HEINEMANN
ADVANCED
SCIENCE

Particle Physics

STEVE ADAMS

Heinemann Educational Publishers
Halley Court, Jordan Hill, Oxford, OX2 8EJ
a division of Reed Educational & Professional Publishing Ltd

OXFORD FLORENCE PRAGUE MADRID ATHENS
MELBOURNE AUCKLAND KUALA LUMPUR SINGAPORE TOKYO
IBADAN NAIROBI KAMPALA JOHANNESBURG GABORONE
PORTSMOUTH NH (USA) CHICAGO MEXICO CITY SAO PAULO

First published 1998

ISBN 0 435 57084 6

2002 2001 2000 99 98
10 9 8 7 6 5 4 3 2 1

Designed and typeset by Gecko Ltd, Bicester, Oxon

Illustrated by Gecko Ltd and Jane Bottomley

Cover design by Gecko Ltd, Bicester, Oxon

Cover photos by Science Photo Library

Printed and bound in Spain by Mateu Cromo

Photo research by Cecelia Weston-Baker

The authors and publishers would like to thank the following for permission to use photographs:

p2: Ben Johnson/Arcaid; **p6 left:** Science Photo Library; **top right:** Science Photo Library; **bottom right:** Chris Honeywell; **p9:** Science Photo Library; **p10:** Science Photo Library; **p13:** Science Photo Library; **p15 left:** Science Photo Library; **right:** Science Photo Library **p21 top:** Science Photo Library; **bottom (×3):** Peter Gould; **p22:** Science Photo Library; **p23:** Peter Gould; **p25:** Science Photo Library; **p26 left and middle:** Science and Society Picture Library; **bottom:** Science Photo Library; **p27:** Science Photo Library; **p29:** Science Photo Library; **p30:** Rex Features; **p32 left:** Science Photo Library; **right:** Science Photo Library; **p33 left:** Science Photo Library **p33 right:** CERN **p34:** Science Photo Library; **p35 top:** CERN; **p35 bottom (a):** CERN; **bottom (b):** Science Photo Library; **p37:** Science Photo Library; **p39 left:** Science Photo Library; **right:** Science and Society Picture Library; **p42:** Science Photo Library; **p45:** Science and Society Picture Library; **p53 left:** Science and Society Picture Library; **right:** Science Photo Library; **p55 top:** Cordon Art of the Netherlands; **p55 bottom:** Science Photo Library; **p60:** Science Photo Library; **p61:** Science and Society Picture Library; **p65:** Science and Society Picture Library; **p70:** Science Photo Library; **p72:** Science and Society Picture Library; **p74:** Science Photo Library; **p75:** Science Photo Library; **p77:** Science Photo Library; **p79 left:** Science Photo Library; **right:** Science Photo Library; **p81:** Science Photo Library; **p83:** Science Photo Library; **p97:** Science Photo Library; **p104:** CERN; **p105 top:** Science Photo Library; **bottom left:** Science Photo Library; **bottom right:** CERN **p112:** Emilio Segre Visual Archives/Paul Ehrenfest; **p115:** The California Institute of Technology; **p124:** Science Photo Library; **p130 top:** Science Photo Library; **bottom:** Rex Features; **p131:** Science Photo Library; **p137:** Science Photo Library; **p140:** British Nuclear Fuels Ltd; **p144:** Science Photo Library.

The author and publishers would like to thank the following for permission to reproduce copyright material:

p40: diagram from *Modern Physics*, Sprout, 1996, John Wiley & Sons Inc, New York; **p58:** diagram from PS210 experiment from LEAR, by Rolf Landua, CERN, Switzerland: **p62:** extract from Rutherford's entry in *Biographical Encyclopedia of Scientists*, 1994, IOPP and Market House Books; **p90:** diagram from *Big Bang Science*, by PPARC PR Office; **p108:** extract by Professor Roger Cashmere, Oxford, on what the Higgs Boson is, 1993; **p116:** diagram from *The Cosmic Background Radiation*, 1974, by Scientific American; **pp136 & 141:** diagrams from *Fission, Fusion and Safety*, by AEA Technology; **p142:** diagram from *Radiation Doses – Maps and Magnitudes*, by The National Radiological Protection Board.

The author and publishers would like to thank the following Examination Boards for permission to reproduce their material:

Northern Examinations and Assessment Board and Edexcel Foundation (London Examinations) for questions on pages 149 to 154.

The publishers have made every effort to trace the copyright holders, but if they have inadvertently overlooked any, they will be pleased to make the necessary arrangements at the first opportunity.

Acknowledgements

I enjoyed seeing this project evolve from an outline plan through several drafts to the full colour proofs and the finished book and am indebted to the highly efficient and professional team at Heinemann who made this possible. I'd like to thank Lindsey Charles, who commissioned the book, Mags Robertson and Cee Weston-Baker who researched the photographs and provided an excellent selection for me to choose from. Clare Farley, the managing editor, was extremely helpful at every stage. Donna Evans showed great patience in copyediting the book.

Of course, the book would never have been written if it was not for Patrick Fullick, and his excellent A-level text. I am also grateful for his comments and constructive suggestions. The style of this book derives from his. Thanks must also go to James Acton, then an A-level student at Westminster School, who read through the first draft and made some very helpful comments. Finally an apology, to Matthew, who kept poking his head around the door of my study and threatening to blow up the computer: I should have more time to play with him now!

Steve Adams November 1997

Dedication For Joseph, Matthew and Sebastian.

How to use this book

Heinemann Advanced Science: Particle Physics has been written to support the nuclear and particle physics options for all syllabuses. It also provides background reading for the modern physics content of the core of advanced-level physics, and preparation for a university course in physics. The style of the book is similar to that of the core book, *Heinemann Advanced Science: Physics*, with the text divided into nine chapters. At the end of each chapter, there are questions to help you find out how much of the material you have understood, and to help you with your revision. Summaries at the end of each chapter provide further help with revision.

In addition to the main text, the chapters of the book contain two types of boxes. The blue tinted *information boxes* contain important information that you need to know. The pink headed *extension boxes* contain more advanced information that can be skipped on first reading if you wish. This will not spoil the story, and you may wish to return to these when you have completed the chapter or gone further with your course. At the back of the book there are also a time-line charting important ideas and discoveries, a glossary of terms, a collection of useful equations and data, and suggestions for further reading and Web surfing.

This book has been written to be an accessible, clear and exciting guide to the story of particle physics, one of the great triumphs of the twentieth century, and to convey the excitement and wonder of the subject. I enjoyed writing it, and hope that you will enjoy reading it.

A word about signs and symbols

If you look through half a dozen different books on physics and compare equations for particle interactions, you will find half a dozen different 'conventions'. My main aims in writing equations in this book have been to make the convention used follow on logically from the equations for simple nuclear reactions which are met at GCSE and in the advanced-level core. By doing this, I hope that the conservation laws will be emphasised.

- In equations, upper and lower prefixes are included. The upper prefix represents baryon number, and the lower prefix represents charge. This is an extension of the scheme familiar to students from simple nuclear transformations, where the upper prefix represents mass number.
- Charged particles are shown with a symbol for charge in all cases, for example, e^- (electron), p^+ (proton), etc.
- Neutral particles have no additional symbol, for example, n (neutron), γ (gamma photon), etc. The exception to this is where charged forms of the particle also exist, for example, π^+ π^- π^o (pions).
- Antiparticles for charged particles are simply indicated by the sign of their charge: e.g. e^+ (positron) and e^-, and p^+ (antiproton) and p^- etc.
- β^- and β^+ are used interchangeably with e^- and e^+ when referring to beta-decays.

The only exceptions to these rules are:

- in Feynmann diagrams, where all prefixes are omitted;
- for the introduction to neutrinos, which are introduced as ν. The notation ν_e ν_m ν_t is used once the different leptons have been met.

CONTENTS

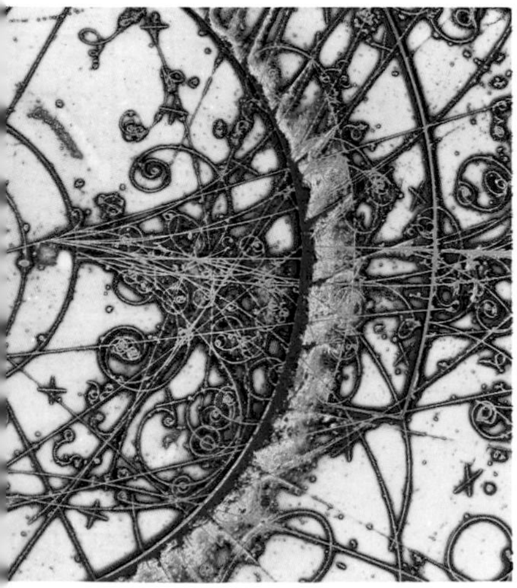

9 Nuclear power

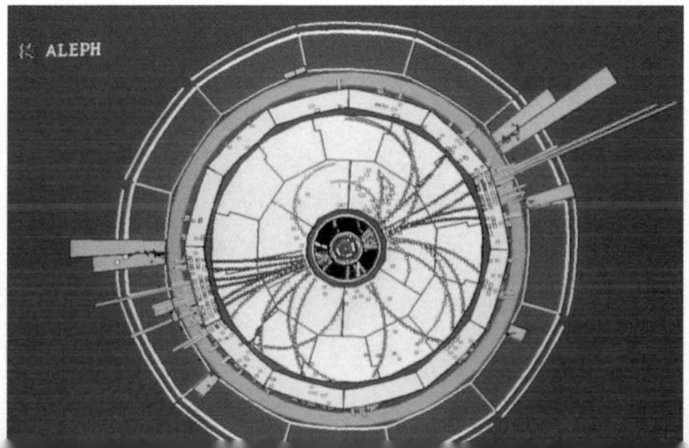

INTRODUCTION

In search of perfect symmetry

'The scientist does not study Nature because it is useful; he studies it because he delights in it, and he delights in it because it is beautiful. If Nature were not beautiful, it would not be worth knowing, and if Nature were not worth knowing, life would not be worth living.'
Henri Poincaré (French mathematician)

Figure 1 The Greek ideal of beauty was copied during the Renaissance. This Villa Rotunda by the architect Palladio has four flights of steps, four terraces, four porticoes, four entrances, and the four facades form a cross crowned by a dome. In this photograph there is almost perfect mirror symmetry about a central vertical line.

Beauty, symmetry and simplicity

Beauty is difficult to define, but many of the things we find beautiful have an internal rhythm or structure that relates one part to another. In a piece of music this may be a particular sequence of chords, a bass riff or a repeated melody, in a building it might be a row of arches or a left-right mirror symmetry and in a poem it could be the regular pattern of rhymes or syllables. These patterns conceal mathematical relationships; Pythagoras discovered the simple sequence of ratios that produces a pleasant harmonic series and the Greeks based much of their architecture and art on a 'golden ratio' of lengths that is pleasing to the eye. The music of Bach contains many intricate mathematical sequences.

The building in the photograph has left–right mirror symmetry, which means you could construct one half of it from a plan of the other half – there is no need for any more information. This illustrates a very important point about symmetry: it is a way of summarising a great deal of information. Think of a perfect sodium chloride (salt) crystal. It will contain billions upon billions of atoms, but it can be completely described very economically. The entire crystal can be constructed by copying and translating a single unit cell. The properties of salt crystals all derive from this unit cell.

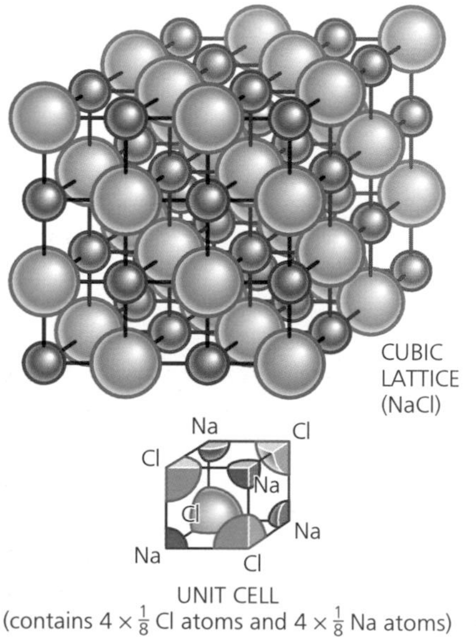

Figure 2 All perfect sodium chloride crystals can be constructed by a repeating pattern of one simple unit cell.

There are many different kinds of symmetry but they all share one characteristic. If something is symmetric then there are certain things you can do to it that leave it unchanged. This is shown in the examples below.

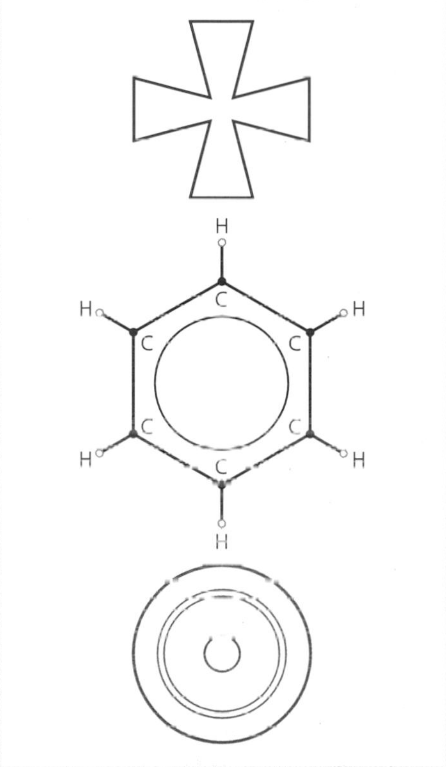

Figure 3 If we consider rotations about the centre of each figure then the first is returned to itself every 90° and the second (a benzene molecule) every 60° – these two are **discrete symmetries**. The third example can be rotated through any angle and has a **continuous symmetry**.

The mathematics of symmetry

What has symmetry got to do with particle physics? In 1918 the mathematician Emmy Noether of the University of Gottingen published a theorem that links the mathematics of symmetry to conservation laws in physics. The consequences of this theorem (see box) are so significant that symmetry has become the single most important guide in the search for a unified theory of all particles and forces. In this quest the work of theoretical and experimental physicists complement one another. The theoretician tries to think up the most general symmetry conditions that existed at the very moment of creation and then uses the mathematics of symmetry (group theory) to create an equation for everything. Particles and forces will then emerge from this equation with all their properties determined by parameters within the equation. The experimentalist, however, continues to build accelerators and crash particles together to learn about the patterns of creation and annihilation among the particles that are produced. These patterns hint at underlying symmetries and so may test existing theories or be used to propose new ones. Ultimately any theory will be judged by how well it agrees with experimental results.

Noether's Theorem

Noether showed that the existence of a symmetry in the mathematical description of the Universe results in a conservation law in physics. To get a feel for how this works think about an isolated particle in otherwise empty space – what general statements can be made about the laws that govern its motion? Firstly, it doesn't matter where the particle is placed, all points in empty space are presumably equivalent, so the laws must have **translational symmetry**. Of course if the particle were to suddenly start moving in a particular direction this translational symmetry would be destroyed, as one direction would be distinguished from all others. So, if translational symmetry is preserved the particle's motion cannot change unpredictably. This leads to the law of conservation of linear momentum!

In a similar way, since nothing is changed if we rotate everything through some angle (space has rotational symmetry), the rotational motion of the particle cannot change arbitrarily either. This leads to conservation of angular momentum!

Finally, the laws would be the same tomorrow or today or a billion years ago, so they also have symmetry with respect to translations in time. This leads to conservation of mass–energy!

space translation symmetry → conservation of linear momentum

time translation symmetry → conservation of mass–energy

rotational symmetry → conservation of angular momentum

This may give the impression that the laws of physics can all be worked out from a few simple assumptions about the nature of space and time coupled with a working knowledge of the mathematics of symmetry. However, this is not really the case, and the present leading contender for a theory of everything is developed from symmetries in ten–dimensional space. Why ten dimensions? Because this is the minimum number that can incorporate the diverse patterns discovered

PCT invariance

As we shall see in chapter 3, beta-minus decay involves the transformation of a neutron to a proton in the nucleus and the emission of an electron and an antineutrino. Free neutrons decay by the same mechanism. This can be written as:

$$ {}^{1}_{0}\mathbf{n} \rightarrow {}^{1}_{1}\mathbf{p}^{+} + {}^{0}_{-1}\mathbf{e}^{-} + {}^{0}_{0}\bar{\nu} $$

A related process is the conversion of a proton to a neutron by collision with an electron:

$$ {}^{0}_{-1}\mathbf{e}^{-} + {}^{1}_{1}\mathbf{p}^{+} \rightarrow {}^{1}_{0}\mathbf{n} + {}^{0}_{0}\nu $$

If you compare these two equations you can see that one can be produced from the other by transferring the antineutrino to the other side of the equation and converting it to a neutrino. This is like algebra where a term can change sides as long as its sign is also reversed. The second reaction is illustrated below by a 'Feynman diagram'. This shows incoming and outgoing particles and adds a new particle that transfers the charge from the proton to the electron (a W^+) and in the process converts the electron to a neutrino:

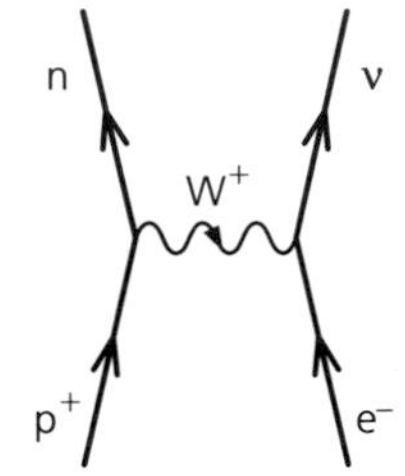

Figure 4(a)

We can use this reaction to illustrate three important symmetry operations.

- **Parity (P)**
  This is space reflection – the coordinates of all particles and events are inverted. It converts particles coming from the left into particles coming from the right and vice versa:
- **Charge conjugation (C)**
  This changes all particles to antiparticles.
- **Time reversal (T)**
  This converts absorbed particles to emitted particles and vice versa.

The three Feynman diagrams below show the effects of applying P, C and T operations in succession to the proton–electron collision above.

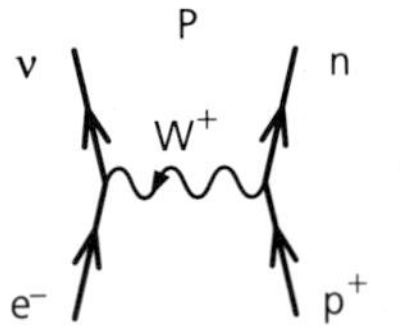

(i) P : 'mirror' reflection

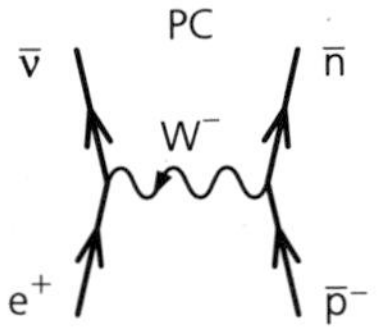

(ii) C : particles replaced by their antiparticles

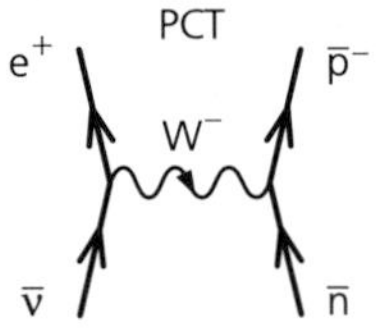

(iii) T : time reversal

Figure 4(b)

Every one of the new diagrams represents a physical process that *can happen* in the physical world. These are very general symmetry operations and it is believed that the combined PCT operation, like that shown above, *always* results in a process allowed by the laws of physics. Surprisingly this is not true for the individual symmetry operations. In particular, the weak interaction that is responsible for beta decays *can* violate parity – that is, a parity reflection of beta decay produces a process that is never observed in nature.

The origin of structure

The idea that symmetry hints at an underlying order based on simpler structures is familiar from chemistry. Mendeleev arranged the elements according to their atomic masses so that elements with similar chemical properties (like sodium and potassium or fluorine and chlorine) fell into the same groups. By letting the periodic pattern guide him he could see gaps in the table and so predicted the properties of then undiscovered elements. In the early days of particle physics there were too few known particles for the patterns to be obvious, but by the 1960s so many particles had been discovered that patterns began to appear. So did gaps, and the symmetries among particle properties allowed theorists like Murray Gell-Mann and Yuval Ne'eman to predict the properties of new particles to fill these gaps. The subsequent discovery of particles with exactly these properties justified the symmetry approach.

The story of particle physics is a mixture of new and often unexpected discoveries and bold predictions based on sweeping generalisations at a fundamental level.

The electron was the first subatomic particle to be discovered, but two unexpected discoveries revealed that it is just one member of a closely related particle family.

Firstly, a close analysis of beta decay showed that it could only obey the known conservation laws if an 'invisible' partner to the electron is created alongside the electron in the decay. This led to the prediction and eventual discovery of the neutrino. Later, whilst looking for a completely different particle, experimentalists discovered the muon, a particle about 200 times more massive than an electron but otherwise its twin – and the muon had its own muon-neutrino as a sidekick. This particle family, called 'leptons', was completed in 1975 by the arrival of an even more massive electron-like particle, the tau – and of course the tau-neutrino.

Meanwhile a wide variety of new heavy particles with similar properties to protons and neutrons were discovered. These 'hadrons' seemed rather arbitrary at first, but this was because their patterns are far more complicated than those of the lepton pairs. Eventually a kind of 'periodic table' of hadrons was constructed called 'the eightfold way' and its success in predicting new hadrons led theorists to look for simple ways to reproduce the essential symmetry of the pattern. To do this they introduced a new family of particles, the quarks, and we are now fairly sure that there are only six quarks arranged in three pairs like the six leptons.

Supersymmetry and superstrings

No one knows why the quark–lepton symmetry exists, but it is very unlikely to be a coincidence. There is a strong suspicion that this correspondence is a requirement of an as yet undiscovered symmetry in the mathematics of a unified theory that can incorporate both quarks and leptons. This is often referred to as a **supersymmetric** theory. And the supersymmetry would have the effect of converting quarks into leptons and leptons into quarks in much the same way that a mirror reflects an object onto an image of itself whilst retaining all the essential relations between parts of the object. Taken to its limit a supersymmetric theory of everything would reduce the variety of 'fundamental' particles in the present 'Standard Model' of particle physics to a single type of particle interacting through a unified force. The appearance of distinct particle families in our experiments is simply the result of a 'broken symmetry' brought about by the relatively low energies available to us in our experiments. At very high energies supersymmetry would rule. Unfortunately the energies concerned are so high that it will be very difficult to create the supersymmetric particles predicted by the new theories, and our best hopes of testing them are by looking for rare events like the decay of the proton that are allowed by supersymmetry but forbidden by the Standard Model. (In the Standard Model the proton is the lightest hadron made up of three quarks, so there is nothing into which it can decay. If quarks can change to leptons however, it can decay to a pion and a positron.)

So where are we now? The Standard Model combines the mathematical symmetries of electromagnetism, leptons and quarks into a composite theory. This is acceptable as far as it goes but it needs many constants to be determined by experiment and it does not incorporate gravity, which is described by Einstein's general theory of relativity as a geometric distortion of space and time. During the last 20 years theorists have shown that supersymmetric theories automatically incorporate gravity, but there are many supersymmetric theories and none have proved entirely successful. On top of this, many physicists are put off by the sheer complexity of the mathematics.

More recently it has been realised that the supersymmetries that emerge from ten-dimensional hyperspace are exactly those that lead to the observed conservation laws and particle patterns in the Standard Model. In this theory all the additional dimensions somehow close up on themselves so that we do not experience them directly. The quarks, leptons etc. of the Standard Model are resonant vibrations of structures called **superstrings** that vibrate in this ten-dimensional hyperspace! If string theory is, as more and more theoretical physicists suspect, the Holy Grail of physics, then we should be able to use it to calculate the values of electron or proton mass from first principles. Unfortunately no one knows how to do this, and whilst superstring theory promises so much there seem to be an enormous number of possible solutions to its equations and no one knows how to select the appropriate ones. It is also almost impossible to test experimentally because the incredibly small scale of the strings (about 10^{20} times smaller than a proton) means that the energies needed to probe matter on this scale are way beyond those we can ever realistically hope to achieve in terrestrial experiments. Edward Witten, one of the leading mathematical physicists developing the superstring model said:

'String theory is twenty-first century physics that fell accidentally into the twentieth century.'

The story continues.

1 High-energy physics

In 1905 Albert Einstein showed that energy has mass and mass has energy. Today, particle physicists use this important idea to probe the very heart of matter and discover its secrets.

The methods particle physicists use are really quite crude, but they are surprisingly effective. Huge machines called **particle accelerators** accelerate subatomic particles to speeds almost equal to the speed of light, and then crash them into one another to see what happens. In these violent collisions some of the kinetic energy of the colliding particles turns into matter, and new particles are made.

In this chapter we shall look at the ways that particles can be accelerated, and learn how to calculate the energy changes which take place when they collide.

Figure 1.2 Albert Einstein (1879–1955). Einstein's special theory of relativity revolutionised our ideas of space and time. The general theory explained gravity as a distortion of spacetime geometry. He received the Nobel prize for his contributions to quantum mechanics, a theory that deeply disturbed him. He was probably the greatest twentieth century theoretical physicist.

PRINCIPLES OF ACCELERATING PARTICLES

Mass and energy

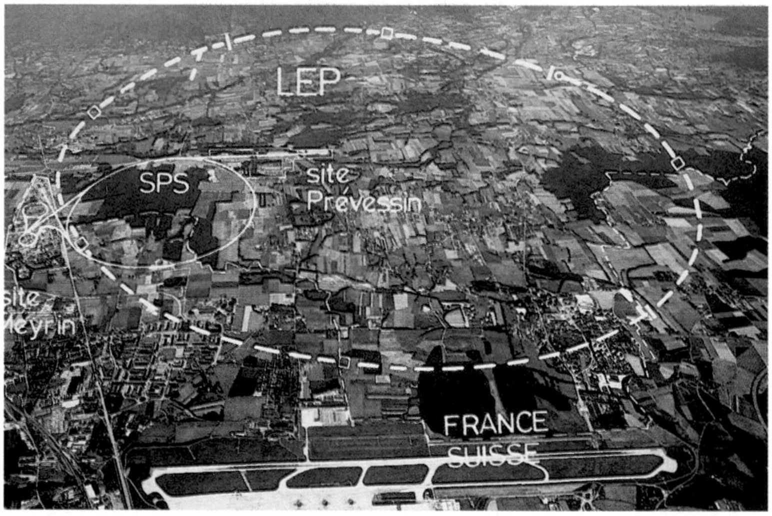

◄ **Figure 1.1** To understand the behaviour of tiny subatomic particles, particle physicists use huge accelerators like this one at CERN. 'CERN' comes from the original name, Conseil Européen pour la Recherche Nucléaire. It is now known as the European Laboratory for Particle Physics, and is funded by fifteen member states.

Newton's laws of mechanics begin to break down when we apply them to objects moving at extremely high velocities. Einstein's theory of relativity predicts that the speed of light is an unattainable limit for any mass, even if we keep supplying it with energy. Einstein also showed that energy itself has mass, so that a moving object has a greater mass than an object at rest. At low speeds this effect is unimportant, but close to the speed of light, c, it becomes extremely important, and an object may have a total mass many times greater than its mass when it is stationary (called its **rest mass**).

Even physicists sometimes misunderstand the meaning of the equation $E = mc^2$, which says that mass has energy and energy has mass – it does not mean that mass can be converted into energy and vice versa.

The energy changes involved in chemical reactions, or when a cup of tea cools down, are tiny compared to the rest energy of the particles involved, so there does not appear to be any change in rest mass. In nuclear reactions and particle collisions the energy changes are a much larger proportion of the rest energy of the particles involved and can be more easily measured.

Figure 1.3 The link between energy and mass is summarised in one of the only equations in physics that is famous enough to be worn on a T-shirt!

Worked example

Alpha decay

When a heavy nucleus decays by emitting an alpha particle the rest mass of the daughter nucleus plus the rest mass of the alpha particle is always less than the rest mass of the original nucleus. This apparent loss of mass is accounted for by the kinetic energy of the two new particles. We can use the alpha decay of uranium-238 as an example.

Atomic and nuclear masses are usually recorded in atomic mass units, u. 1 u is about equal to the mass of a proton. More accurately it is 1.661×10^{-27} kg, 1/12 the mass of a carbon-12 atom.

${}^{238}_{92}U \rightarrow {}^{234}_{90}Th + {}^{4}_{2}He$	mass of U-238 atom	$m_1 = 238.0508$ u
$m_1 \rightarrow m_2$ and m_3	mass of Th-234 atom	$m_2 = 234.0437$ u
	mass of He-4 atom	$m_3 = 4.0026$ u

$$\Delta m = m_1 - (m_2 + m_3) = 0.0045 \text{ u}$$
$$\text{or } \Delta m = 7.5 \times 10^{-30} \text{ kg}$$

The energy equivalent of this mass defect is:

$$E = c^2 \Delta m = 6.7 \times 10^{-13} \text{ J}$$

This is in the form of kinetic energy, most of which goes to the alpha particle because of its much smaller mass (this follows from conservation of linear momentum).

You might think that the prime purpose of an accelerator is to increase the velocity of particles, but this is not really true. Once a particle is travelling at, say, 99% of the speed of light it is not going to increase its velocity very much, no matter how much more energy is supplied. However, its mass increases as it gains energy to a value γm_o where the 'γ-factor' depends on velocity. Table 1.1 shows that γ changes from 7 to 22 when the velocity increases from $0.99c$ to $0.999c$. The velocity increase is about 1% but the mass increase is nearer 300%. Clearly the main purpose of an accelerator is to increase the mass of the particles, not to make them go faster.

Table 1.1 Changes in gamma with the ratio v/c.

v/c	γ
0.010	1.000
0.100	1.005
0.500	1.155
0.800	1.667
0.900	2.294
0.950	3.203
0.990	7.089
0.999	22.37

Mass and velocity

The rest mass of a particle is its mass when it is at rest relative to the instruments which are used to measure its mass. Since we know that mass and energy are equivalent, it follows that we can use $E = mc^2$ to find the particle's rest energy from its rest mass. For example, the rest mass of an electron is 9.1×10^{-31} kg, and its rest energy is 8.2×10^{-14} J.

The symbol m_o is used to represent rest mass, while the symbol m represents the total mass of a particle in motion. Rest mass is constant, while m increases with velocity v according to the relationship:

$$m = \frac{m_o}{\sqrt{1 - \frac{v^2}{c^2}}}$$

This is often written as:

$$m = \gamma m_o \text{ where } \gamma = \frac{1}{\sqrt{1 - \frac{v^2}{c^2}}}$$

This 'gamma-factor' is a measure of how important relativistic effects are. If the velocity of a particle is close to the speed of light, then $\frac{v^2}{c^2}$ will be close to 1 and γ becomes very large indeed. For a particle travelling at 99.9% of the speed of light (that is $v = 0.999c$), $\gamma = 22.4$, which means that the total mass of a particle moving at this speed is 22.4 times its rest mass. Table 1.1 shows how γ changes with the ratio v/c.

Accelerators

How do we go about accelerating anything? When we throw a ball we have to get hold of it and apply a force to it as we move our hand in the direction of the throw. The work we do is equal to the product of the force applied and the distance through which it moves before we release the ball. Most particle accelerators work on much the same principle. We use charged particles because we can 'get hold of them' using electric and magnetic fields. The electric field exerts a force on the charged particle that accelerates it and increases its energy. Magnetic fields can be used to change the direction of a moving charge. This is particularly useful as the charges can be made to move around a ring and acceleration can continue during many orbits of the ring.

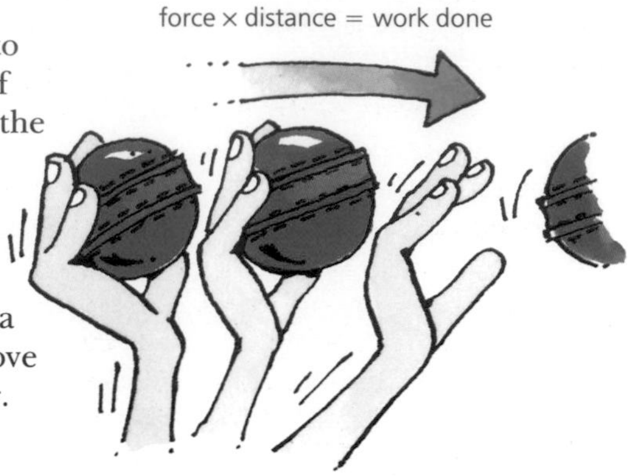

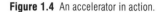

Figure 1.4 An accelerator in action.

The electric field

An electric field is a region of space in which a charged particle experiences a force. The strength of the electric field E at some point is defined as the force that would be exerted per unit positive charge placed at that point:

$$\boldsymbol{E = \frac{F}{q}} \qquad (E \text{ is measured in N C}^{-1} \text{ or V m}^{-1})$$

The magnitude of the electric field is also equal to the magnitude of the potential gradient at the point, that is the change of voltage per metre. If a uniform field is set up between two electrodes a distance d apart with a p.d. V between them then the magnitude of the field strength is:

$$\boldsymbol{E = \frac{V}{d}}$$

The force on a positive charge is:

$$\boldsymbol{F = Eq}$$

Accelerating a charge through a potential difference of V volts increases its kinetic energy:

$$\boldsymbol{\Delta \text{KE} = qV}$$

The energy gained when a particle carrying a charge equal to the electronic charge e is accelerated through 1 volt is called an 'electronvolt' (eV). From the equation above this can be expressed in joules:

$$\boldsymbol{1\,\text{eV} = 1.6 \times 10^{-19}\,\text{C} \times 1\,\text{V} = 1.6 \times 10^{-19}\,\text{J}}$$

Useful units in nuclear and particle physics are the mega-electronvolt or MeV and the giga-electronvolt or GeV.

$$\boldsymbol{1\,\text{MeV} = 10^6\,\text{eV} \qquad 1\,\text{GeV} = 10^9\,\text{eV}}$$

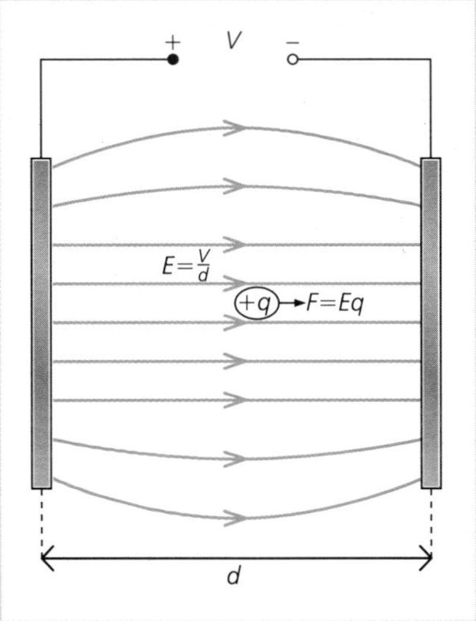

Figure 1.5 The *E*-field.

Apart from artificial particle accelerators there are two sources of high-energy particles in nature, both of which have revealed the existence of new particles. The first of these sources is radioactive nuclei which eject particles as they decay. The second is the mysterious cosmic rays that reach us from outer space.

Radioactive decays typically produce particles with energies of a few MeV and were particularly important in the discovery of the nucleus (the Rutherford scattering experiment in 1911), splitting the atom (also Rutherford, in 1919) and the discovery of the neutron (Chadwick, 1932). A close analysis of beta decay prompted Pauli to suggest the existence of the neutrino (actually an antineutrino in beta decay) although this particle was not detected until 1956.

Cosmic rays are extremely high-energy particles, often atomic nuclei, that arrive from deep space. They contain the most energetic particles we have ever detected – as high as 10^{11} GeV (1 GeV = 10^9 eV) – and create showers of new particles as they collide with molecules in the Earth's atmosphere. Although several particles had been discovered or predicted by 1930 the study of cosmic rays in the 1930s and 1940s suddenly produced a host of new particles (e.g. positrons, muons and the strange particles, see pages 50, 45 and 79,).

Since 1950 most discoveries have been made using accelerators of ever-increasing energy (and ever-increasing cost).

The earliest accelerators were simple electron tubes like the ones used in school laboratories or inside a TV tube to produce an electron beam. These accelerate electrons through a few kilovolts. Modern accelerators reach much higher energies. From 1989 to 1995 **LEP** (the Large Electron Positron Collider) at **CERN** near Geneva produced a collision energy of 89–94 GeV. In 1996 it was upgraded to about 170 GeV. The **SPS** (the Super Proton Synchrotron, also at CERN) exceeds 600 GeV. The **Tevatron** at **Fermilab** near Chicago was the first device to exceed 1 TeV (1 tera-electronvolt = 1000 GeV). However, an even more powerful machine, the **SSC** (Superconducting Super Collider) was cancelled for financial reasons. The next big accelerator will replace LEP and run in the existing tunnel early in the twenty-first century – this is the **LHC** (Large Hadron Collider) designed to collide protons and antiprotons at over 40 TeV! However, if even bigger accelerators are too expensive to build, the future of particle physics may well lie with a return to the study of energetic cosmic rays or else some ingenious development to produce high-energy collisions more cheaply.

Figure 1.6 The Tevatron at Fermilab (diameter 2 km) – at 1000 GeV protons have a velocity of 0.999999 *c*.

PRACTICAL PARTICLE ACCELERATORS

There are two basic designs of particle accelerator. In a **linear accelerator** the charged particles are accelerated in a straight line, while in a **circular accelerator** the particles travel round and round in a circle.

An important advantage of the circular accelerators is that particles are accelerated on every orbit whereas linear acceleration occurs as they pass once only along the length of the accelerator. However, linear accelerators (called LINACs for short) have one very important advantage over circular accelerators (such as **synchrotrons**) when it comes to accelerating electrons. Whenever a charged particle is swung in a circle it radiates energy. The greater its centripetal acceleration the greater the rate of radiation, so high-energy electrons in circular accelerators lose a lot of the input energy as 'synchrotron radiation'. A linear accelerator does not have this problem since there is no centripetal acceleration. For this reason the most powerful electron accelerators are LINACs. The problem is not serious for protons of comparable energy (since they travel more slowly and so have smaller centripetal accelerations) so LINACs are only used with protons as preliminary stages of acceleration before the protons are injected into a synchrotron ring.

Linear accelerators

A cathode ray tube or electron tube is the simplest linear accelerator. A potential difference *V* volts is maintained between the anode and cathode and electrons accelerate in the field between them, converting electrical potential energy (EPE) to kinetic energy. This is fine for 'low' energies (e.g. 10 keV) but not much use if we want very high energy (say 1 GeV) because it would require a single potential difference of a billion volts. This is impracticable – voltages of even a few hundred thousand volts are difficult to insulate. However, the same effect can be achieved by accelerating the electrons in a number of distinct steps using lower voltages rather than supplying all the energy in one go.

The **Stanford Linear Accelerator** can accelerate electrons to 30 GeV. This produced much of the early evidence for the internal structure of protons and neutrons by scattering high-energy electrons from nuclei.

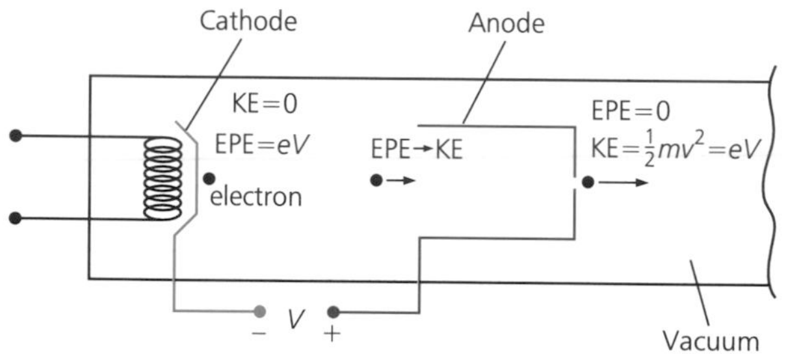

Figure 1.7 A cathode ray tube.

Figure 1.8 The Stanford Linear Accelerator (SLAC), a 3 km 'electron gun'.

The principle of the linear accelerator was first developed by Wideröe in 1928. A series of drift tubes are arranged in a straight line. Radio-frequency voltage pulses are then used to accelerate the charged particles in a series of steps until they reach very high energy. (The use of an alternating voltage rather than a direct voltage has the advantage that transformers can be used to produce high voltages for acceleration in each stage. However, the apparatus must be designed and operated in such a way that the particles are always accelerated in the same direction as they move from one drift tube to the next.) The principle is explained and illustrated in figure 1.9.

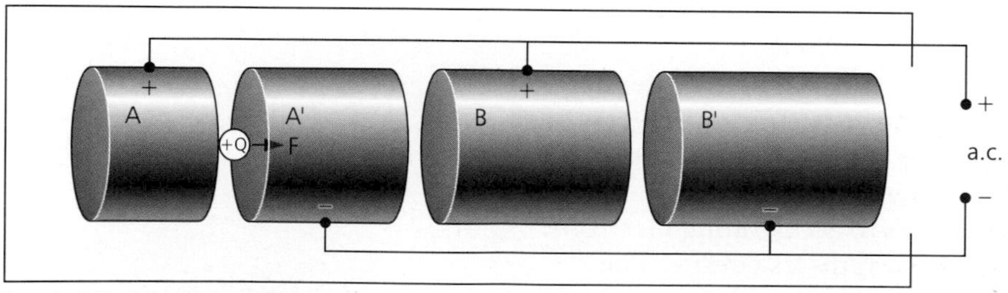

The principle of the linear accelerator.
A, A' and BB' etc. are drift tubes.
Acceleration occurs in gaps between tubes – as ion moves from A to A' it is in an electric field produced by the p.d. between the two tubes.
When the ion is inside a particular tube it is in an equipotential region and so experiences no force.
By the time it reaches the gap between tubes A' and B half a cycle of the a.c. has occured and so B is now negative with respect to A' and the ion experiences another accelerating force.
Since the ion velocity increases, the distance between successive gaps must increase.

Figure 1.9 The principle of the linear accelerator.

Advantages of LINACs:
- high beam intensities
- well-collimated beams (the beam cross-section is small)
- smaller energy losses (especially for electrons) – no synchrotron radiation

Disadvantages:
- each pair of electrodes accelerates particles once only
- high energy machines are very long.

LINAC calculations

Assume that ions or electrons arrive at gaps between the drift tubes when the peak voltage V is across them.

The increase in energy will then be eV in each gap.

While non-relativistic equations remain valid:

$$\mathbf{KE} = \tfrac{1}{2} mv^2 = neV \qquad \textbf{after } n \textbf{ gaps}$$

So the speed of ions or electrons is:

$$v = \sqrt{\frac{2neV}{m}}$$

The time taken to move from one gap to the next will be half the period of the a.c. supply ($1/2f$) so the separation of the nth and $(n+1)$th gaps must be:

$$s_n = \frac{1}{2f} \times \sqrt{\frac{2neV}{m}} \propto \sqrt{n}$$

That is, the tube lengths increase in the ratios $\sqrt{1}:\sqrt{2}:\sqrt{3}$ etc.

At higher energies this relation will break down as the mass of the particles increases with their velocity.

The cyclotron

The **cyclotron** was invented by Ernest Lawrence in 1929. The design was based on Wideröe's drift idea for a linear accelerator but with one literally *revolutionary* difference: the particles move in spiral paths inside a circular machine.

In Wideröe's machine the ions cross a different accelerating gap during each half cycle of the applied a.c. By making the particles move in circles Lawrence could use just two semi-circular electrodes ('dees') and send the

The magnetic field

When an electric current (I) passes at right angles to a magnetic field (B) there is a force (F) on the length (l) of current-carrying conductor given by $F = BIl$ in a direction predicted by Fleming's left-hand rule. A beam of charged particles is also a current and can be deflected by an applied magnetic field. The force on a charge q moving at velocity v perpendicular to a magnetic field of strength B is:

$$F = Bqv$$

This acts at 90° to the velocity of the particle so it does no work on it and does not affect its kinetic energy. Its effect is to make the particle move in a curved path by providing a centripetal force:

$$Bqv = \frac{mv^2}{r}$$

So

$$r = \frac{mv}{Bq}$$

The radius of the charge's orbit will increase if its momentum increases. In the cyclotron particles are injected close to the centre of the pair of 'dees' and then spiral outwards as they gain kinetic energy.

charges backwards and forwards across *the same gap* increasing their kinetic energies each time. An applied magnetic field maintains the circular paths and the distance travelled inside each hollow electrode increases naturally as the particles increase the radius of their orbits. The first cyclotron was built in 1931 and used a pair of magnets just 11 cm in diameter to produce protons of kinetic energy 80 keV. The following year Lawrence built a cyclotron which accelerated protons to 1 MeV. It had a diameter of 26 cm.

For the cyclotron to work with an alternating supply of constant frequency, the orbiting charges must spend the same time on each orbit, regardless of their kinetic energy. It turns out that this will occur naturally as long as the particle motion can be described accurately by the equations of Newtonian mechanics. For a particular charged particle in a particular magnetic field there is a unique frequency (the **cyclotron resonance**) at which the accelerating voltage must alternate. It will then change the relative polarity of the two 'dees' while the charge is inside one of them so that each time it enters the gap between 'dees' it will be accelerated by the peak voltage in the direction it is already travelling.

The cyclotron resonance frequency is:

$$f = \frac{Bq}{2\pi m}$$

If B = 20 m T, and the particle is a proton with $q = 1.6 \times 10^{-19}$ C and $m = 1.67 \times 10^{-28}$ kg then $f \approx 3.0$ MHz.

Cyclotrons can produce continuous proton beams up to about 25 MeV.

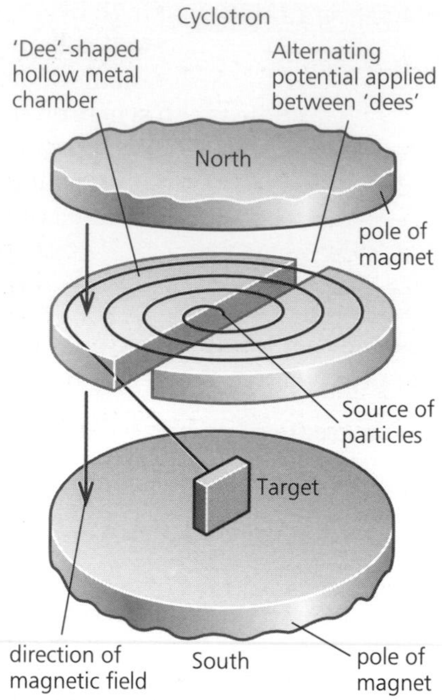

In a cyclotron the charged particles from a source at the centre follow a spiral path until they emerge to strike a target. The magnetic field bends the tracks of the particles, while the alternating field between the 'dees' accelerates them.

Figure 1.10 The principle of a cyclotron.

Cyclotron resonance

The radius of orbit for a moving charged particle in a magnetic field is:

$$r = \frac{mv}{Bq}$$

The time of orbit is therefore:

$$T = \frac{2\pi r}{v} = \frac{2\pi mv}{Bqv} = \frac{2\pi m}{Bq}$$

This is completely independent of the particle speed. At higher speeds the particle moves in a larger orbit but takes the same time. The fact that the orbital time is independent of particle energy (up to relativistic energies) allows the cyclotron to work with a fixed frequency a.c. supply and so accelerate *continuous* beams of particles. The frequency of the a.c. or 'cyclotron resonance' frequency is:

$$f = \frac{1}{T} = \frac{Bq}{2\pi m}$$

Above about 25 MeV the relativistic mass increase becomes significant and the time for particle orbits becomes larger than that calculated on the assumption of constant mass.

Eventually charges arrive too late to be accelerated by the voltage between the dees and end up completely out of step with the a.c. supply. One way to avoid this is to use an enormous voltage so that large energies are reached in just a few orbits. However, a more effective approach is to change the accelerating frequency in step with the accelerating charges. A machine designed to do this is called a synchro-cyclotron or synchrotron.

Positron Emission Tomography

Apart from basic research into matter, cyclotrons have also been useful in medicine. Many hospitals have their own cyclotrons on site to produce the radioactive nuclei used for tracers to label molecules used in biochemical reactions. The reason for locating the cyclotron within the hospital is because the half-life of some of the tracers used is very short. Oxygen-15, used in **PET** scans, has a half-life of 2 minutes and must be inhaled by the patient almost as soon as it is created.

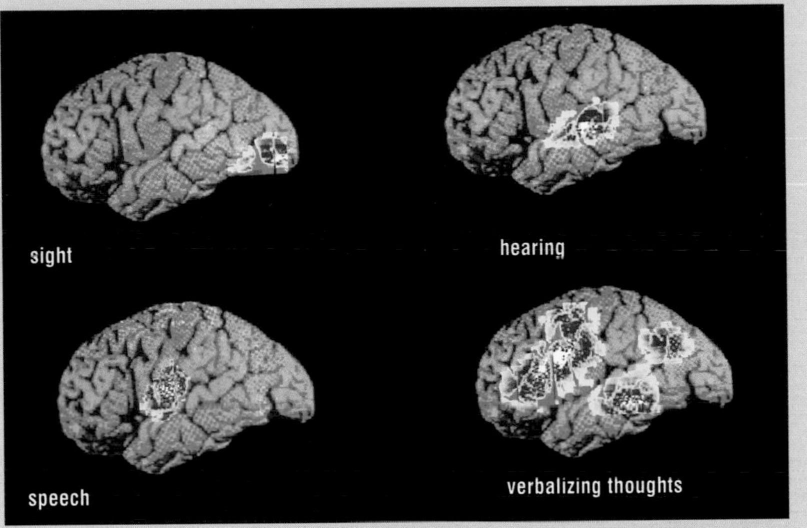

Figure 1.11 PET stands for positron emission tomography and can produce detailed images of the brain. It relies on the simultaneous detection of a pair of gamma rays emitted when a positron from a decaying nucleus annihilates with an electron. The gamma rays are emitted in opposite directions from the point of annihilation and so allow the experimenter to locate the position of this event – and hence the original nucleus – very precisely. In the photograph above gamma-ray emission (red and yellow areas) show regions of increased blood flow corresponding to particular brain activities.

The synchro-cyclotron

In a synchro-cyclotron the frequency of the accelerating voltage is gradually decreased as the particle kinetic energy rises. This process is carried out in a series of steps during each of which the beam settles into a stable circular orbit before the frequency is reduced and the beam moves out to a larger stable orbit. This continues until the beam reaches the edge of the 'dees'. In principle any energy can be achieved so long as a large enough magnet is available. In practice this sets a limit to the useful size of a synchro-cyclotron and so most modern high-energy proton accelerators use a slightly different principle.

The synchrotron

Instead of reducing the frequency and allowing the orbital radius to increase, we can increase the magnetic field strength and keep the charged particles in an orbit of fixed radius. The advantage of this is that we only need to provide a magnetic field at the circumference of the orbit and not over all of a large circular area. This allows larger higher energy machines to be built (the ring at CERN has a circumference of 27 km).

The path followed by a particle of mass m and charge q, moving through a magnetic field of strength B at speed v has a radius of curvature given by:

$$r = \frac{mv}{Bq}$$

As the particles accelerate the magnetic field is increased to keep them on the same orbit. The particles take less and less time to complete their orbit so the frequency of the accelerating a.c. must increase as well. The magnets perform two functions in the synchrotron – they bend the beam into a circular path (by the motor effect force) and focus it to keep as many particles as possible on the ideal orbit. Bending is achieved using dipole magnets whereas beam focusing uses quadrupole magnets (four poles).

Effective focusing is very important as it:

- enhances the beam intensity
- reduces beam cross-section (so that smaller evacuated beam tubes and smaller gaps between magnetic poles can be used).

Several **radio-frequency (rf) cavities** are positioned around the ring. These contain the alternating electric fields synchronised with the beam's orbital period and accelerate the charges. In a proton synchrotron the radio frequency must be increased as the particle velocity increases. In an electron synchrotron the electrons are already travelling at very close to the speed of light when they are injected. Their orbital frequency remains more or less constant – so a constant a.c. frequency can be used.

Particles are usually injected into the synchrotron using a LINAC which intersects the main ring at a tangent. The incoming beam is deflected onto its orbital path by a dipole magnet and the accelerated beam is extracted by deflecting it out of the ring in a similar way. A synchrotron has several extraction points which allows the same machine to be used by several different research groups at the same time.

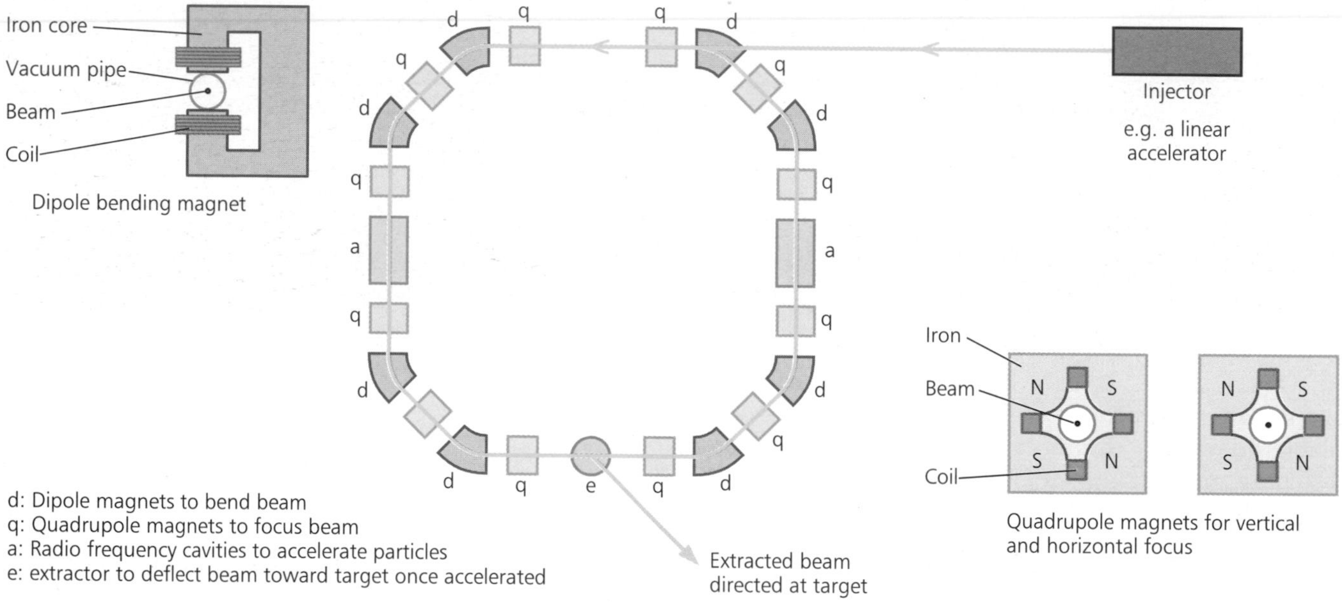

Figure 1.12 The principle of a synchrotron.

The largest synchrotron is the large electron–positron collider (**LEP**) at CERN. This has a circumference of 27 km and operates in an underground tunnel which crosses the Swiss–French border near Geneva. Up until 1996 it accelerated electrons to energies of 50 GeV and collided them with positrons (antielectrons) of the same energy moving in the opposite direction. This energy was chosen to correspond closely to the rest energy of Z^0 particles, and so increase the chance of creating them. The 1996 upgrade, which almost doubled the collision energy, was also 'tuned' to produce particular types of particle – pairs of W^+ and W^- particles. (When LEP2 was first switched on the beam kept failing; it was being absorbed somewhere. On investigation two empty beer bottles were discovered inside the beam tube!) At close to the speed of light electrons and positrons complete about 11 000 orbits of LEP per second.

The Tevatron at Fermilab near Chicago accelerates protons and antiprotons to 1000 GeV or 1 TeV. It has a circumference of 6 km. Although 1 TeV is far in excess of the energy produced by LEP, protons and antiprotons are composite particles (made up of quarks) and collisions between them give energy to all the particles involved so are usually pretty complicated. Electrons and positrons are fundamental, so all the available energy goes into a simpler collision. New particles are usually (but not always) discovered in the very energetic but complex collisions in proton–antiproton accelerators, but precision measurements and detailed tests of theory are usually carried out using electron–positron colliders. The proton–antiproton collision energies in the LHC will be comparable to the typical energy of particles 10^{-12} s after the Big Bang and will be used to look for the hypothetical Higgs particle. (LHC can also be used to collide heavy ions at up to 1000 TeV.)

Figure 1.13 This photograph of the LEP was taken when the beam was switched off (LEP is switched off each winter to reduce the demand on the local electricity supply grid). If you stood beside LEP2 when it was operational a 30 second exposure to the synchrotron radiation would give you just 50% chance of surviving the next 24 hours!

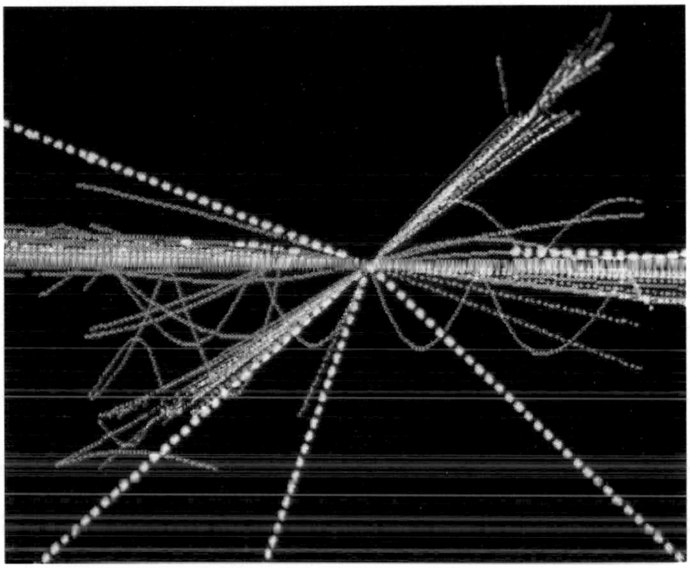

Figure 1.14 The point of these huge machines is to make new particles in violent collisions like this one in the OPAL detector on the LEP ring at CERN.

Appropriate units

Particle energies are usually given in GeV. For example, the rest energy of a proton is 0.938 GeV. The energy and mass of a particle are related by Einstein's equation,

$$E = mc^2 \qquad \text{so} \qquad m = E/c^2$$

and an appropriate unit for mass is the GeV/c^2. In this unit the proton's rest mass is 0.938 GeV/c^2 In these units mass–energy correspondence is emphasised.

The speed of light, c, plays a fundamental role in the equations of high-energy physics so it is usual to express velocities in terms of it.

For example, $v = \beta c$ (so $\beta = 0.9$ for a particle moving at 90% of the speed of light).

This system of units can be extended to momentum if we remember that the mass of a moving particle is increased by the 'gamma-factor' ($m = \gamma m_o$).

$$p = mv = \gamma m_o v = \gamma m_o \beta c$$

β and γ are both dimensionless numbers so the appropriate units of linear momentum are the same as the units of $m_o c$, that is GeV/c^2 times c, or GeV/c.

Summary

units of energy:	GeV
units of mass:	GeV/c^2
units of momentum:	GeV/c

Beware! None of these are SI units, so they would need converting if you want an answer in joules etc.

Operating a large accelerator complex like CERN can generate some quite unexpected problems. The ring itself is entirely underground but is not horizontal; this is deliberate – it ensures the ring remains in the same rock strata and so stabilises it against geological deformation. However, a few years ago researchers noticed that precision measurements of electron and positron energies were varying on a near monthly cycle. It seems the tidal effect of the moon on nearby Lake Geneva was pressing on one end of the ring and distorting it slightly. This caused a periodic variation of beam length with the lunar cycle! Another problem occurs every time a TGV train leaves Geneva station. Its electrical supply returns to earth and some currents run through the metallic conductors in the LEP tunnel causing electrical disturbances to sensitive equipment.

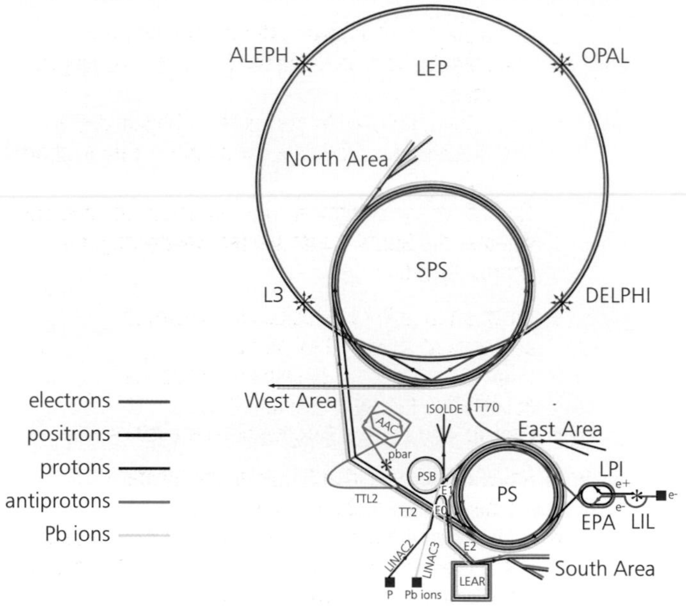

Figure 1.15 The CERN complex. The LEP ring, with its four main experimental sites – ALEPH, DELPHI, OPAL and L3, dominates CERN but there are many other facilities too. Old accelerators like the Proton Synchrotron (PS) and Super Proton Synchrotron (SPS) can provide high- and low-energy proton beams as well as acting as pre-injectors for LEP. The PS is also used to decelerate antiprotons for the neighbouring Low Energy Antiproton Ring (LEAR), the only place in the world where antimatter can be studied at low energies.

Summary

- Physicists use particle accelerators to investigate the behaviour of subatomic particles.
- A particle which is at rest relative to the instruments used to measure its mass has a **rest mass** m_o. Travelling at velocity v relative to the measuring instruments, its mass m is given by the relationship $m = \gamma m_o$, where

$$\gamma = \sqrt{\frac{1}{1 - \frac{v^2}{c^2}}}$$

- In a **linear accelerato**r (or LINAC) charged particles are accelerated in a straight line by a series of **drift tubes**.
- LINACs to produce particles with high energy must be very long. However, for electrons LINACs have the advantage that no synchrotron radiation is produced.
- In the **cyclotron** charged particles move in a spiral path through a constant magnetic field, accelerated by an alternating voltage.
- In the **synchroton** charged particles are accelerated through a field which increases in strength as the energy of the particle increases, keeping the particles in the same orbit. This requires a uniform magnetic field over the circumference of the orbit alone, rather than over the entire circular area.

QUESTIONS

1 Radium-226 has a half-life of 1620 years and decays by emitting alpha particles of energy 4.78 MeV. These decays can be used to provide back-up power in an orbiting satellite.
- **a** What is the primary source of energy for the satellite likely to be?
- **b** What is the energy of a 4.78 MeV alpha particle in joules?
- **c** What is the activity of 1 g of radium-226?
- **d** What is the minimum mass of radium-226 needed to generate 25 W of power?
- **e** Suggest how the energy of the alpha particles may be converted to electricity.

2 An electron is accelerated through a potential difference of 2000 V.
- **a** What is its resultant kinetic energy in (i) eV, (ii) keV, (iii) MeV, (iv) J?
- **b** What would be the energy in keV of (i) a proton and (ii) a helium 2+ ion accelerated through the same potential difference?
- **c** Use the expression KE $= \frac{1}{2}mv^2$ to calculate the velocity of the electron ($m_e = 9.11 \times 10^{-31}$ kg).
- **d** Why, in this case, is it acceptable to use the non-relativistic equation?

3
- **a** Use the Newtonian equation for kinetic energy to calculate the accelerating voltage that would accelerate (i) an electron and (ii) a proton to 10% of the speed of light ($m_p = 1.67 \times 10^{-27}$ kg).
- **b** Explain why this equation becomes increasingly inaccurate at higher and higher energies.

4 Uranium-239 is a short-lived isotope formed when uranium-238 absorbs a neutron. This is a very common occurrence inside a nuclear reactor. U-239 decays, by emitting a beta particle, to neptunium. The energy released in the decay is 1.29 MeV.
- **a** Write down an equation for this decay.
- **b** Use the non-relativistic equation for kinetic energy to calculate the velocity of the emitted beta particle – comment on your result and the validity of this method.
- **c** The ratio of the total energy of the beta particle to its rest energy is equal to the 'gamma factor' for the particle, calculate this value ($m_e = 0.511$ MeV/c^2).
- **d** Use the calculated value of γ to determine the velocity of the electron.
- **e** Would it be necessary to use relativistic equations to calculate the velocity of a 1.29 MeV proton?

5 The rest mass of an electron is 9.110×10^{-31} kg.
The rest mass of a proton is 1.673×10^{-27} kg
1 u = 1.661×10^{-27} kg
- **a** Express the rest masses in atomic mass units (u).
- **b** Express the rest energy of the particles in (i) J, (ii) eV, (iii) MeV, (iv) GeV.
- **c** Express the rest masses in GeV/c^2.

6 The rest mass of a proton is 0.94 GeV/c^2. It is accelerated through a total potential difference of 50 GeV.
- **a** What is its total mass (in GeV/c^2)?
- **b** What is its total energy (in GeV)?
- **c** What is its velocity?
- **d** What is its linear momentum in GeV/c?

7 The power of solar radiation reaching the outer layers of the Earth's atmosphere is about 1400 W m^{-2}. The Earth's orbit has a radius of about 1.5×10^{11} m.
- **a** Calculate the total power output from the Sun.
- **b** Calculate the rate at which the Sun is consuming its rest mass.
- **c** If the Sun continues to consume hydrogen at this rate, how long could it last (mass of the Sun is about 2×10^{30} kg)?
- **d** Explain why your answer to (c) is unrealistic and say whether the Sun's actual lifetime will be longer or shorter than this.

8
- **a** What is the ratio of velocities for electrons accelerated through 1 kV and 2 kV?
- **b** What is the ratio of velocities for electrons accelerated through 1 GV and 2 GV?
- **c** Explain why (a) and (b) give different values.

9
- **a** Show that the relation between energy and momentum for a photon is $p = E/c$.
- **b** Write down the general equation that relates energy and momentum for a particle of non-zero rest mass.
- **c** Show that the equation you have given in (b) approaches the relation in (a) if the particle energy is sufficiently high.
- **d** Suggest a suitable condition for 'sufficiently high energies'.

10 A nucleus of uranium-238 is at rest when it decays by alpha emission to thorium-234.
- **a** Use the data below to calculate the loss of rest mass in the decay.
  atomic mass of U-238 = 238.05082 u
  atomic mass of Th-234 = 234.04364 u
  atomic mass of He-4 = 4.00260 u
  1 u = 1.661×10^{-27} kg
- **b** How much energy (in MeV) is released in this decay? Where does it go?
- **c** What conservation laws are relevant to this decay?
- **d** Why is it unnecessary to consider the rest energy or binding energy of the orbital electrons?
- **e** How is the energy shared between the alpha particle and the recoiling nucleus?

QUESTIONS

11 According to special relativity an electron could never be accelerated up to or beyond the speed of light.

a What happens to the mass of an electron as its velocity approaches *c*?
b What is the mass of a photon of energy *E*?
c How can it be possible for photons to travel at the speed of light?

12 What are the advantages and disadvantages of a collider compared to a fixed target experiment?

13 Find the total energy available to form rest energy of new particles when:
a A proton with kinetic energy 14 GeV has a head-on collision with an antiproton with the same kinetic energy.
b An antiproton with kinetic energy 28 GeV collides with a stationary proton. (Take the rest energy of a proton to be approximately 1 GeV).
c Explain the difference and comment on its significance for accelerator design.

14 In a cyclotron charged particles are deflected into circular orbits by a magnetic field perpendicular to their paths.
a Assuming particle mass is constant and equal to m_0, derive an equation for the radius of curvature of the particle path if it has velocity *v* and charge *q* and moves perpendicular to a magnetic field of strength *B*.
b What is the orbital period of this particle?
c Why is it convenient that the orbital period is independent of particle velocity?
d Explain what is meant by the *cyclotron resonance frequency* and calculate its value for a 0.5 MeV proton moving in a magnetic field of strength 0.5 T.
e At high energy the period does depend on particle velocity. Why is this a problem for the operation of a cyclotron and does the period increase or decrease with energy?
f Explain why 25 MeV is about the practical limit for the acceleration of protons in a cyclotron. Would the limit for electrons be at a higher or lower energy?

15 The synchro-cyclotron gets round the problem of increasing period with energy by changing the a.c. frequency applied to the 'dees' in step with the changing orbital frequency. This allows bunches of particles to be accelerated to even higher energy.
a Above about 700 MeV these machines become uneconomic, why?
b Explain how the principle of the synchrotron differs from that of a synchro-cyclotron.
c What is the main advantage of a synchrotron?

16 **a** What is synchrotron radiation?
b Why is synchrotron radiation more of a problem when accelerating electrons than when accelerating protons?
c How are very high-energy electron beams usually produced?

17 **a** What is the average electric field strength along a 3 km linear accelerator that produces 20 GeV electrons?
b Will there be any significant gravitational deflection of the beam over this distance?

18 The cancellation of the Superconducting Super Collider raises the question of whether or not a new generation of higher energy accelerators (beyond the proposed and accepted plan for LHC at CERN) will ever be built. Imagine you had to advise the government whether or not to invest in particle accelerators. What would be your arguments for and against the investment?

2 Detectors

An ideal particle detector would reveal the presence of all types of particles. It would show their trajectories and collisions in three-dimensional space and allow us to calculate charge, momentum and energy. It would resolve positions to within a fraction of a millimetre and react quickly enough to detect millions of events per second and output data on them directly to a computer for processing. Some modern detectors come close to achieving all of this, but most detectors are a compromise solution. In this chapter we will look at the development of particle detectors from the **spinthariscopes** used by Rutherford to the large layered detectors used at modern accelerators like CERN and Fermilab.

DETECTING HIGH-ENERGY PARTICLES

Essential principles

When a charged particle moves through a medium it interacts with atoms in the medium. This interaction is electromagnetic, and usually results in ionisation or excitation of the atoms in the medium. Particle physics experiments involve particles with energies which are typically many millions of times the ionisation energy of an atom, so they are likely to affect large numbers of atoms as they travel through matter. This situation has been likened to firing a bullet through a large crate of eggs, where a line of smashed eggs remains as a 'memory' of the bullet's path.

There are three possible ways in which high-energy particles may be detected when they interact with matter.

- If the high-energy particles ionise atoms in matter as they pass through it, the ions and electrons produced may be detected as tiny electrical signals using suitably positioned electrodes. This principle is used in the **ionisation chamber** and the **Geiger counter**, and in more modern detectors such as **drift tubes** and **multiwire proportional chambers**. It is also the principle behind the use of semiconductor diodes as detectors. In such detectors, high-energy particles passing through the semiconductor material free electrons in the material. This allows a pulse of electric current to flow through the diode, which can then operate a counting circuit.
- A second method of detection is possible if the high-energy particles create ions which produce visible tracks. The tracks can be photographed and used to analyse particle trajectories. This is used in the **cloud chamber**, **bubble chamber**, **photographic emulsions** and the **spark chamber**.
- A third way of detecting high-energy particles can be used if the particles produce excited atoms which lose energy by emitting photons of light. The photons can be counted by a photomultiplier, and may be used as signals which trigger a camera or other recording device as in a **scintillation counter**.

Notice that all of these mechanisms rely on an *electromagnetic* interaction. Most of these detectors will not directly detect neutral particles, whose existence and properties must be inferred from the behaviour of the charged particles with which they collide or into which they decay.

The photographs and diagrams here show particle detectors that are commonly used in school laboratories.

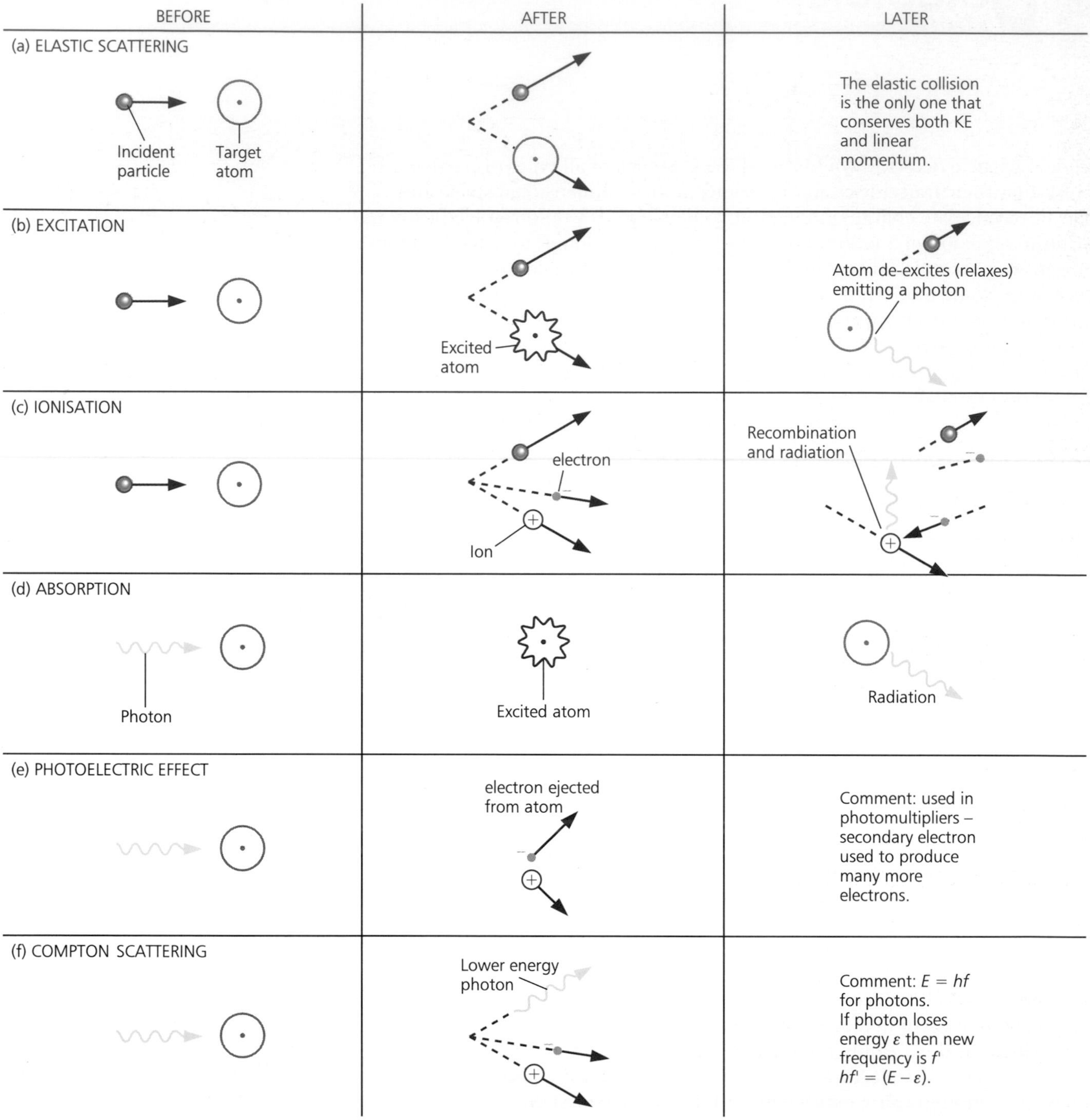

Figure 2.1 Interaction between high-energy particles and matter.

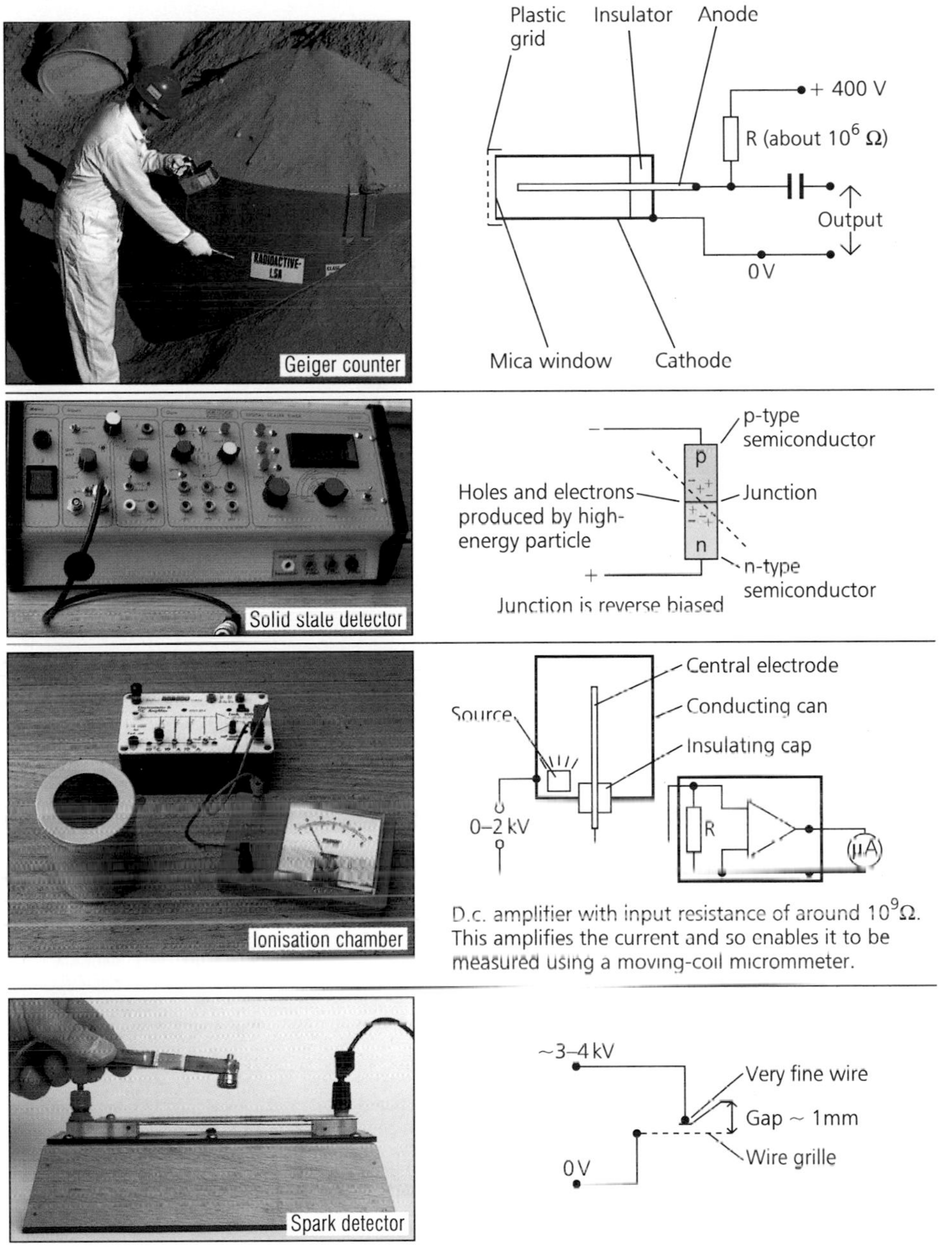

Figure 2.2 Particle detectors used in school.

The cloud chamber

Cloud chambers are rarely used nowadays although many early discoveries were made with them. A cloud chamber produces particle tracks in much the same way that an aircraft's exhaust fumes cause a visible track across the sky. In both cases condensation causes tiny drops of liquid to form in a gas. In the atmosphere water droplets form a long thin cloud along the exhaust trail of the aircraft. In the cloud chamber drops of alcohol condense around the ions left in the wake of a passing particle.

The cloud chamber was invented by Charles Wilson when he was trying to produce artificial mists to investigate atmospheric effects in the laboratory. As early as 1896 he showed that X-rays (which were known to ionise air) would produce a diffuse cloud in the chamber, but it was not until 1910 that he demonstrated the paths of alpha and beta rays through the chamber. This was the first time anyone had seen the tracks of individual subatomic particles – Wilson received the Nobel prize for this work in 1927.

The cloud chamber

To produce particle tracks it is essential that the air inside the cloud chamber is **supersaturated** with vapour. At any particular temperature there is a maximum concentration of vapour that can remain in the air, and any extra vapour will condense out to form a liquid. The amount of vapour that a given volume of air can hold increases with temperature, so there is more vapour in saturated warm air than in saturated cold air. If saturated warm air is suddenly cooled the vapour will condense out onto any dust particles or ions present in the air. If there are no suitable particles to initiate condensation the vapour does not immediately condense out but becomes supersaturated. If a high-energy particle passes through this supersaturated vapour condensation occurs and droplets rapidly grow onto the ions left in the wake of the particle. These droplets soon become large enough to see and photograph.

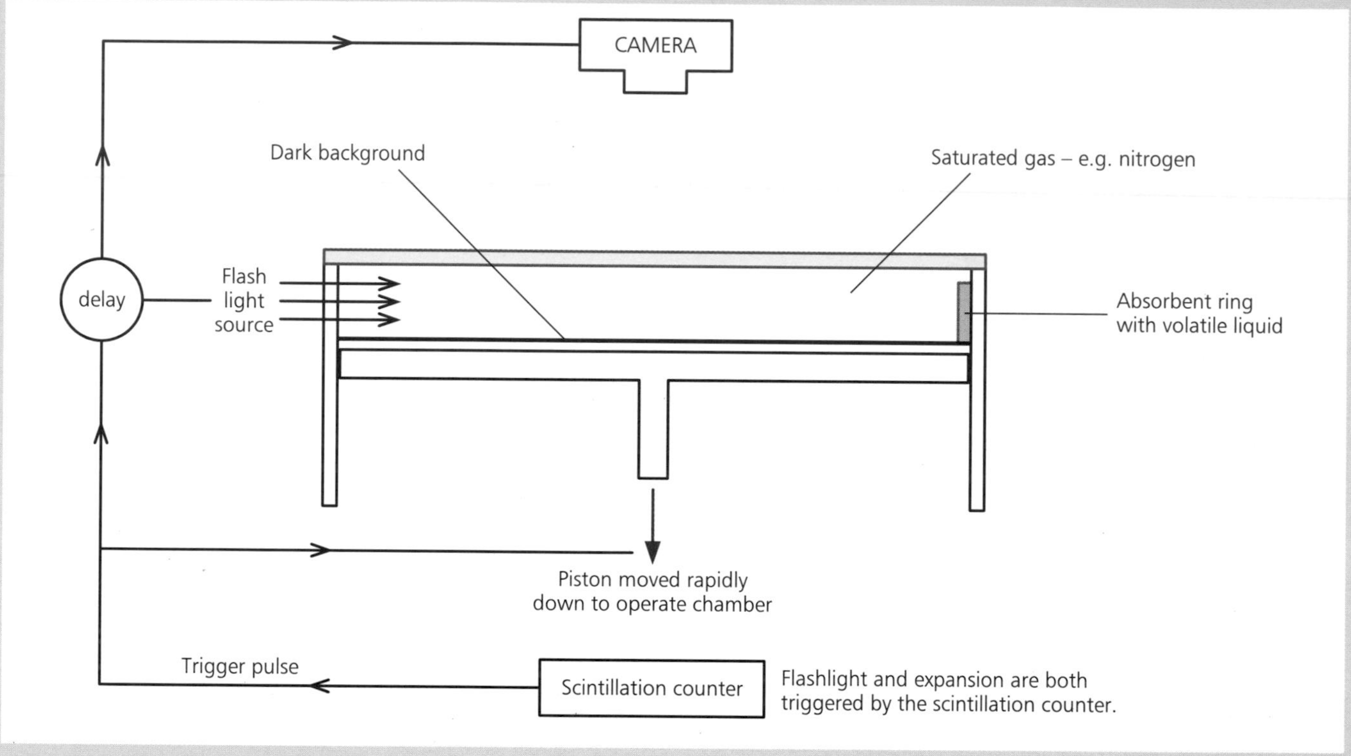

Figure 2.3 An expansion cloud chamber.

There are two ways in which a supersaturated vapour may be generated in a cloud chamber. One way is to saturate the air with alcohol and then rapidly expand the chamber so that the temperature falls due to the work done by the gas in expansion (this type of chamber is called an 'expansion chamber'). The second way is to have a temperature gradient in the chamber produced by placing dry ice (solid carbon dioxide) under the viewing surface. Saturated vapour near the top of the chamber becomes supersaturated as it cools and falls. This produces ideal conditions for viewing the particle tracks just above the viewing surface and is the technique used in many school cloud chambers.

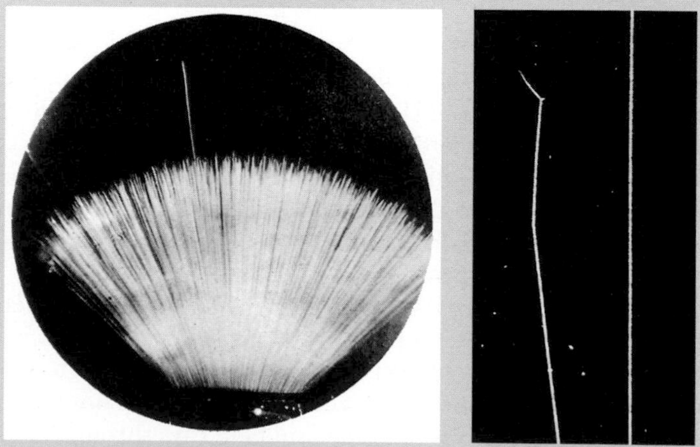

Figure 2.4 Cloud chamber tracks.

The beauty of the expansion cloud chamber is its ability to show the actual trajectories of individual subatomic particles. It also has 'memory', as the trail of droplets persists for a while after the particle that produced them has gone. This means a cloud chamber can be triggered to expand when a detector close to it (e.g. a **scintillation counter**) detects an 'interesting' event, producing a record of that event. However, air has a low density and high-energy particles will travel a long way through it before they stop or collide. Because of this, it is difficult to capture an image of an event in a predictable way. Also, the time taken between expansions means the device has a long 'dead time' and many events are inevitably missed.

The bubble chamber

The paths of alpha particles from a school source just about stop in a cloud chamber 10 cm across. These alpha particles have an energy of a few MeV so it is obvious that little of interest will be likely to be recorded by a cloud chamber if it is used to look at the particles produced by a modern accelerator (whose energies are measured in GeV). By the 1950s it was clear that some other kind of detector was required that could capture the long tracks of very high-energy particles and that could be operated repeatedly with little time lost between observations.

Donald Glaser invented the **bubble chamber** in the early 1950s, and it was first used to observe particle tracks in 1954. The bubble chamber acts as both target and detector for the incident particles which usually collide with superheated liquid hydrogen inside it. The principle is very similar to that of the cloud chamber except that the much greater density of the liquid medium means that incident particles will have many more interactions per unit length of their paths and so will not travel so far. This allows more energetic particle tracks to be captured and photographed inside the chamber. Glaser won the 1960 Nobel Prize for his invention.

The bubble chamber

When a bottle of beer is opened the sudden drop in pressure allows dissolved carbon dioxide in the beer to form bubbles throughout the body of the liquid. However, if you look closely you can see that the bubbles tend to stream from tiny bumps or irregularities on the inside surface of the glass. A bubble chamber works on a similar principle. In the bubble chamber very pure liquid hydrogen is pressurised to prevent it from boiling. In operation the pressure is suddenly released and the boiling point falls (as it does for water at reduced atmospheric pressure). Because the hydrogen is pure it does not boil, but becomes temporarily superheated (it remains liquid at a temperature above its boiling point). Bubbles form inside the hydrogen wherever ions or impurities are present. Bubbles grow rapidly around the ions left in the wake of a high-energy particle.

Figure 2.5 Bubbles in a beer bottle.

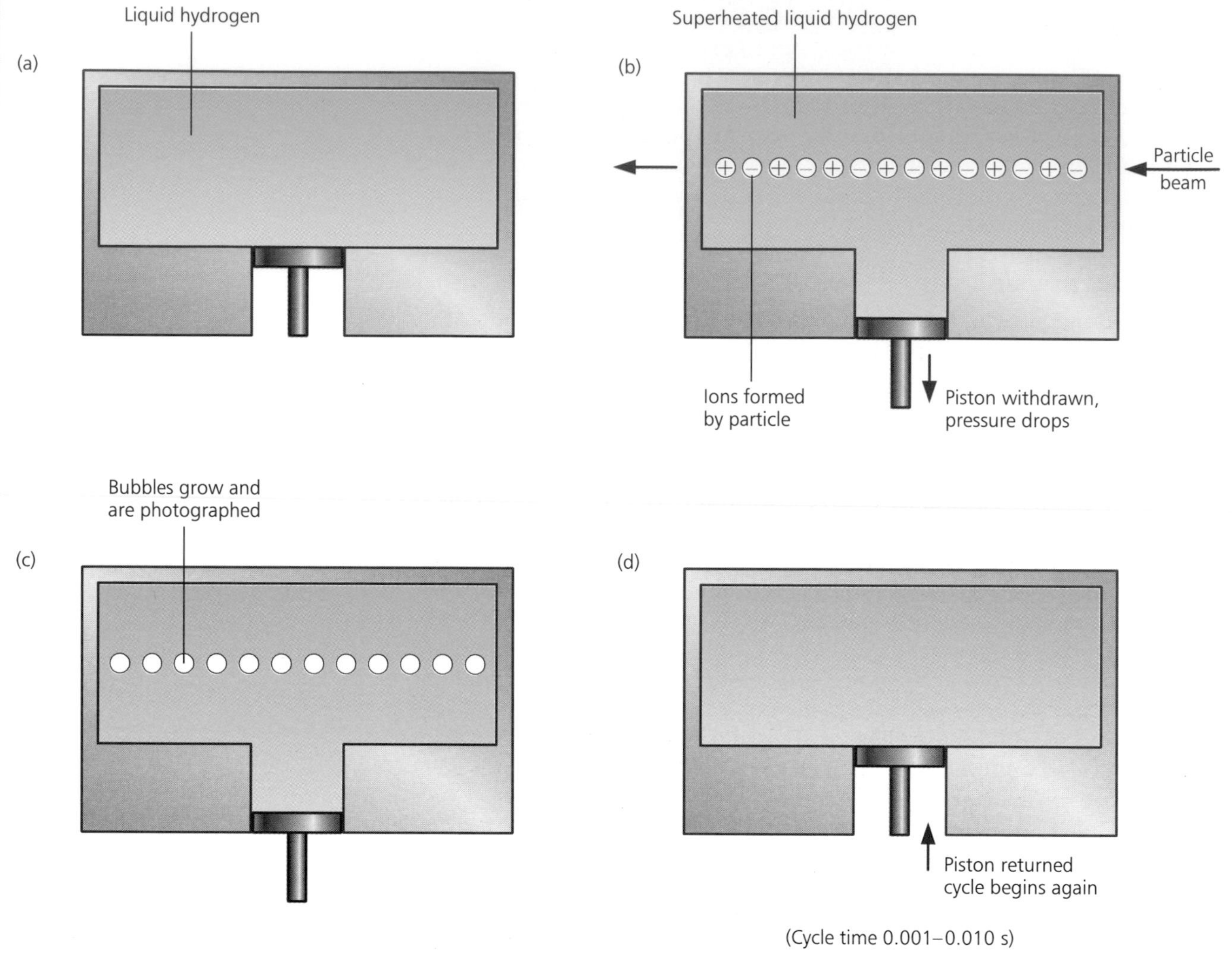

Figure 2.6 A bubble chamber.

Bubble chambers use liquid hydrogen because this is the simplest element, but it does have a drawback – the apparatus must be cooled to about 20 K (–253 °C) to liquefy the hydrogen. Many bubble chambers were built and used during the 1960s and 1970s and some are several metres in diameter. Like the cloud chamber these devices have a dead time after each expansion before the next event can be detected. This dead time is around one second, during which many events may be missed.

In practice bubble chambers are triggered to operate when pulses of particles from an accelerator are due to arrive. The 2 m bubble chamber at Brookhaven starts to expand 15 ms before the particles arrive. On arrival the particles leave trails of rapidly growing bubbles. About 1 ms after their arrival an arc light flashes to allow photographs of the tracks to be taken. (In 1964 the Brookhaven chamber was first to detect the omega-minus particle.)

Analysing particle tracks

Individual particle tracks have several characteristics that can be used to identify the properties of the particles that made them.

- **Track length**: this is related to the particle energy, but also depends on the type of particle. For example, a 100 MeV proton makes a longer track than a 70 MeV proton but an electron of similar energy does not interact so strongly with matter and makes a much longer track than either of the two protons.
- **Track thickness**: this is related to charge. Highly charged particles tend to produce thicker tracks but velocity also plays a part. Faster particles produce thinner tracks since they spend less time near each atom of the medium, and so interact with matter less strongly.
- **Track curvature**:
  (i) Usually a magnetic field is imposed perpendicular to the particle paths. This exerts a force on the particle in a direction predicted by Fleming's left-hand rule. If the direction in which the particles are travelling is known then the sign of their charge can be worked out from the direction in which they are deflected.
  (ii) As particles move through a medium they lose energy. This reduces their momentum and as the radius of curvature of their path becomes smaller, they turn more sharply. If this is visible in the track, the direction of motion of the particles can be deduced.
- **Missing tracks**: it is sometimes obvious that events in a bubble chamber are connected even though no visible track connects them. This is a good indication that a neutral particle is involved in the reaction.

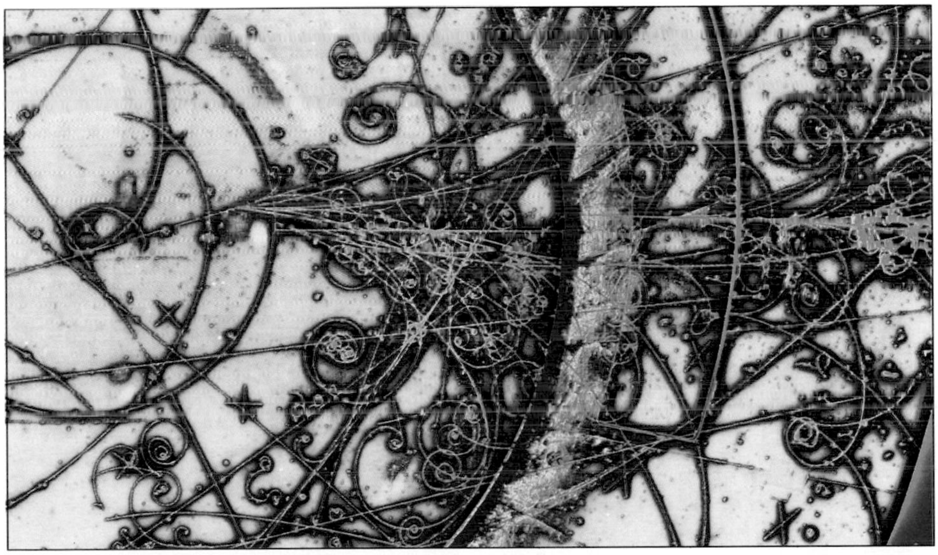

Figure 2.7 Tracks in a bubble chamber. The magnetic field direction would be perpendicular to the page.

Calculating energy and momentum from radius of curvature

The radius of curvature (r) for a charge (q) moving at velocity (v) perpendicular to a magnetic field (B) is:

$$r = \frac{mv}{Bq} = \frac{p}{Bq}$$

where p is the linear momentum.

This also holds for relativistic velocities as long as relativistic momentum is used:

$$p = \gamma m_o v$$

Once p is known the particle energy can be calculated:

$$\textbf{kinetic energy KE} = \frac{p^2}{2m} \ \textbf{(non-relativistic)}$$

$$\text{or } \textbf{total energy } E = \sqrt{p^2c^2 + m_o{}^2c^4} \ \textbf{(relativistic)}$$

We can learn a lot about individual particles from their tracks but more information comes from the *relation* between the tracks when a collision occurs. Here the laws of conservation of energy, momentum and charge can help to identify unknown particles from the behaviour of familiar ones.

Momentum conservation in 2D

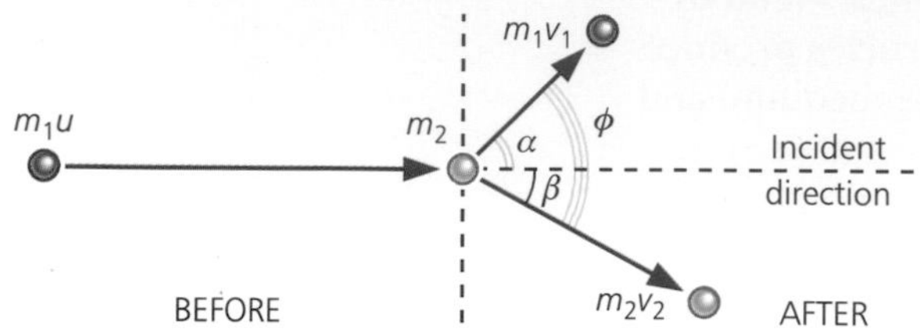

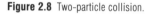

Figure 2.8 Two-particle collision.

Many particle collisions are between high-energy incident particles and almost stationary target particles. This is the case in a bubble chamber. We can analyse these collisions using the laws of conservation of energy and momentum (in the equations below momentum has been resolved parallel (2) and perpendicular (3) to the incident particle direction). If the collision is elastic (kinetic energy is conserved (1)):

$$\tfrac{1}{2}m_1u^2 = \tfrac{1}{2}m_1v_1^2 + \tfrac{1}{2}m_2v_2^2 \qquad (1)$$

$$m_1u = m_1v_1 \cos\alpha + m_2v_2 \cos\beta \qquad (2)$$

$$m_1v_1 \sin\alpha = m_2v_2 \sin\beta \qquad (3)$$

These equations lead to some useful general results:

- For
  - $m_1 = m_2$ $\quad \phi = 90°$
  - $m_1 > m_2$ $\quad \phi < 90°$
  - $m_1 < m_2$ $\quad \phi > 90°$
- If the incident particle is the more massive there is a maximum scattering angle for the incident particle:

$$\alpha_{max} = \frac{m_2}{m_1}$$

A proton can deflect no more than 0.03° when it scatters from an electron and an alpha particle can deflect no more than 14.5° when it scatters from a proton.

- There is also a maximum amount of incident kinetic energy that can be transferred to the target particle. This maximum value occurs when the collision is head-on. The fraction is then

$$\frac{4m_1m_2}{(m_1 + m_2)^2}$$

This will only approach unity if the masses of the particles are similar.

(a) **(b)** **(c)**

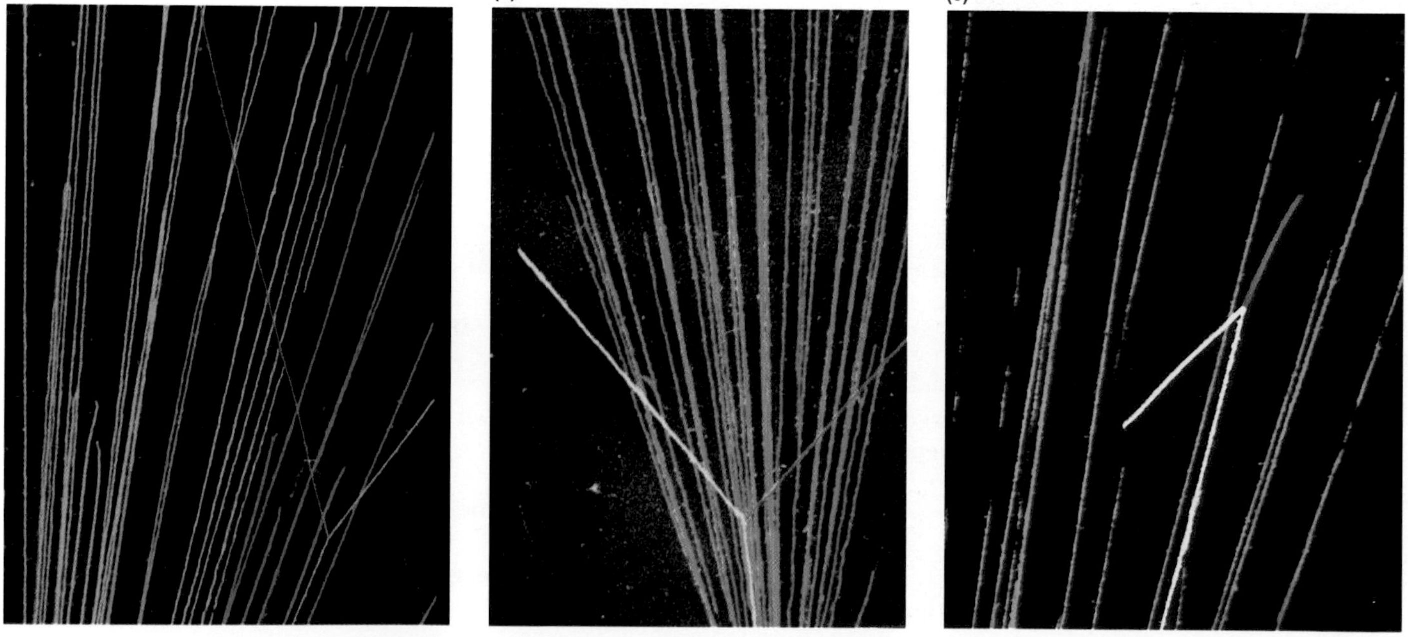

Figure 2.9 Three bubble chamber photos showing collisions between particles of different or the same mass. The incident particle is shown in yellow in each case. (a) Particle 1 more massive. (b) Particles of equal mass (90 degree angle) (c) Particle 1 of less mass. In all three cases the second particle is initially stationary.

Bubble chambers have the advantage of resolving particle tracks but they are sensitive for only a few milliseconds each second and their resolution is limited by the size the bubbles have to grow to become visible.

COUNTERS AND DETECTORS

Scintillation counters

One of the earliest particle detectors was the **spinthariscope**. This is an eyepiece focused on a small thin screen coated in zinc sulphide. When alpha particles strike the screen the zinc sulphide is excited and later emits photons of visible light. A tiny flash of light is emitted for each alpha particle hitting the screen and an observer can count the rate of arrival of particles. To carry out experiments like Geiger and Marsden's observations of Rutherford scattering would involve sitting in a darkened room for some time while your eyes grow accustomed to the darkness. You would then sit for hours on end taking turns to make counts of arrival rates at different scattering angles. It is hardly surprising that Geiger went on to invent the Geiger counter!

Solids like zinc sulphide used in the early scintillation counters rapidly absorb the flashes of light they emit, so they can only be used when spread in thin layers on a screen. However, certain organic crystals (like naphthalene and anthracene) are transparent to their own fluorescent radiation so can be used in large quantities and the light emitted can be directed to a **photomultiplier**.

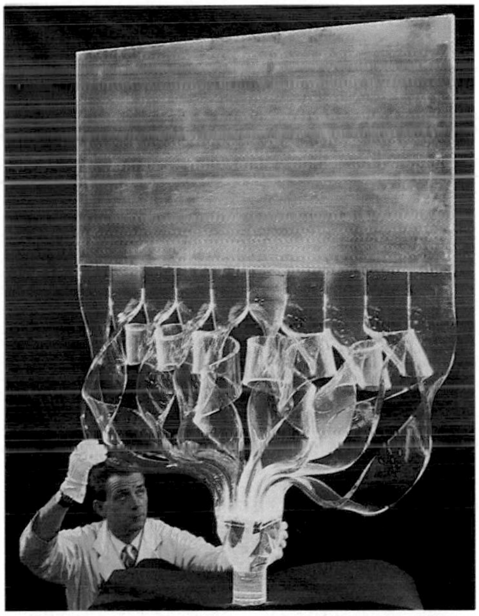

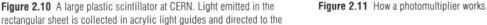

Figure 2.10 A large plastic scintillator at CERN. Light emitted in the rectangular sheet is collected in acrylic light guides and directed to the circular 'pipe' below. The light guides are all the same length so they do not affect the relative arrival time of light from different parts of the scintillator.

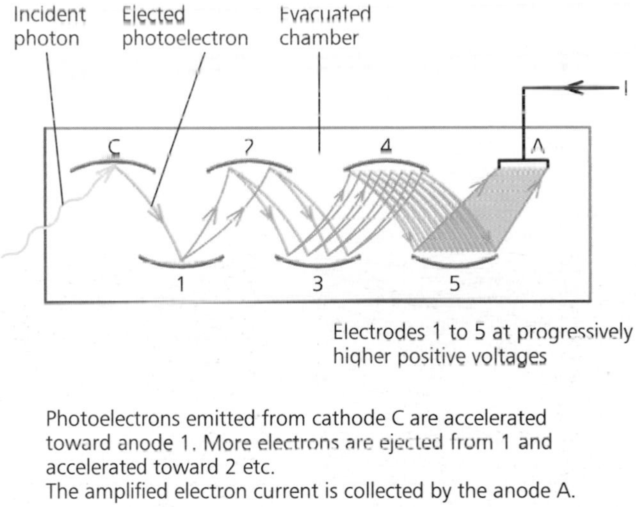
Incident photon
Ejected photoelectron
Evacuated chamber
I
C
2
4
A
1
3
5
Electrodes 1 to 5 at progressively higher positive voltages
Photoelectrons emitted from cathode C are accelerated toward anode 1. More electrons are ejected from 1 and accelerated toward 2 etc.
The amplified electron current is collected by the anode A.

Figure 2.11 How a photomultiplier works.

A photomultiplier connected to a scintillation counter will produce an electrical pulse whenever a particle passes through the scintillation counter. A second scintillation counter and photomultiplier placed some distance away along the path of the particle will only produce a simultaneous electrical pulse if the same particle passes through it too (these particles are moving almost at the speed of light so the time to travel between the two detectors can be neglected). The outputs of the two detectors can be connected to a '**coincidence counter**' which will register only these simultaneous signals. In this way the path of the particle can be determined.

Čerenkov counters

If a charged particle moves through a medium faster than the speed of light in that medium it creates the optical equivalent of a sonic boom. This is an electromagnetic shock wave of visible radiation called **Čerenkov radiation**. The radiation is emitted at an angle to the particle's path that increases with the velocity of the particle. The velocity of light in the medium is determined by the medium so it is possible to build detectors that will reveal only particles moving above a particular velocity.

Speed of light in medium is $c^1 = \frac{c}{n}$
(n = refractive index)

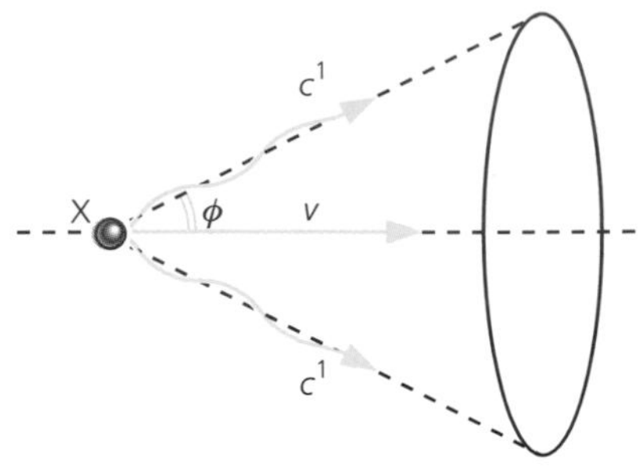
X
ϕ
v
c1
c1

Particle at X has $v > c^1$

Photons are emitted at an angle ϕ to its motion

$$\cos\phi = \frac{c^1}{n} = \frac{c}{nv}$$

Figure 2.12 Čerenkov radiation.

Spark counters

A simple spark counter consists of a fine metal wire above a metal grille. If the voltage between these two conductors is increased the air between them will eventually break down and conduct (dry air at atmospheric pressure breaks down in electric fields exceeding about $3 \times 10^6\,\mathrm{V\,m^{-1}}$). It does this violently as electrons torn from air molecules are accelerated in the field between the electrodes. These electrons gain enough kinetic energy to ionise more molecules by collision and there is an avalanche of charge flow resulting in a spark. If the voltage is now reduced slightly the air between the electrodes is on the verge of electrical breakdown and an ionising source such as a high-energy particle or X-ray or gamma ray will trigger more sparks. One immediate advantage of spark counters over cloud chambers and bubble chambers is their speed of response – their main disadvantage is that they give little or no information about the particle trajectory.

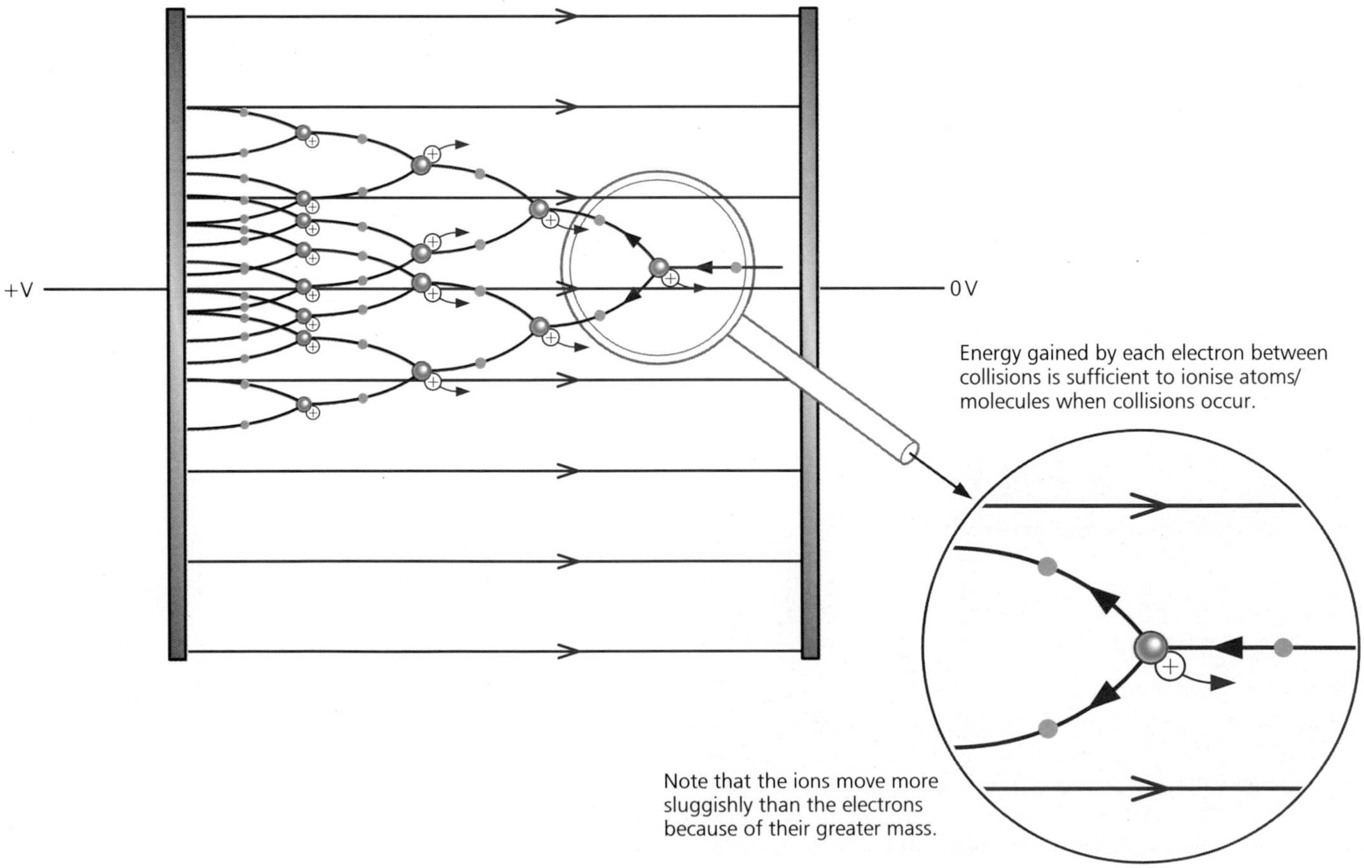
+V
0 V
Energy gained by each electron between collisions is sufficient to ionise atoms/molecules when collisions occur.
Note that the ions move more sluggishly than the electrons because of their greater mass.

Figure 2.13 Mechanism of spark formation and electrical discharge in gases.

Spark detectors

The spark chamber

During the 1950s and 60s the basic idea behind the spark detector was developed in several ways. Marcello Conversi invented the **flash tube**, a sealed glass tube filled with neon and placed between metal electrodes. When a high-energy particle passes through the tube it ionises the neon and the electric field induces a visible discharge as in a discharge tube or fluorescent lamp. This is visible at the end of the tube so an array of flash tubes viewed end on will record the path of the particle. As with the cloud chamber the ions created by the particle persist in the tubes after the particle has passed, so the system has memory and can be triggered by a scintillation counter to switch on the high voltages and photograph the array. Arrays of flash tubes were later replaced by spark chambers in which the glass tubes were removed and parallel layers of metal electrodes were spaced in a chamber of inert gas.

The wire spark chamber

This idea was developed by Frank Kiernan at CERN who replaced the metal plate electrodes with wires. Every time a spark is produced a tiny current flows in the wires nearest to it. These electrical signals can be detected and analysed automatically to calculate the path taken by the particle to a within a few millimetres accuracy. There are several advantages to this approach:

- it is no longer necessary to photograph the array
- electrical detection is more sensitive than photography so the sparks do not have to grow so large to be recorded. This reduces the dead time of the detector, making it much faster, operating at up to 1000 times per second
- the electrical signals need little extra processing before being analysed by computer.

Figure 2.15 A spark chamber in operation at CERN. The tracks of ionising particles appear as red lines in the picture above.

Figure 2.14 The spark chamber and wire spark chamber.

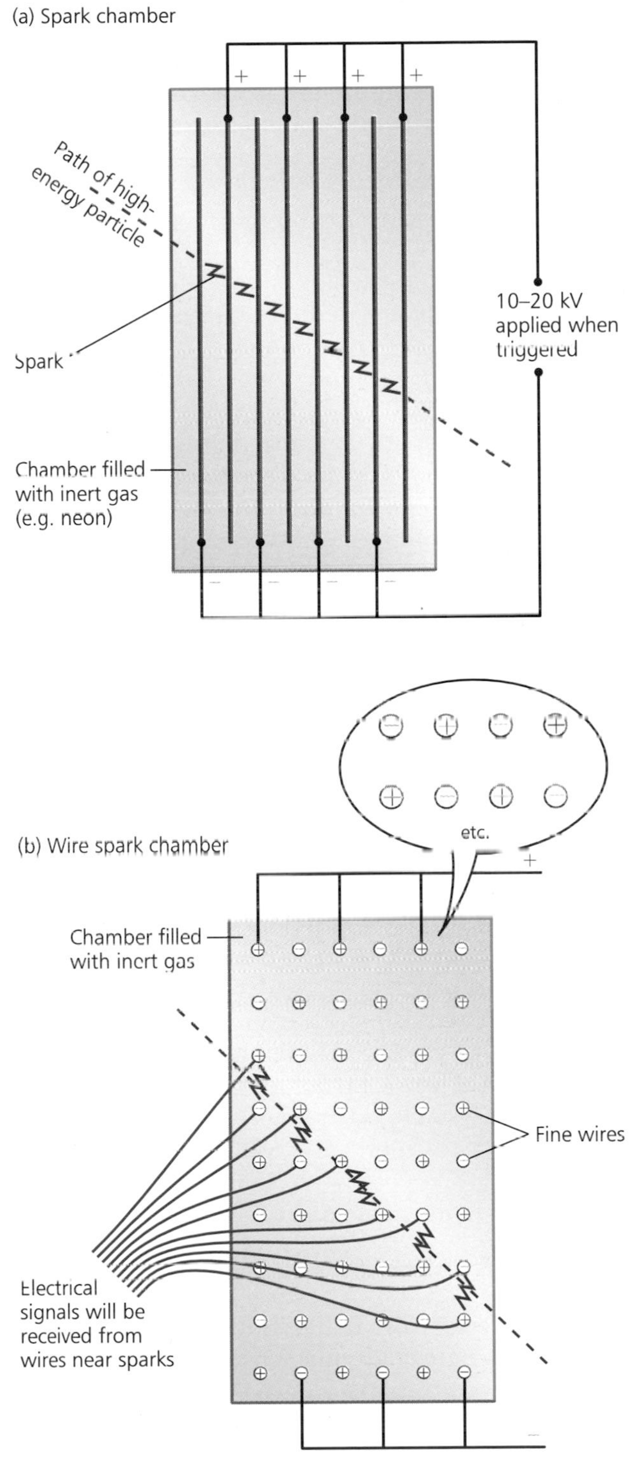

N.B. (i) Supply connections only shown at edges of chamber although *all* wires are connected to supply.
(ii) Signal leads only shown for responding wires above although all wires do have signal leads attached.

Georges Charpak and the drift chamber

The 1992 Nobel Prize for Physics was awarded to Georges Charpak of CERN for 'his invention and development of detectors in high-energy physics'. His team developed two new types of detector which revolutionised the imaging of subatomic particles and played a part in several discoveries which led to other Nobel Prizes. Both the **multiwire proportional counter** and the **drift chamber** are faster and more accurate than the spark chambers they replaced.

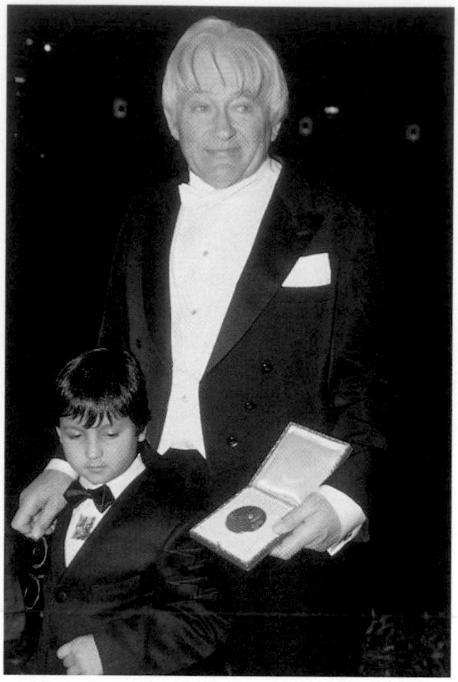

Figure 2.16 Georges Charpak was awarded the 1992 Noble prize for his invention of the multiwire proportional chamber. The Nobel prize has been awarded for the invention or development of particle detectors on three other occasions: Wilson (1927) for the cloud chamber, Powell (1950) for the use of photographic emulsions, Glaser (1960) for the bubble chamber.

The multiwire chamber and the drift chamber

The multiwire proportional counter is rather similar to a Geiger–Müller tube in that it responds to the electrons accelerated in the intense electric field very close to a fine wire. It is much faster than the spark chamber because it responds immediately to the electrons freed by the particles rather than being triggered later and sweeping up the ions along the particle path. It is also more accurate because the very fine wires (about 20 μm in diameter and just a few millimetres apart) act independently of one another. These detectors can pinpoint a particle's path to within a millimetre and respond to a million particles a second.

The **drift chamber** goes one step further. As well as recording the wires that respond to a particle it records the *time* at which they respond (to do this they need to be triggered by multiwire detectors). Electrons produced by the particle take time to reach the intense field near the fine wires and cause the avalanche of charge that is responsible for the electrical signal. The later their arrival time (after the trigger signal) the further from the wire they were produced, so recording the arrival time allows the particle's trajectory to be calculated with much greater accuracy. With wires spaced several centimetres apart, particle trajectories can be determined to within 50 μm.

Although the idea of the drift chamber is simple in principle there were many technical problems to be overcome before the technique was perfected. One problem is calculating how much distance corresponds to how much delay, as the drifting electrons are continually supplied with energy from the electric field but dissipate it in collisions with molecules in the gas. The electric field must be set up so that a balance is struck between these two effects so that the distances can be calculated. Another problem is that the inert gases in the chamber must be very pure – only one part per million of oxygen in the chamber would destroy its effectiveness. Drift chambers may be several metres in size.

Charpak's detectors also find uses in medicine and industry where their speed of response gives a great advantage over traditional photographic techniques.

The time projection chamber

In particle physics the drift chamber has been taken still further by David Nygren who has invented a Time Projection Chamber (TPC) in which particles moving through a large gas-filled cylinder release electrons that then drift *up to a metre* to the ends of the chamber where they hit segmented electrodes. The time and position of arrival together allow a 3-dimensional image of the particle path to be reconstructed. (A large TPC is used in the ALEPH detector at CERN which is used to analyse the results of Z^0 decays.)

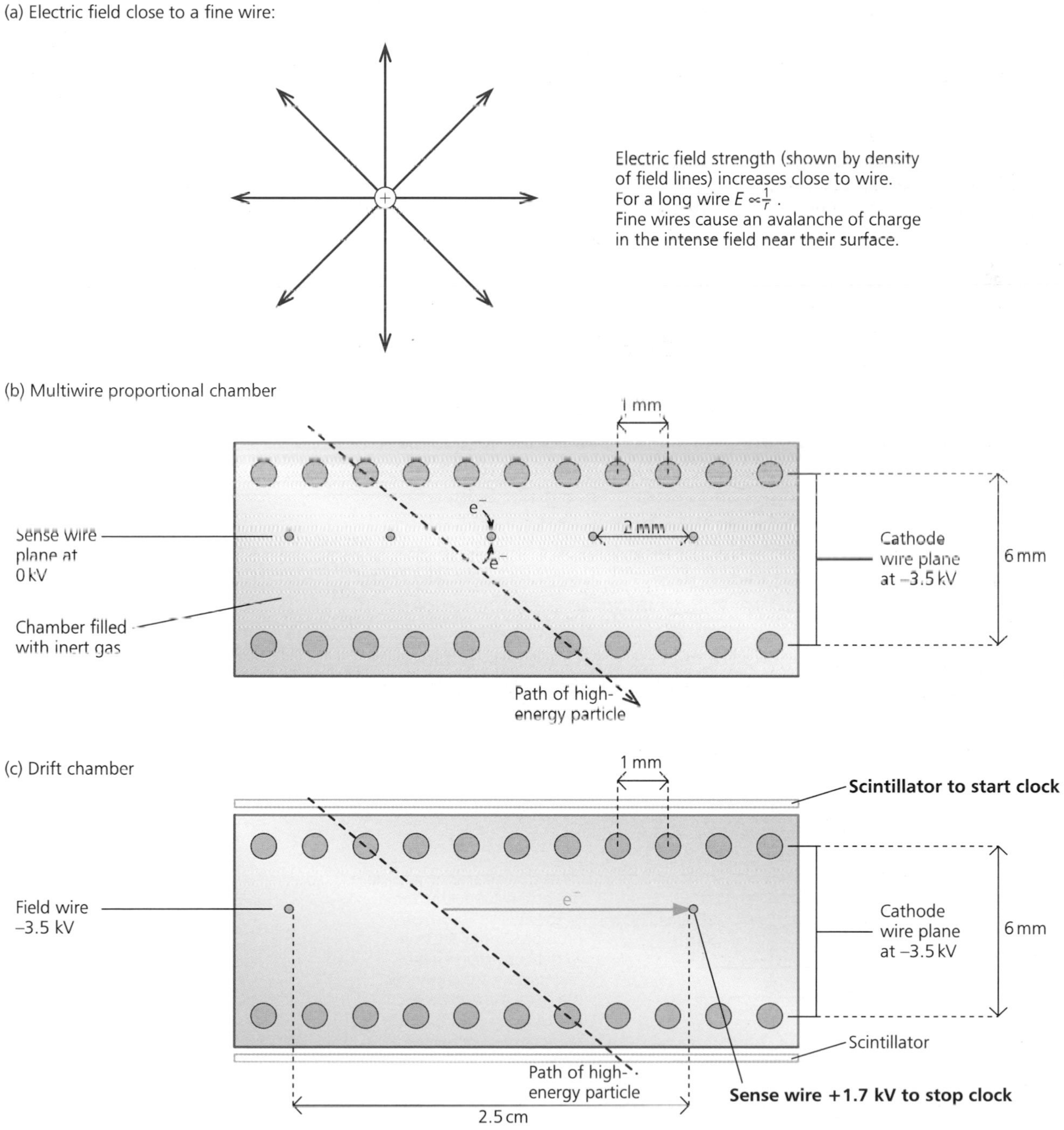

Figure 2.17 Sketches of the multiwire proportional counter and the drift chamber.

Figure 2.18 Many thousands of fine wires collect the electrons released by high-energy particles as they pass through the drift chamber.

Figure 2.19 The time projection chamber works back from the arrival of tiny electrical signals to determine their origin on the track of a high-energy particle. This photograph shows one end of the TCP at the PEP collider at SLAC.

Solid state detectors

Intrinsic (pure) semiconductors would be insulators at absolute zero. This is because all their outer electrons are used in bonding (valence band full) and none are free to conduct (conduction band empty). They differ from true insulators in that the energy gap between their valence and conduction bands is less than 1 eV and so comparable to the thermal energy available to an electron at room temperature. This means there will always be some electrons which break free of their bonds and are able to move through the structure in the conduction band. If a high-energy particle passes through the semiconductor it will supply enough extra energy to promote many more electrons and the conductivity of the semiconductor will temporarily increase due to the increase in both electrons and holes. This can be used to produce an electrical signal to record the particle.

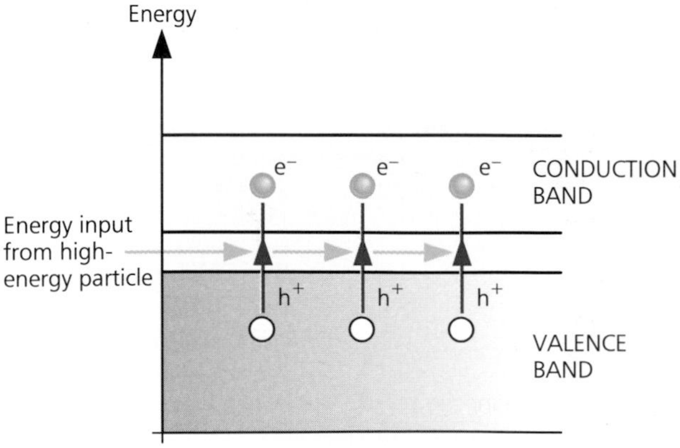

When a high-energy particle hits a semiconductor some of the energy absorbed promotes more electrons to the conduction band. This increases the number of charge carriers (both electrons e^- and holes h^+) and reduces semiconductor resistance.

Figure 2.20 Energy band diagram for a semiconductor.

Silicon strip detectors (SSDs) can resolve detail that is too fine to be captured in a bubble chamber photograph (below 10 μm). They consist of a line of semiconductor diodes on a single chip. Each diode stores the charge freed by high-energy charged particles and can be read like an electronic memory of the event. They are particularly useful in detecting particles that have lifetimes around 1 ps (like tau-leptons or particles containing bottom quarks) because they can distinguish the point at which they are created from the point where they decay (which is only a few millimetres away). They were crucial in the recent discovery of the top quark and also have applications in astronomy and medicine.

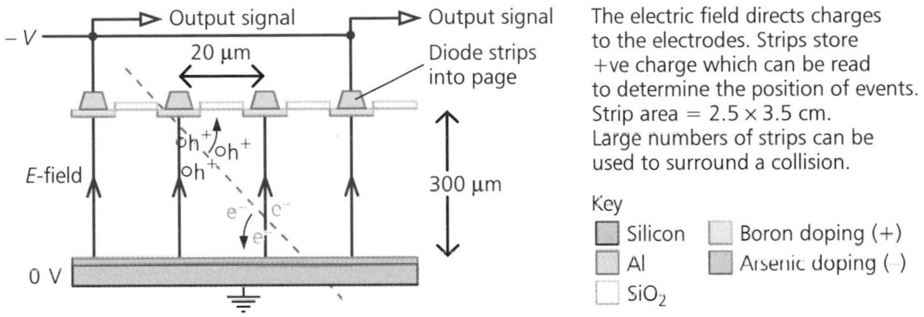
Output signal
Output signal
−V
20 μm
Diode strips into page
E-field
300 μm
0 V
The electric field directs charges to the electrodes. Strips store +ve charge which can be read to determine the position of events. Strip area = 2.5 × 3.5 cm. Large numbers of strips can be used to surround a collision.
Key
Silicon
Al
SiO2
Boron doping (+)
Arsenic doping (−)

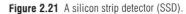

Figure 2.21 A silicon strip detector (SSD).

Charge coupled devices (CCDs) are also single chips but are divided into an array of 'pixels', perhaps 250 000 on a 1 cm square chip. These pixels or picture elements attract and store the charge released by high-energy particles and form a 2-dimensional image of the particle track with a resolution approaching 100 μm. Two disadvantages of using CCDs are that they have to be kept at very low temperatures (around 120 K) and it takes time to read the information stored on them.

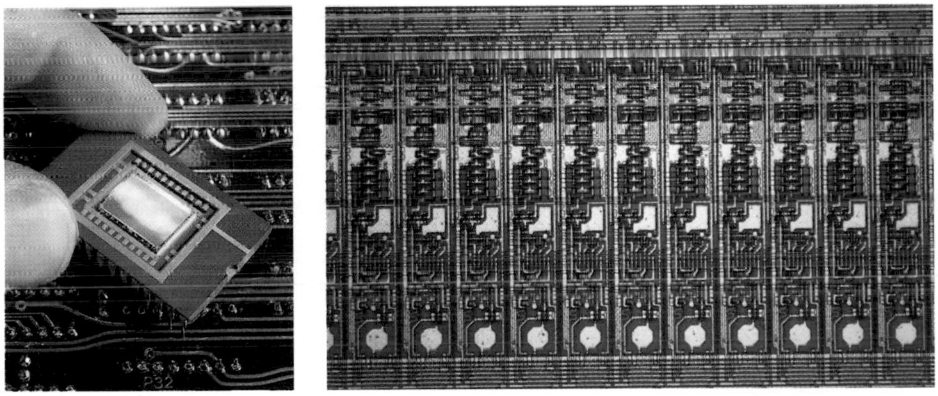

Figure 2.22 The pictures show a pixel detector read out chip. The close-up shows an area of 1 mm × 2 mm containing 12 separate read-out channels. The entire chip contains 1000 read-out channels (around 80 000 transistors) covering a sensitive area of 8 mm × 5 mm.

Layered detection

So far we have discussed individual detectors, but real experiments often use a combination of detectors to provide a range of information about the events being studied. At **LEP** (the large electron–positron collider at CERN) four large **composite detectors** surround the beam tube at the places where the beams cross and collisions occur. Each of these massive detectors (**ALEPH, DELPHI**, **L3**, and **OPAL**) are run by large international teams consisting of hundreds of physicists. The aim is to detect as many of the particles produced in the electron–positron annihilation as possible and to calculate their energies. To do this large detector assemblies, each typically 10 m in each direction and having a mass of several thousand tonnes, are wrapped around the beam tube at the annihilation points.

These large detectors are all different, but the basic layout is similar in each case. The layer nearest the beam tube contains the **tracking detectors** which reveal the trajectories of charged particles. These tracking detectors are themselves complex, with a silicon vertex detector close to the beam followed by a drift chamber to trigger a time projection chamber (TPC) beyond it. In ALEPH the TPC measures 3.6 m in diameter by 4.4 m long and is used to make precise measurements of particle momenta and direction. It has to be large because the high-energy particles produced will deflect only a few millimetres as they cross it. The next layer is a dense material like lead glass that stops all electrons, positrons and photons, and which is full of detectors that measure the energy dissipated by the particles as they stop. This part is an **electromagnetic calorimeter** (i.e. it measures the heat dissipated). The advantage of this is that it helps in identifying some neutral particles like neutral pions which leave no trace in the tracking detector but which decay to photons. The third and outer layer of the composite detector has a dual role – it is made of iron and forms part of the electromagnet that bends the particle tracks. It also stops all the heavier particles (hadrons, like mesons and protons) and measures their energy. This is a **hadron calorimeter**. Muons will penetrate all of these layers so there is an outer muon detector consisting of drift tubes (anything that registers here must be a muon since other charged particles have already been stopped). The highly penetrating, weakly interacting neutrinos will not be stopped in the detector but their energy can be calculated from the difference between the known energy of the annihilation and the total energy measured in the calorimeters.

Figure 2.23 View of the end cap of the DELPHI layered particle detector at CERN.

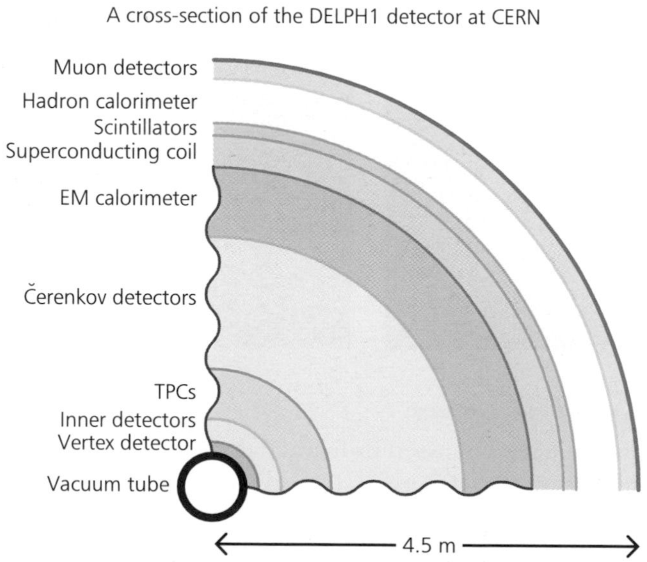

Figure 2.24 Collisions take place inside DELPHI once every 30 μs and a great deal of 'pre-selection' must take place to decide which events are worth analysing in detail. The detector is capable of resolving particle positions with great precision – from 5 μm near the collision point to 1 mm at a distance of 5 m. Information from the detector passes through 200 000 electronic channnels to be analysed by fourteen computers. Information from a typical event requires over a million pieces of information to be stored.

Figure 2.25 The superconducting magnet in the DELPHI detector is the largest in the world. It was made at the Rutherford Appleton Laboratories in Oxford and transported by road to CERN in 1987. It produces a field strength of 1.2 T in a solenoid 7.4 m long and 6.2 m in diameter.

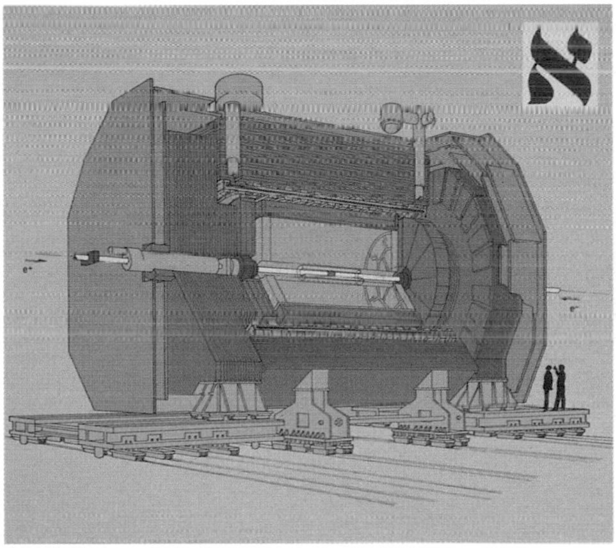

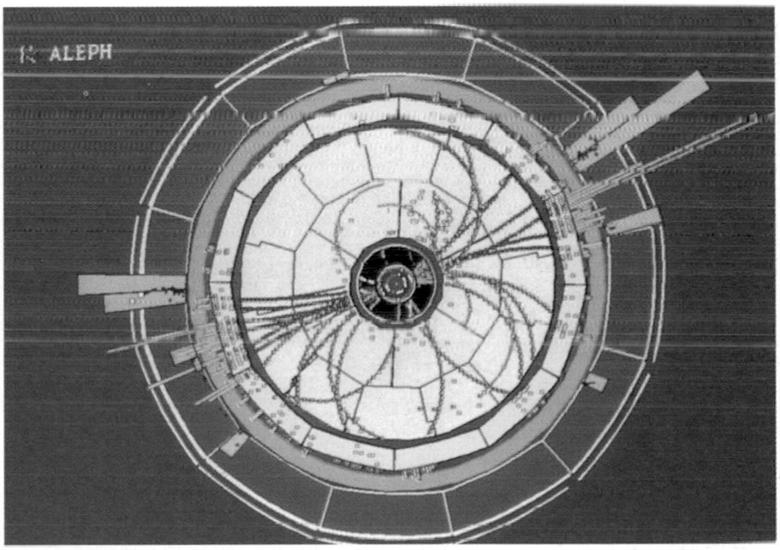

Figure 2.26 (**a**) Cutaway of the ALEPH detector. (**b**) Computer representation of a collision event between an electron and a positron inside ALEPH.

SUMMARY

- The detection of charged particles relies on their electromagnetic interactions with matter.
- Most detectors cannot detect uncharged particles. The existence of uncharged particles must usually be deduced from the path of charged particles with which they collide or into which they decay.
- **Table 2.1** Summary of particle detectors.

Detector type	Principle of operation	Use
ionisation chamber	measures average ionisation current in chamber	to measure the activity of a strongly ionising source
Geiger counter	detects individual ionising events in a low pressure gas	to monitor activity of radioactive sources
solid state detector	detects individual events as they release holes and electrons in a semiconductor material	as for a Geiger counter
spark counter (air)	detects breakdown of air due to ionising radiation	to detect alpha particles or cosmic ray bursts
cloud chamber	ionising particles produce a track of droplets in a saturated vapour	records tracks of low energy ionising particles
bubble chamber	ionising particles produce a track of bubbles in a superheated liquid	records tracks of higher energy particles and shows collisions and decays
photographic emulsion	ionising particles produce tracks in the emulsion as they pass through	to record high resolution particle tracks – particularly important in early cosmic ray studies
scintillation counters	emit photons when high-energy particles pass through them	useful for triggering other detectors that record tracks or time of arrival
Čerenkov detectors	particles moving at greater than the speed of light in some medium emit an 'EM-shock wave'	characteristic direction in which photons are emitted can be used to determine particle path
spark counters	electrical breakdown between electrodes in a gas	gives a rapid response and light emitted can be detected
multiwire proportional counters	electrical breakdown in a gas produces currents in wires close to the ionising event	many wires and rapid response allow accurate path determinations
drift chamber	ions produced in a gas drift toward electrodes	time of arrival relative to a trigger signal locates the original ionising event
time projection chamber	similar to a drift chamber but with large electrode separation and segmented end electrodes	allows a precise 3D image of the particle tracks to be constructed from time and position of ion arrival
vertex detector	silicon diodes in an array record charges freed by passing high-energy particles	used close to beam tubes, these record precise tracks of short-lived particles
charge coupled devices	pixelated detectors that store charges released by particles	store particle tracks as an array of charges that can be read off into a computer
calorimeters	count photon showers emitted by particles as they stop in a dense material (e.g. lead glass)	to measure particle energies
layered detectors	combination of above	to identify particles and make precise measurements of charge, energy, momentum and paths

- The characteristics of particle tracks used to identify the particles that made them include: track length, track thickness, track curvature, missing tracks, and the relationships between tracks (using conservation of momentum).

QUESTIONS

1 a Neutral particles are difficult to detect. Why?
b Why are neutrinos much more difficult to detect than neutrons?
c Why are photons easier to detect than either neutrons or neutrinos?

2 a What is the minimum velocity at which electrons will emit Čerenkov radiation in water (refractive index 1.33)?
b What kinetic energy does this correspond to?

3 The photograph shows an electron spiralling in the magnetic field of a bubble chamber at the Lawrence Berkeley Laboratory.
a In which direction did the electron move along the track? Explain.
b What was the direction of the magnetic field? Explain.
c What other information would you need to calculate the initial energy of the electron?

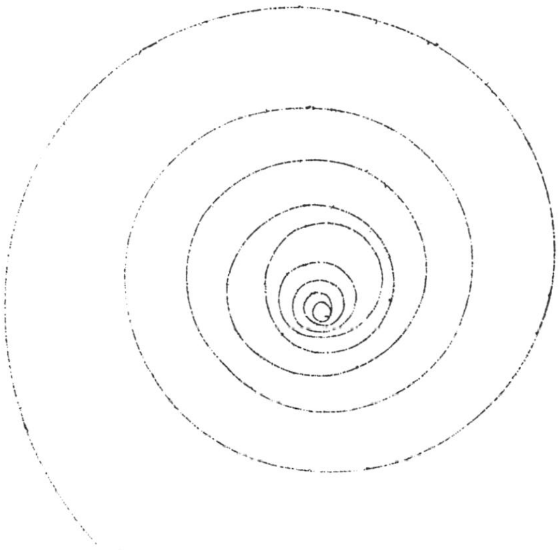

4 a What is the main difference between a cloud chamber and a bubble chamber?
b What are the advantages of a bubble chamber over a cloud chamber for investigating high-energy charged particles?
c Can you think of any events that would be shown more clearly in a cloud chamber? Explain.

5 A muon is very similar to an electron, but its mass is about 200 times greater. What are the similarities and differences between electron and muon tracks in a bubble chamber if:
a Both particles enter the chamber at the same speed?
b Both particles enter the chamber with the same kinetic energy?
Assume that there is a uniform magnetic field perpendicular to the chamber and that neither particle undergoes a violent collision with a proton in the chamber.

6 a Give one advantage of a multiwire detector over a bubble chamber.
b Why is it important, in multiwire chambers, that the wires themselves are very fine?
c What additional information is obtained in a time projection chamber?

7 Large detectors like ALEPH and DELPHI at CERN are *layered detectors*.
a What is the point in having many layers?
b What kinds of particles and events would be recorded by the innermost layers?
c What kinds of particles will *not* be recorded in any layers?
d How is it possible to calculate the energy of the particles in (**c**) even though they have not been detected?
e What is measured by an 'electromagnetic calorimeter'?

8 High-energy particle detectors use large extremely powerful superconducting magnets.
a Why do they need such powerful magnets?
b Why is it important that the magnets maintain a strong field over a large volume?

3 Leptons

How do we classify things? In biology we identify similar characteristics (e.g. scales or a backbone) in different organisms. Now that we know a lot more about DNA we know that the patterns of characteristics are connected to a hidden level of order in the genetic code. A similar thing is true in chemistry where Mendeleev constructed the Periodic Table by grouping elements according to their chemical properties. We now know that this periodicity results from a more fundamental pattern in the way electrons orbit nuclei. There is a moral here – large scale patterns or symmetries in nature are often explained by simple combinations of more fundamental units.

Once physics developed the means to probe inside the atom and nucleus a whole host of new particles began to emerge. These new particles had a wide range of properties and interactions. Some were very massive, some massless, some seemed to consist of smaller parts while others were apparently pointlike, they had various spins and charges, some were stable and some decayed almost as soon as they were created. Patterns began to emerge from the many discoveries and experiments, and a simpler more fundamental picture gradually formed. This is the **Standard Model** which we shall explore in the next four chapters.

THE MYSTERIES OF BETA DECAY

Electrons

The electron was the first subatomic particle to be discovered (by J.J. Thomson in 1897) and remains one of the fundamental particles in the Standard Model.

Properties of the electron

Rest mass = 9.1×10^{-31} kg	about 1/1840 of the mass of a proton
Charge = -1.6×10^{-19} C	this is the smallest unit of free charge
Size	pointlike as far as we can tell
Spin = $\frac{1}{2}$ unit	all spin $\frac{1}{2}$ particles are called **fermions**

Beware! Particle **spin** is a quantum mechanical property and does not mean that the electron simply rotates about an axis. See the box on page 43 for more information about the strange properties of spin.

Orbital electrons generate a magnetic field (like the field produced by a current in a coil) but this is not sufficient to account for all the magnetic effects observed in atomic spectra. It was realised around 1925 that the electron has an intrinsic **magnetic moment** as well (that is, an isolated electron is also a tiny magnet in its own right).

Interactions: electromagnetic (affected by electric and magnetic fields), weak nuclear force (as in beta decay), gravitation (they have weight), but not the strong nuclear force. (We shall find out more about the nature and properties of forces in chapter 7.)

However, in the 1920s the high-energy electrons emitted in beta decays caused great concern because they did not seem to be obeying the conservation laws. When a radioactive decay occurs the energy of the products is the energy-equivalent of the mass-defect for the reaction. This suggests that a particular decay will release a certain amount of energy as motion of the products, and in alpha decay this is certainly the case. The alpha particles from a particular decay have a discrete energy spectrum that produces tracks of certain lengths in a cloud chamber (see figure 3.2). Scientists expected that the electrons emitted in beta decay would also have a distinct energy spectrum, depending on the radioactive decay producing them.

Figure 3.1 Thomson carried out a series of brilliant experiments on the cathode rays produced when electricity passes through an evacuated Crooke's tube. He concluded that the rays were actually a stream of negatively charged particles with mass much less than that of a hydrogen atom – electrons.

Figure 3.2 The length of an alpha particle's track is a measure of its energy. In this photograph the alpha particles are emitted with two distinct energies. The shorter tracks correspond to a decay which leaves the new nucleus in an excited state. It will decay to its ground state by emitting one or several gamma rays.

Measuring the beta-energy spectrum

The energy of a beta particle can be measured electromagnetically by the amount it deflects in a magnetic field. The beta particles emitted from a source are collimated into a narrow beam so that their initial direction is well defined. The beam is directed into a magnetic field perpendicular to the particle velocities. This exerts a force on the beta particles (by the 'motor effect') which deflects them into semicircular paths (this is the same principle used in the mass spectrometer). Higher energy beta particles have greater momentum and are deflected less than those of lower energy. If all the beta particles from a particular source have the same energy they would follow paths with the same radius of curvature. A discrete energy spectrum would result in several distinct paths.

What actually happens is the beta particles from a particular source follow a *continuous* range of paths from very small radius of curvature up to a maximum radius determined by the source used. This implies that the beta particles are emitted with a continuous range of energies from zero up to some maximum.

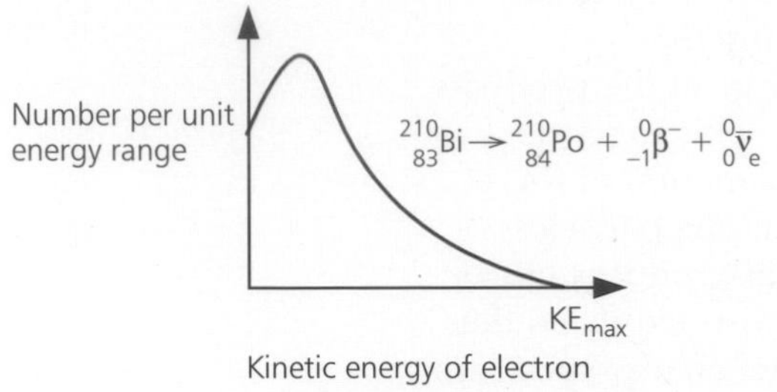

Figure 3.3 The graph shows that beta particles emitted from a particular source can have any energy from zero up to a maximum (where the graph intercepts the KE axis). If the energy released in the decay is equal to this maximum kinetic energy the question arises as to what happens to the rest of the energy when a lower energy beta particle is emitted?

Experiments to measure the beta particle energies showed that they have a continuous energy spectrum from very low values up to some limit. Despite this a number of physicists clung on to the idea of a discrete spectrum and explained away the continuous results as due to secondary effects as the beta particles leave the atom. Their reluctance to accept the evidence was linked to the difficulty of explaining it. If the same input energy (from the mass defect in the decay) results in different output energies, then what has happened to the missing energy? The experiment that finally convinced the doubters was carried out by Chadwick in 1927 in which he used a calorimeter to measure the total energy of all the beta particles emitted from a particular source in a known time. The energy per beta particle was calculated and was found to be less than the energy of the decay. This confirmed that the beta particles really do not carry away all the energy. By 1929 the continuous energy spectrum for beta decay was an accepted mystery.

The calorimeter experiment

Calorimeters measure the energy absorbed from particles that stop in the calorimeter. The argument about beta spectra came down to whether the observed continuous spectrum was really what the electrons gained in the decay or merely what remained after other interactions when they left the atom. The calorimeter would be warmed by both sources of energy so should give an energy per decay equal to the upper limit of the beta spectrum, that is the energy equivalent of the mass defect for the reaction. Ellis and Wooster working under Chadwick set up the crucial experiment in 1925. They chose a bismuth-210 (then known as radium-E) source because it produces a good continuous spectrum with few secondary effects. It has a half-life of about 5 days, and an energy spectrum with mean energy 0.39 MeV and upper limit 1 MeV. The temperature changes measured over a period of 26 days were just 10^{-3} K and these allowed them to determine the energy released per electron to be 0.34 MeV with an error of about 10%. This showed conclusively that the energy of the decay does not all go to the electrons.

$$^{210}_{83}\mathbf{Bi} \rightarrow ^{210}_{84}\mathbf{Po} + ^{0}_{-1}\beta^{-}$$
$$m(\mathbf{Bi\text{-}210}) = \mathbf{209.984105\,u} \quad \text{(atomic mass)}$$
$$m(\mathbf{Po\text{-}210}) = \mathbf{209.98285\,u} \quad \text{(atomic mass)}$$
$$\Delta m = \mathbf{209.984105\,u - 209.982857\,u = 0.001248\,u}$$
(note that electron masses cancel)
$$\Delta E = \mathbf{0.001248 \times 931\,MeV = 1.16\,MeV}$$

Ellis and Wooster's experiment suggested that either energy conservation is violated by beta decays, or that something that does not interact with the calorimeter is also emitted and carries away the missing energy.

Energy and momentum in a two-particle decay

It has probably occurred to you that this discussion of beta spectra has ignored the kinetic energy of the recoiling nucleus. There is a very good reason for doing this, since if linear momentum and kinetic energy are both conserved, then the energy must divide in the inverse ratio of the particle masses. This is shown on the next page.

Assume the original nucleus is at rest and let the masses of the product particles be M and m. After the decay the two particles move in opposite directions with speeds u and v respectively.

$Mu = mv$ **to conserve linear momentum** **(1)**

$\frac{1}{2}Mu^2 + \frac{1}{2}mv^2 = E$ **where E is the energy equivalent of the mass defect for the decay** **(2)**

from (1): $v = \dfrac{M}{m}u$

$$\therefore \tfrac{1}{2}mv^2 = \tfrac{1}{2}m\left(\frac{M}{m}\right)^2 u^2 = \left(\frac{M}{m}\right)\tfrac{1}{2}Mu^2$$

that is: $\mathbf{KE}_{\text{mass } m} = \dfrac{M}{m}\,\mathbf{KE}_{\text{mass } M}$

For the beta decay of Bi-210 the ratio M/m is about 400 000, so the error involved in ignoring the KE of the new nucleus really is negligible. (Even for alpha decay this ratio is about 50, so the error would still be only 2%.)

Enter the neutrino

By the early 1930s beta decay spectra had produced a crisis in physics. Niels Bohr, one of the prime architects of Quantum Theory, even suggested that energy conservation might have to be abandoned for individual particle events and retained only as a statistical law. However, Wolfgang Pauli had other ideas and in 1930 he sent a letter to a gathering of experts on radioactivity in Tübingen. In the letter he proposed the existence of a new particle that carries away the missing energy but is not stopped in the calorimeter or detected by a photographic plate or ionisation detector. The new particle's properties would be tenuous to say the least.

- The particle must be *neutral*, since beta decays conserve charge without it. This means that it *does not interact electromagnetically*.
- The particle must be *massless or of very low mass*, since the total mass of the most energetic electrons and new nucleus account for almost all the available energy. (If it has zero rest mass then it must travel at the speed of light.)
- The particle must have *one half unit of spin* (like the electron) to conserve angular momentum in the decay.
- It must not interact with protons or neutrons (otherwise it would stop in the calorimeter). This means that it *does not interact by the strong force*.

We detect most particles by their electromagnetic interaction with atoms. The only significant interaction for this new particle is the **weak interaction** involved in the beta decay that forms it. The term *weak* means that the probability of these decays occurring is very small, even in favourable circumstances, so they are very difficult to detect – in fact they were not detected until 1956.

Pauli originally called this new particle a 'neutron' (not what we know as neutrons, which were discovered in 1932) but Enrico Fermi christened it '**neutrino**' (meaning 'little neutral one') in 1933 and this name stuck. However, this is not the end of the story. By 1933 Paul Dirac had derived a relativistic quantum theory for the electron, known as the Dirac Equation. One consequence of this equation is that electrons and neutrinos are classified as members of a particle family known as the **leptons**. According to Dirac, when particles interact with one another, the total number of leptons must remain constant. Since none of the particles present before the decay occurs is a lepton, the conservation of leptons would be violated if beta decay produced a single electron, and it would also be violated if the decay produced an electron and a neutrino (two leptons).

The solution suggested by Dirac's work was that the new particle must be an antineutrino (symbol $\bar{\nu}$), the antimatter counterpart of a neutrino (symbol ν).

The antineutrino also enables linear momentum and angular momentum to be conserved. Pauli suggested that one way to demonstrate the existence of the particle would be to show that the recoil of the new nucleus and the path of the emitted beta ray in a cloud chamber do not lie along the same line. Assuming the original nucleus was at rest, the three momentum vectors for the decay products should form a closed triangle. In practice at the time the recoil was too small to detect.

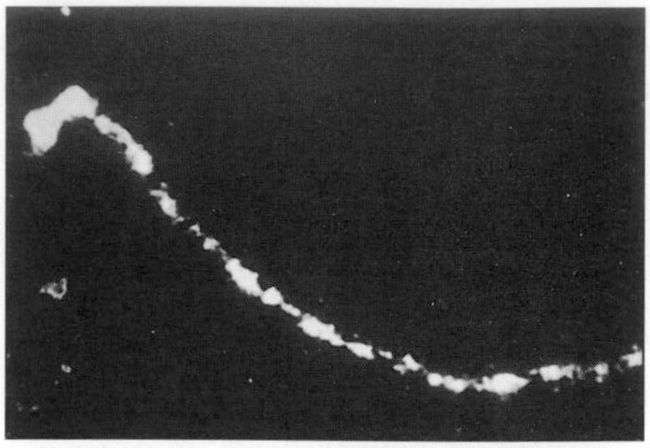

Figure 3.4 Beta decay occurs when a nuclear neutron decays to a proton. Free neutrons are unstable and also decay by the same mechanism. This cloud chamber photograph was taken in 1957 by S. Szalay and J. Csikay and shows the effect of the invisible antineutrino. The short green track is the proton, the red track is the emitted electron.

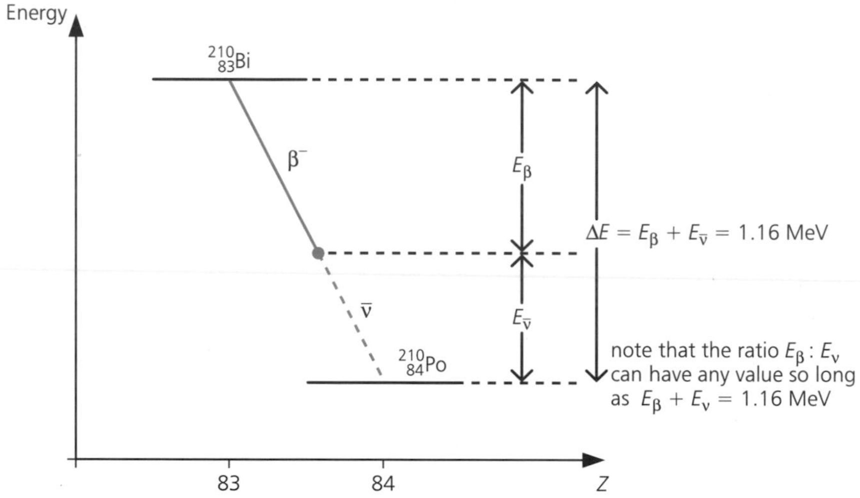

Figure 3.5 How energy is conserved in beta decay.

Beta decay revisited

We are familiar with the conservation of nucleon number in nuclear reactions like alpha and beta decay. The conservation of leptons can be represented in a similar way by introducing **lepton number**. If electrons and neutrinos have lepton number 1 then antielectrons and antineutrinos must have lepton number –1. Beta decay creates an electron and an antineutrino so there is no change in lepton number (1 – 1 = 0).

	$^{210}_{83}\mathrm{Bi}$ →	$^{210}_{84}\mathrm{Po}$ +	$^{0}_{-1}\beta^-$ +	$^{0}_{0}\bar{\nu}$
nucleon number	210	210	0	0
charge	83	84	–1	0
lepton number	0	0	1	–1

It is important to bear in mind that the lepton/antilepton pair emitted in beta decay are *created* in the decay and were not present previously either in the nucleus or locked inside the neutron that decays.

Spin

All magnetic fields are produced by moving charges. At an atomic level these fields arise from the orbital motion of the electrons and from their spin. Spin was first proposed by Goudsmit and Uhlenbeck in 1925 to explain the splitting of some spectral lines into two closely related components. For example, the intense yellow colour from a sodium discharge tube (also used in street lighting) is due to the 'sodium D-lines'. These come from an electron transition in the sodium atom when certain excited electrons drop back to the ground state and release energy as a visible photon in the yellow part of the visible spectrum. Close inspection shows that the light consists of two distinct wavelengths at 589.0 nm and 589.6 nm. There must be two very close quantum jumps taking place resulting in slightly different energy changes. This can be explained if the electron has a magnetic moment due to its spin that can align parallel or antiparallel with the magnetic field of the atom (due to orbital motion). When they are parallel the electron energy is increased slightly and when they are antiparallel it is reduced. This interaction should split other spectral lines too, an effect that was soon verified.

Particle spin is quantised. That is, particles can only have discrete values of spin angular momentum. The quantum of spin angular momentum is $h/2\pi$ (Planck's constant divided by 2π, written as $\hbar$ and called 'h-bar'). All particles in nature are either **fermions**, with half-integer spin, or **bosons**, with integer spin. Which of these groups a particle belongs to determines more than just its magnetic moment. Fermions obey the **Pauli Exclusion Principle** which prevents any two from being in exactly the same quantum state at the same time whereas bosons will tend to cluster in the lowest available energy state. This has very significant physical results. The Periodic Table and all chemical properties derive from the hierarchical structure of electrons in atoms: no more than two electrons can occupy the same orbit, one 'spin-up' and the other 'spin-down'. On the other hand, when a large scale quantum level is empty there is no limit to how many bosons can occupy it. Photons are bosons and the coherent light of a laser is an example of a state occupied by a very large number of similar bosons.

All the neutrons and protons in the nucleus and the electron and antineutrino created in beta decay are fermions, that is they each have half-integer spin. The quantum mechanical rules that determine how spins can combine make it impossible for an even number of fermions to have the same total spin as an odd number. This rules out any decay that creates a single fermion since this would change the total number of spin-half particles from even to odd or vice versa. Angular momentum would not be conserved if beta decay merely emitted an electron, or if the antineutrino had zero or integer spin. Antineutrinos (and therefore neutrinos too) must be fermions.

Spin, but not as we know it!

A simple classical model of the electron would be a tiny massive charged sphere spinning about its own axis. This would give a qualitative explanation of its electromagnetic and gravitational interactions and, since current loops generate magnetic fields, explain its magnetic moment. Unfortunately the model does not stand up to experimental investigation. Electron properties can produce strange and subtle effects and our best physical model is quantum mechanical.

The spin of the electron determines its angular momentum, but quantum mechanical angular momentum is quantised, and behaves in a rather strange way. Electrons have a spin of exactly $\frac{1}{2}\hbar$, like all fermions.

However, you might reasonably expect that the angular momentum about any arbitrarily chosen axis could be any fraction of this since it is presumably a projection of the electron's angular momentum onto the axis chosen for measurement. But this is not the case. The *projection* of angular momentum is also quantised, so however we measure the spin of an electron we always get a result of $\frac{1}{2}\hbar$ and the orientation of the spin axis always lies parallel or antiparallel to our measurement axis. If a cricket ball behaved in a similar way then, no matter how the bowler bowled it, its spin axis would be parallel or perpendicular to the bat when the batsman hits it.

The theory of spin in the Dirac Equation showed that the property is genuinely non-classical and even requires four-dimensional spacetime to explain it! One very strange consequence is that the electron must rotate through 720° to return to its original state!

(In quantum theory a particle state is described by a vector in an imaginary infinite dimensional space called Hilbert Space. When a spin-half particle is turned through 360° its state vector changes sign in Hilbert Space. It must be turned through a further 360° to get back to its original state. State vectors for particles with integer spin return to their original state when rotated through 360°.)

Figure 3.6 When the spin of an electron is projected along any chosen axis and then measured, the result is always $\frac{1}{2}\hbar$.

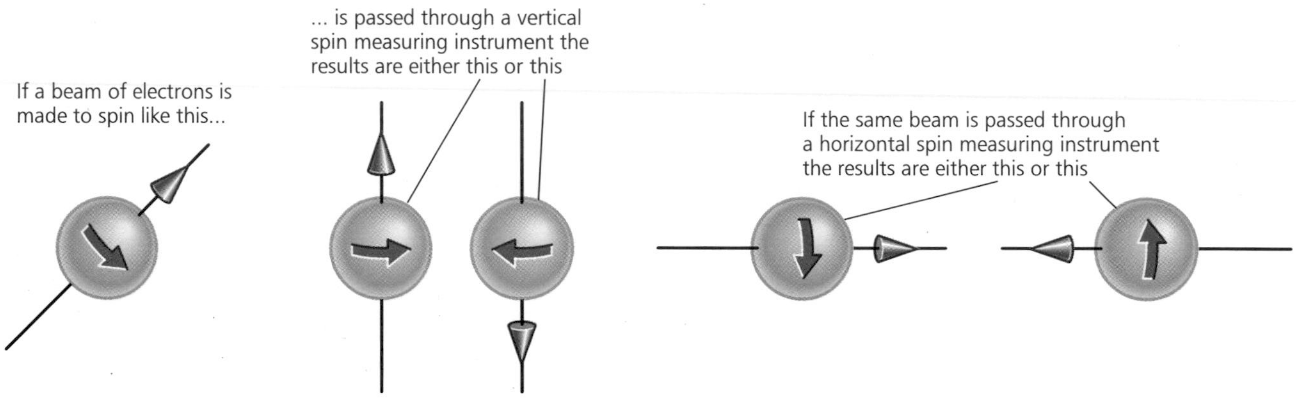

If a beam of electrons is made to spin like this...
... is passed through a vertical spin measuring instrument the results are either this or this
If the same beam is passed through a horizontal spin measuring instrument the results are either this or this

Detecting neutrinos

Over a quarter century passed between Pauli's prediction of neutrinos and their detection by E. Cowan and F. Reines in 1956. The reason for this long delay is that neutrinos only interact by the weak force and this interaction occurs very rarely. To a neutrino the Earth itself is barely different from empty space and most of those that fall on its surface from space (they are created in nuclear reactions in the Sun) pass right through with no interaction at all. To increase the chance of detection you need a very intense source and a very large number of particles in the detector with which the neutrinos could interact. This explains the delay in detecting neutrinos, as intense antineutrino sources were not available on Earth until the invention of nuclear reactors and accelerators. Many fission products are neutron-rich and so undergo beta decays emitting electrons and antineutrinos.

What can detect these antineutrinos? Cowan and Reines used a liquid scintillator in which the incident antineutrinos induce an '**inverse beta decay**'. That is they strike a proton and convert it to a neutron. Since an antilepton annihilates in this process another antilepton must be created – and so an antielectron (positron) is emitted. When this 'inverse beta decay' occurs, the positron soon annihilates with an electron to release gamma ray photons. These can be detected, but to confirm the event Cowan and Reines also had to detect the neutron created in the reaction. They did this by detecting another burst of photons expected to occur about 5 microseconds after the first when the neutron had slowed down sufficiently to be captured by the nucleus of cadmium atoms in a suitably positioned target.

$$^{0}_{0}\bar{\nu} + {}^{1}_{1}\mathbf{p}^{+} \rightarrow {}^{0}_{0}\mathbf{n} + {}^{0}_{1}\beta^{+}$$

N.B. β^+ represents an antielectron (e^+) or positron.

On 14 June 1956 Cowan and Reines sent a telegram to Pauli to inform him that his tiny neutral particle had finally turned up.

Incidentally, about 10^{12} neutrinos are passing through you every second.

THREE GENERATIONS OF LEPTONS

An unexpected alien: the muon

The electron, positron, neutrino and antineutrino form a close family group of leptons. However in 1936, while trying to detect a new nuclear particle called the pion in cosmic rays, C.D. Anderson and S.H. Neddermeyer discovered a cloud chamber track that turned out to be another lepton. If we could see the tracks of these leptons, called **muons** (symbol μ), we would be surrounded by a thick mesh of fine threads, as muons continue to pass through us and the atmosphere as they arrive from outer space.

Although there was considerable confusion about the identity of the new particle, it eventually became clear that its properties are remarkably like those of an electron or positron, but with one very significant difference – it is 207 times more massive than an electron. This much larger mass also means muons are more penetrating than electrons since they interact less strongly with matter and radiate less. Unlike electrons, muons are unstable and decay with a half-life of 2 μs, forming electrons and neutrinos.

This decay illustrates a very important point which particle physicists still cannot fully explain. The muon and its neutrino (and their antiparticles) also form a close family and cannot be created or destroyed in isolation. The 'muon family' is like a second generation of the 'electron family' but with a greater mass. This second generation is distinct from the first, so that as well as **total lepton number L** being conserved, **muon-lepton number L_μ and electron–lepton number L_e** are also separately conserved.

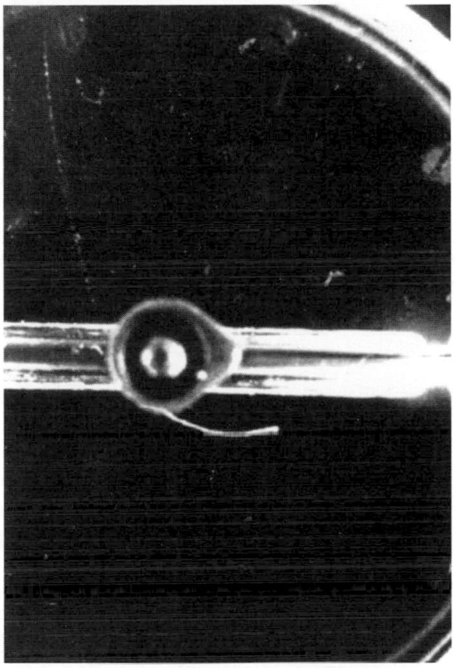

Figure 3.7 A positive antimuon enters from top-left, slows down after interacting with a Geiger counter, and stops in a cloud chamber.

$$ {}^{0}_{-1}\mu^- \rightarrow {}^{0}_{-1}e^- + {}^{0}_{0}\bar{\nu}_e + {}^{0}_{0}\nu_\mu $$

charge	$-1 =$	-1	$+0$	$+0$
lepton number L	$+1 =$	$+1$	-1	$+1$
electron-lepton number L_e	$0 =$	$+1$	-1	$+0$
muon-lepton number L_μ	$+1 =$	0	$+0$	$+1$

We must now distinguish between the generations of leptons, which means that Pauli's particle is called the *electron-neutrino* and the corresponding particle for the muon is the *muon-neutrino*.

The third generation

The second generation muon family repeats the pattern of the electron family at higher mass, although muons play little part in ordinary matter and seem rather 'unnecessary'. However, in 1974 Martin Perl in Hamburg detected the creation and decay of another much more massive (about twice the mass of a proton!) lepton, the **tau** particle (symbol τ). Once again it was accompanied by its own distinct **tau-neutrino** and once again there is **conservation of tau-lepton number L_τ**. We now believe that there are only three generations of leptons (see pages 88–90) but the reason for this repeating pattern remains a mystery.

Testing time dilation with muons

Einstein's special theory of relativity predicts that 'moving clocks' will run slow.

This is called *time dilation*. The 'moving clock' is slowed by a factor γ (where

$$\gamma = \frac{1}{\sqrt{1 - \frac{v^2}{c^2}}}$$

as before and v is the speed of the moving clock.)

However the effect is small unless the relative velocity is comparable to the speed of light, making it difficult (but not impossible) to test this experimentally with normal clocks. Muons are ideal subjects for this experiment since they form when cosmic rays strike the atmosphere and hurtle down to Earth at very nearly the speed of light. They also have a clock on board – their own half-life. Time dilation can be tested by measuring how much the half-life of a moving muon is extended (since its time passes slowly relative to ours).

Slow-moving muons in the laboratory have a half-life of about 2 μs.

High-energy muons are created at an altitude of about 60 km.

It would take about $t = \frac{6 \times 10^4\,\text{m}}{3 \times 10^8\,\text{m s}^{-1}} = 2 \times 10^{-4}\,\text{s}$

for these muons to reach the ground.

This is about 200 times the laboratory half-life so, if time is unaffected by motion, the proportion of muons reaching the surface will be a mere $1/2^{200}$ of the number created at the top of the atmosphere. This is less than one muon in 10^{60} which means effectively *none*.

Experiments to measure muon flux at various altitudes have been carried out and show that about *one in eight* of these muons makes it all the way down to the surface of the Earth. Eight is two-cubed, so the flux of moving muons has halved just three times during an Earth-time in which 200 half-lives would elapse. Viewed from the Earth, time for the moving muons is about 1/70 of its terrestrial rate. This is $\frac{1}{\gamma}$ for the muons and tells us that their mass has also increased about 70 times.

Summary of lepton properties

Generation	Particle	Symbol	Relative mass	Relative charge	Spin	L	L_e	L_μ	L_τ
1	electron	e^-	1	–1	$\frac{1}{2}$	1	1	0	0
1	electron-neutrino	ν_e	0?*	0	$\frac{1}{2}$	1	1	0	0
1	positron	e^+	1	+1	$\frac{1}{2}$	–1	–1	0	0
1	antielectron-neutrino	$\bar{\nu}_e$	0?	0	$\frac{1}{2}$	–1	–1	0	0
2	muon	μ^-	207	–1	$\frac{1}{2}$	1	0	1	0
2	muon-neutrino	ν_μ	0?*	0	$\frac{1}{2}$	1	0	1	0
2	antimuon	μ^+	207	+1	$\frac{1}{2}$	–1	0	–1	0
2	antimuon-neutrino	$\bar{\nu}_\mu$	0?	0	$\frac{1}{2}$	–1	0	–1	0
3	tau	τ^-	3490	–1	$\frac{1}{2}$	1	0	0	1
3	tau-neutrino	ν_τ	0?*	0	$\frac{1}{2}$	1	0	0	1
3	antitau	τ^+	3490	+1	$\frac{1}{2}$	–1	0	0	–1
3	antitau-neutrino	$\bar{\nu}_\tau$	0?	0	$\frac{1}{2}$	–1	0	0	–1

Interactions:

All leptons take part in weak interactions and (presumably) gravitation.

Charged leptons interact electromagnetically.

No leptons interact by the strong nuclear force.

*Neutrino mass has been shown to be very small but there is nothing that forbids it from being non-zero. No experiment so far has definitely shown that neutrinos have mass, but the answer to this question has important implications for the Standard Model and for cosmology as we shall see later on.

SUMMARY

- The **Standard Model** is the model developed by physicists to explain and predict the behaviour of subatomic particles.
- The first subatomic particle to be discovered was the electron.
- Subatomic particles may have **spin**. A simple model of a particle with spin is a tiny spinning magnet, although the true picture is much more complex than this.
- The existence of the **antineutrino** was suggested to explain the continuous spectra of high-energy electrons, emitted in beta decay.
- Because **neutrinos** interact only through the weak force, it was more than 25 years before direct evidence for the neutrino was obtained.
- There are three 'generations' of leptons – the electrons, the muons and the tau particles each with its accompanying neutrino.

QUESTIONS

1 **a** Why did Pauli need to introduce a new particle to explain beta-decay spectra?
b What are the properties of the new particle?
c Why does it turn out to be an antineutrino rather than a neutrino?
d Write down an equation for the beta decay of carbon-14 to nitrogen-14 and explain how the relevant conservation laws apply to this decay.

2 Neutrinos are incredibly difficult to detect.
a Why?
b How *are* they detected?

3 **a** Write down an equation showing how a collision between an electron-neutrino and a neutron can result in the creation of a proton and an electron.
b How does this reaction compare to the decay of a free neutron?
c Suggest a similar reaction that may occur if a muon-neutrino collides with a neutron.
d How do we know that electron-neutrinos and muon-neutrinos are distinct particles?

4 Pi-zeros have a lifetime of 8×10^{-17} s.
a How far does light travel in 8×10^{-17} s?
b A pi-zero is created in an experiment and moves off at 0.995*c*. If it decays after exactly one lifetime (in its own rest frame) how long does it 'live' in the laboratory?
c How far from its point of origin does it decay?

5 Electrons are closely related to muons and tau particles.
a State two properties which are the same for all three particles.
b How do they differ from one another?
c Explain why the muon and tau particles are unstable and yet the electron is stable.

6 It has been suggested that neutrinos emitted from nuclear reactions in the Sun may oscillate between electron-neutrinos, muon-neutrinos and tau-neutrinos, as they travel to the Earth.
a What distinguishes a muon-neutrino from an electron-neutrino or a tau-neutrino?
b Would any conservation laws be violated if an electron-neutrino changed to a muon-neutrino?

7 Muons are created when cosmic rays strike the upper atmosphere at an altitude of about 60 km. According to the box on page 46, only about 3 muon half-lives elapse as they travel through the atmosphere to sea level. (Muon half-life is approximately 2μs.)
a Assume the muons are moving at close to the speed of light. Approximately how far does a muon travel in 6μs?
b If it was possible for an observer to ride on one of these muons, how deep would they think the Earth's atmosphere is?
c How far does terrestrial observer see these muons travel?
d What do you conclude about the effect of relative motion on distances? (From the point of view of an observer riding on the muon, the Earth's atmosphere is rushing towards him at almost the speed of light.)

8 **a** Why do we think neutrinos have little or no mass?
b How can the maximum kinetic energy of an electron emitted in beta decay set an upper limit to the possible mass of an anti-neutrino?

4 Antimatter

Paul Dirac was one of the greatest mathematical physicists of the twentieth century. He believed that correct physical theories could emerge simply from the beauty of mathematical equations and was prepared to let that be his guide in searching for a fundamental description of Nature. This approach is very different from that of Einstein or Feynman both of whom used visual models to help construct abstract theories.

In the 1920s Dirac was concerned about the electron. He knew it could be described by the new quantum theory of Schrödinger and Heisenberg, but he also knew that electrons in atoms travel very fast and that at high speeds their behaviour has to be described by the equations of special relativity. Unfortunately quantum theory and special relativity were not compatible and there were aspects of the quantum equations that seemed awkward and ugly to Dirac. He set about trying to construct an equation that was mathematically beautiful and yet combined the relativistic and quantum mechanical properties of the electron. The equation he created is known as the Dirac Equation, one of the most beautiful and accurate equations in physics.

Equations are elegant symbolic ways of describing the relationship between particle properties, but we must always interpret them. The Dirac Equation had some surprises in store – not only did it allow physicists to calculate properties of the electron to unprecedented accuracy, and put the theory of spin on a firm (albeit four-dimensional) footing, it also predicted a completely new form of matter.

FROM NEGATIVE ENERGY TO ANTIMATTER

A sea of negative energy

Before the Dirac Equation, free electrons were thought to have only positive energies. The minimum energy, E_o, is the rest energy, equal to m_oc^2, and a free electron could have any value above this corresponding to its total energy mc^2, where m is the relativistic mass γm_o. The Dirac Equation also predicted the energy of a free electron, but its solution to this problem was a symmetric pair of positive *and negative* energies. For every positive energy state there is another allowed state corresponding to a negative energy electron. This result follows from the relativistic expression for total energy (which is a quadratic equation relating the energy E to the momentum p and rest mass m_o):

$$E^2 = p^2c^2 + m_o^2c^4$$
$$E = \pm\sqrt{p^2c^2 + m_o^2c^4}$$
$$E_o = \pm m_oc^2$$

This worried Dirac. To understand why he was worried, think about a hydrogen atom. If the electron in this atom is excited into a higher energy level there will be empty allowed energy levels below this into which the electron will spontaneously fall, emitting energy as electromagnetic photons. So, if there is an infinite range of allowed negative energy states, what is to prevent positive energy electrons from making quantum jumps into them and disappearing in a flash of gamma radiation? This was a serious problem for

Dirac's theory, for it seemed to imply that ordinary matter, which is full of electrons, should be completely unstable and should disappear in an apocalyptic explosion!

N.B. These hypothetical negative energy electrons are *not* what we call antimatter, they are negative energy states for matter.

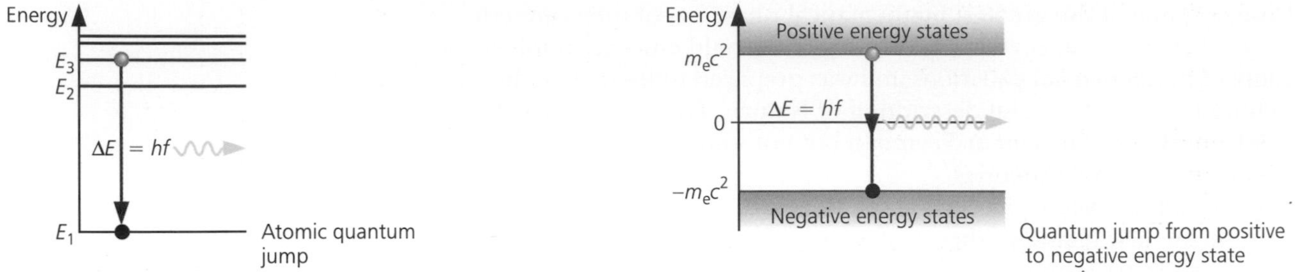

Figure 4.1 If vacant negative energy states are available why don't all the positive energy electrons make quantum jumps into them?

Dirac came up with a brilliant but rather disturbing solution. The outer electrons in many-electron atoms cannot fall into lower energy states because these states are already occupied by electrons and the Pauli Exclusion Principle forbids two electrons from occupying the same quantum state. Perhaps positive energy electrons cannot jump into negative energy states for the same reason – all the negative energy states are already occupied. The Universe is filled with an infinite sea of negative energy electrons 'on top' of which is the world of positive energy in which we live!

This is all very well but it looks as if Dirac introduced negative energy states only to get rid of them with an arbitrary and very peculiar idea. What difference do they make? How can the existence of the negative energy states be demonstrated? One way to do this would be to provide enough energy to promote one of the negative energy electrons into a positive energy state so that we can observe it as an ordinary electron created at some point in space. How much energy would be needed? The forbidden energy gap between the lowest positive and negative energy electrons is equal to twice the rest energy of the electron, so if a gamma ray photon of at least this energy was to travel through space it might just do the job.

However, this gamma ray would not just create a new positive energy electron, it would also knock a 'hole' in the negative energy sea of electrons, and this would look like a *positively charged particle*. The charge on the 'hole' would be equal and opposite to that of the electron, and so would its spin (that is, a lack of spin half will look like spin half against the background sea of negative energy electrons). At first Dirac wondered whether it might be a proton, but further analysis showed that it would have the same mass as the electron. It is a kind of mirror-image electron sharing many of the electron's properties but carrying an opposite charge. It also has one very special property. If an electron collides with it the electron can drop into the hole emitting the energy it loses as gamma-ray photons. As far as the positive energy world is concerned the electron and 'hole' **annihilate**. For this reason these 'holes' in the negative energy sea are described as '**antimatter**', in this case **antielectrons** or **positrons**. The creation of a particle/antiparticle pair is called **pair production** and their mutual annihilation is **pair annihilation**.

Pair production by gamma-ray photons

Rest energy of the electron $= m_e c^2$

Photon energy $= hf = \dfrac{hc}{\lambda}$

To promote a negative energy electron: $\dfrac{hc}{\lambda} \geq 2m_e c^2$

$$\lambda \leq \frac{hc}{2m_e c^2} \approx 10^{-12}\,\text{m}$$

which is in the gamma ray region of the electromagnetic spectrum.

In practice energy and momentum cannot be conserved if a single photon causes pair production so the process only occurs in the presence of other particles which can participate in the event and balance the conservation laws, e.g. when a gamma ray passes close to a nucleus.

Similarly, if a positron and electron meet the annihilation cannot result in a single photon, it usually produces a pair of gamma-ray photons.

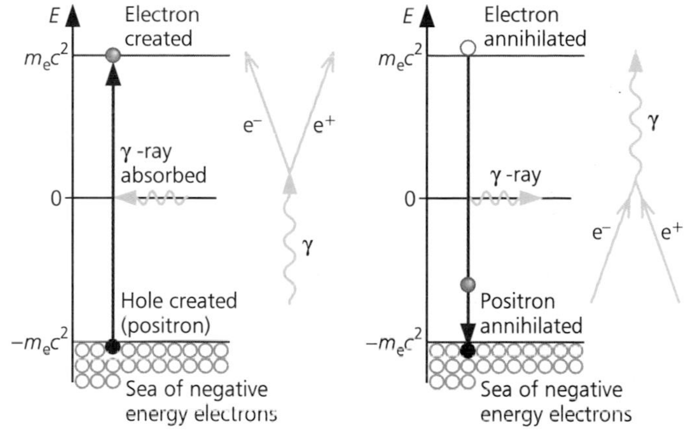

Figure 4.2 Pair production.

We now believe that all particles have antimatter counterparts that resemble them in every respect but the sign of their charge and the handedness of their spin. These matter/antimatter pairs annihilate if they come together.

Antimatter particles can be denoted by putting a bar over the symbol for the matter particles. For example, $\bar{n}$ is an antineutron and $\bar{\nu}$ an antineutrino. For charged particles it is often more convenient to use their charge to distinguish them. For example e^- is an electron and e^+ is a positron (these are also sometimes written as β^- and β^+ in beta decays).

Equations for annihilation and creation reactions:

${}^0_0\gamma \rightarrow {}^0_1e^+ + {}^{\ 0}_{-1}e^-$ Pair production/creation (in the presence of a nucleus).

${}^0_1e^+ + {}^{\ 0}_{-1}e^- \rightarrow 2\,{}^0_0\gamma$ Pair annihilation (two gamma rays are needed to conserve momentum).

Backwards in time

The negative energy sea of electrons should not be taken too seriously. It is an analogy, a convenient story to help us understand the implications of the Dirac Equation. Richard Feynman also came up with a good story about antimatter, thinking of it as ordinary matter *travelling backwards in time!* This incredible idea can be seen if we draw some simple diagrams of pair annihilation and creation. Figure 4.3(a) shows a pair of electrons approaching and repelling by exchanging a photon (see chapter 7). Figure 4.3(b) shows pair annihilation to a proton followed by pair creation. If the positrons in figure 4.3(b) are replaced by electrons moving backwards in time we get figure 4.4.

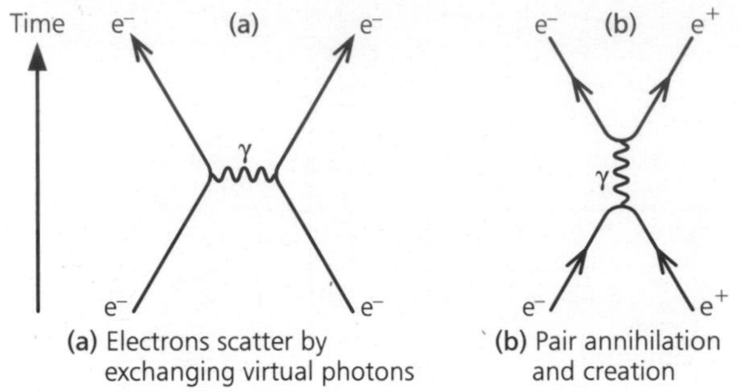

Figure 4.3 Imagine rotating diagram (a) through 90°. It would look very much like diagram (b). The only difference is that time and space axes have been interchanged. Feynman interpreted the annihilation and creation reactions as electrons scattering back and forth in time rather than space.

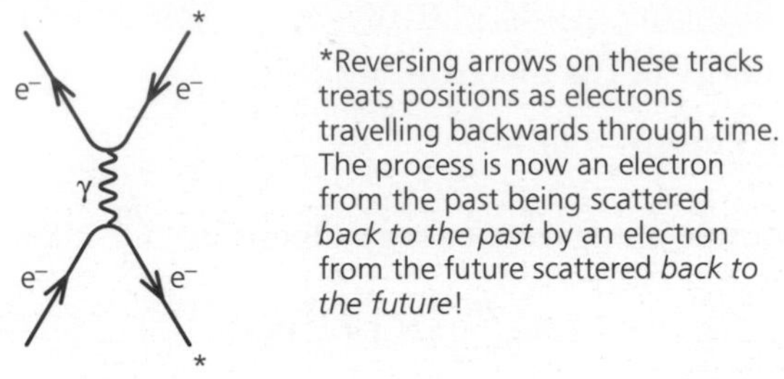

e⁻
e⁻
γ
e⁻
e⁻
*
*
*Reversing arrows on these tracks treats positions as electrons travelling backwards through time. The process is now an electron from the past being scattered *back to the past* by an electron from the future scattered *back to the future*!

Figure 4.4 Compare this diagram with figure 4.3(b). The arrows on the tracks of the positrons in figure 4.3(b) have been reversed, so that here they are shown as electrons travelling backward through time. If antimatter really is matter travelling backwards through time then it is no surprise to discover that antiparticles have exactly the same mass, spin and magnitude of charge as their matter counterparts.

The discovery of the positron

Dirac predicted the positron in 1928, and it was discovered in 1932 by Carl Anderson at Caltech. Anderson was using a cloud chamber to investigate cosmic rays, and had noticed that the curvature of tracks in a magnetic field indicated the presence of both positive and negative charged particles in about equal numbers. This was a surprise because most physicists thought that tracks were formed by electrons knocked out of atoms by cosmic gamma-rays. It seemed very unlikely that the positive particles were protons and the tracks were not distinct enough to have been formed by such a massive positive particle. Anderson even suggested that the tracks may be electrons travelling toward the incoming cosmic rays but there seemed no sensible origin for these.

A very simple experiment settled the argument. Anderson placed a 6 mm lead plate across the centre of the chamber and compared the curvature of the unidentified tracks for a particle that passed through the plate. Interactions with the plate dissipate some of the particle's energy and momentum so its path curves more sharply after it has passed through. This allowed him to determine the direction of its motion and so confirm its charge. It really was positive. Moreover its ionising power seemed very similar to that of an electron. The positron had been discovered.

Anderson's work was developed by Blackett and Occhialini who used Geiger counters to detect cosmic rays and then trigger the expansion of the cloud chamber. This is a much more efficient way to capture cosmic ray events and showed that cosmic ray particles generate positrons when they collide with atomic nuclei.

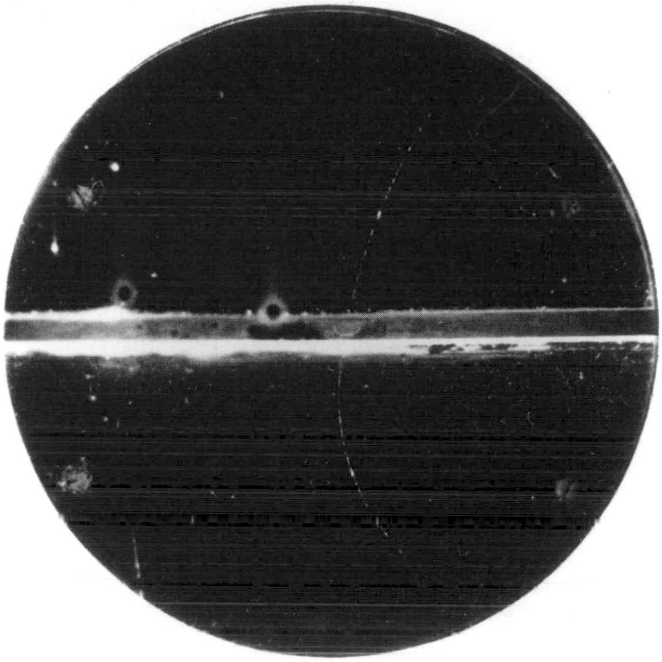

Figure 4.5 Use the change in curvature of the particle's track as it passes through the 6 mm lead plate to determine its direction of motion. Use Fleming's left-hand rule to show that it must have a positive charge. The magnetic field is into the page.

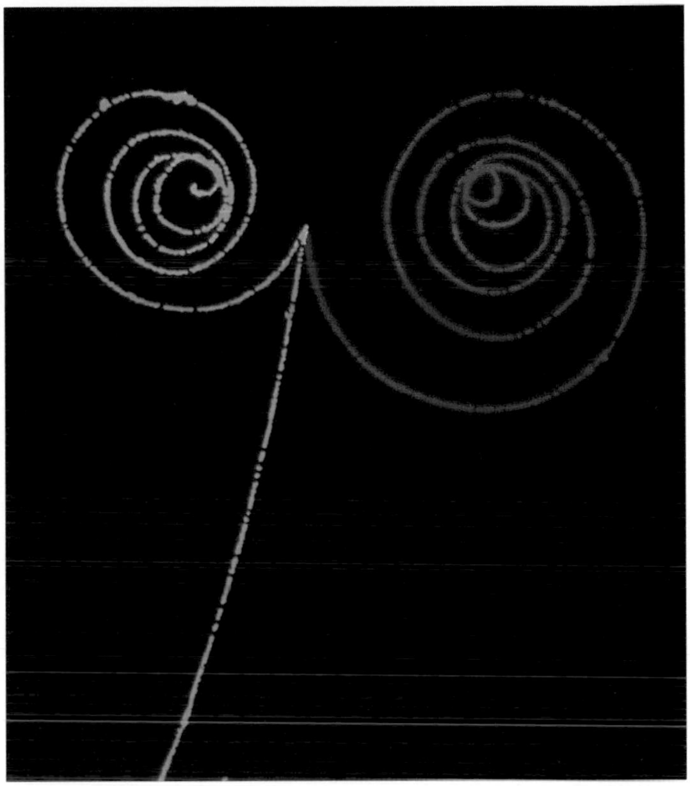

Figure 4.6 Pair production. A gamma ray emerging from the top centre has created an electron–positron pair, which spiral in opposite directions in the magnetic field. The third particle is a displaced atomic electron.

Beta-plus decay

Beta decay occurs in nuclei like carbon-14 that have too many neutrons to be stable. The underlying process is the conversion of a neutron to a proton and the creation of an electron and antineutrino.

$$^{14}_{6}\mathrm{C} \rightarrow {}^{14}_{7}\mathrm{N} + {}^{0}_{-1}\beta^{-} + {}^{0}_{0}\bar{\nu}_{e}$$
$${}^{1}_{0}\mathrm{n} \rightarrow {}^{1}_{1}\mathrm{p}^{+} + {}^{0}_{-1}\beta^{-} + {}^{0}_{0}\bar{\nu}_{e}$$

Free neutrons are also unstable and decay to protons. The half-life for this decay is 11.7 minutes. Protons can only convert to neutrons if energy is supplied. This can happen in some proton-rich nuclei (usually artificially produced) if the energy advantage gained by the nucleus is sufficient to 'pay' for the conversion of the proton. Such a nucleus undergoes **beta-plus decay** and emits a positron and neutrino. This was discovered by Irène and Frédéric Joliot-Curie in 1934. A neutrino accompanies the positron in order to conserve lepton number (the positron, being an antielectron, has lepton number –1).

An example of β^+ decay:

$$^{22}_{11}\mathrm{Na} \rightarrow {}^{22}_{10}\mathrm{Ne} + {}^{0}_{+1}\beta^{+} + {}^{0}_{0}\nu_{e}$$
$${}^{1}_{1}\mathrm{p}^{+} \rightarrow {}^{1}_{0}\mathrm{n} + {}^{0}_{1}\beta^{+} + {}^{0}_{0}\nu_{e}$$

Almost all nuclei that can decay by β^+ emission can also decay by another mechanism – '**K-capture**'. In this case the nucleus captures an inner (K-shell) electron and a neutrino is emitted. The electron converts a nuclear proton to a neutron:

$$^{22}_{11}\mathrm{Na} + {}^{0}_{-1}\mathrm{e}^{-} \rightarrow {}^{22}_{10}\mathrm{Ne} + {}^{0}_{0}\nu_{e}$$

Pair creation and annihilation and the conservation laws

Energy and momentum are conserved in all particle reactions. This can place restrictions on the allowed transformations. It might seem reasonable that an electron and positron meet and annihilate to a single gamma-ray photon that carries away all their energy and momentum, but this is not possible.

Imagine watching an electron and positron approach and annihilate one another. If we watch from their mutual centre of mass they will come towards us with equal velocities from opposite directions. Their masses are equal so the total linear momentum in this reference frame is clearly zero. If each particle has total energy W the gamma-ray photon will have to carry away an energy $E = 2W$. However, photons carry both energy E *and* momentum p, and as $p = E/c$ this gamma ray would have linear momentum $p = 2W/c$ in some direction. This would violate conservation of momentum and so the process is forbidden.

If a *pair* of photons is created in the annihilation then these must have equal energy and travel in opposite directions in the centre-of-mass frame so that their momenta cancel. Pair production is a time reversal of pair annihilation so cannot occur *in isolation* from a single gamma-ray photon. However, the chance of two gamma rays of the right energy meeting to produce an electron/positron pair is vanishingly small. What actually happens is that a high-energy gamma-ray photon passes close to a nucleus which also recoils as the pair is produced. In this way energy and momentum can be conserved. (Pair annihilation to a single photon can also occur near a nucleus.)

It should be pointed out that electrons and positrons do not have to annihilate, they can also scatter from one another. In a particular interaction there is a probability for each outcome. These probabilities are called 'cross-sections' and the larger the value of cross-section for a particular process the more likely it is that it will occur. Cross-sections for scattering and annihilation will depend on factors such as the particle energy and their distance of closest approach.

THE ANTIMATTER WORLD

Strange reflections

Dirac's prediction of antimatter is not restricted to the electron and positron, it applies to all particles. The antimatter world is like a 'mirror-reflection' of the matter world. Just as a mirror image is related to its object by symmetry so an antiparticle is related to its particle by a symmetric transformation. When you stand in front of a mirror the image is constructed of points projected from you to an equal distance behind the mirror. Front and back are reversed and the image ends up with the opposite handedness to the object it reflects. Antimatter inverts the charge of matter. It also changes the orientation of the particle's spin with respect to its magnetic moment (a kind of 'handedness').

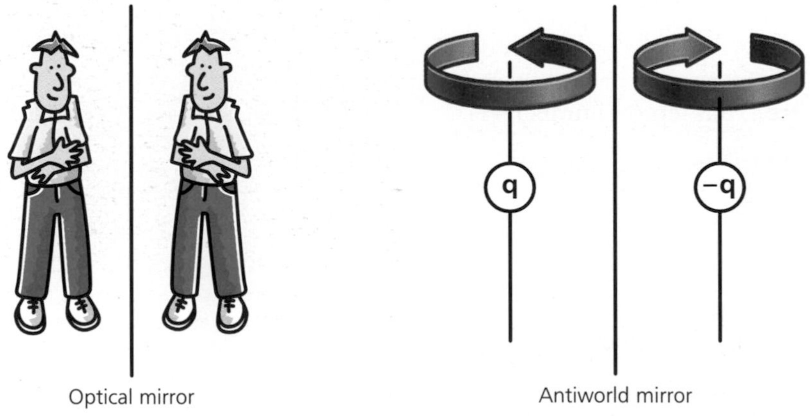

Figure 4.7 Mirror reflection and particle 'reflection'.

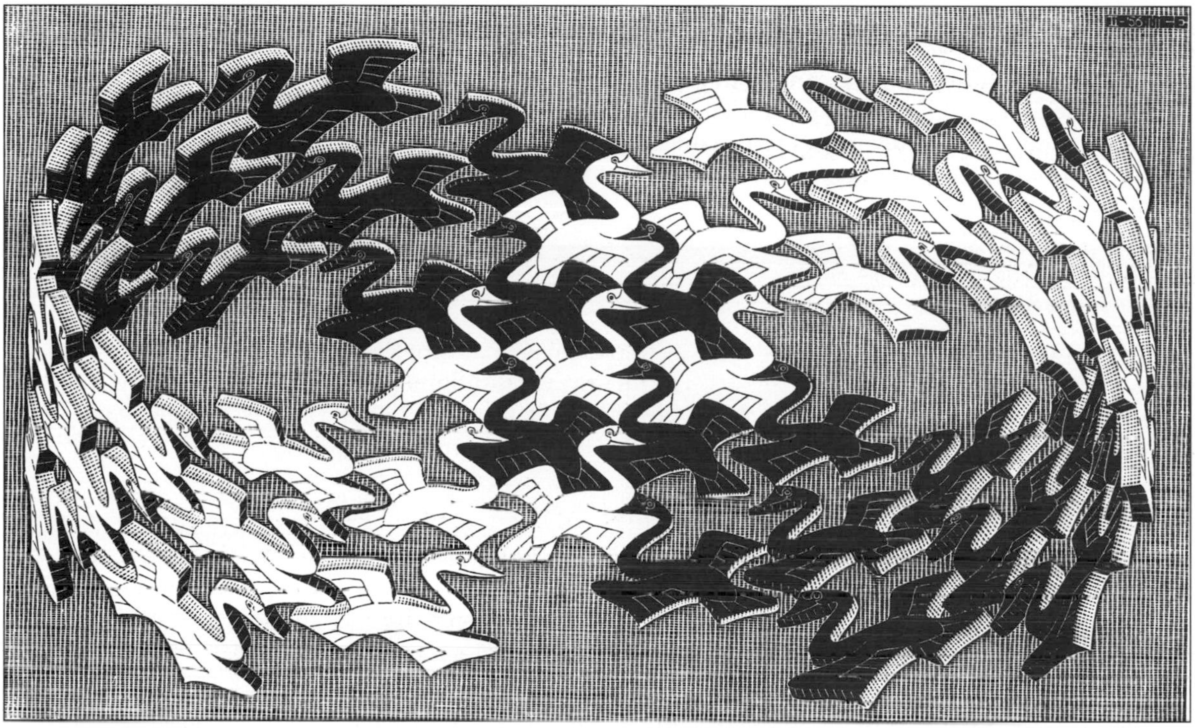

Figure 4.8 The symmetry between matter and antimatter is similar to that between the black and white birds in this picture drawn by the artist Escher. If black is swapped for white they swap roles. If in addition the picture is reflected about a central vertical line it becomes indistinguishable from the original. Matter and antimatter swap roles if we reflect all their coordinates and charges. (Reversing time has the same effect.)

The antiproton

The **antiproton** was discovered in 1955 by Emilio Segrè and his team using the Bevatron at the Lawrence Berkeley Laboratory (LBL). Copper nuclei were bombarded by energetic protons, and antiprotons were produced in some of the proton–proton collisions above 5.6 GeV. The main experimental problems lay in separating the rare events that produced antiprotons from the large number of events that produced pions (the pion is a less massive particle related to the nucleons). The equation below shows how antiprotons were produced – some of the kinetic energy of the incident proton created a proton–antiproton pair in the collision.

$${}^{1}_{1}p^{+} + {}^{1}_{1}p^{+} \rightarrow {}^{-1}_{-1}p^{-} + {}^{1}_{1}p^{+} + {}^{1}_{1}p^{+} + {}^{1}_{1}p^{+}$$

Antiprotons should have the same mass as a proton but deflect in the opposite direction in a magnetic field. The momentum of the antiprotons was determined from the curvature of their path in a magnetic field. Their velocity was determined by direct timing (using two scintillation counters placed 12 m apart) and by the Čerenkov radiation they emit (since they are travelling faster than light in the medium). Their mass was then calculated from the momentum and velocity and found to agree with this prediction.

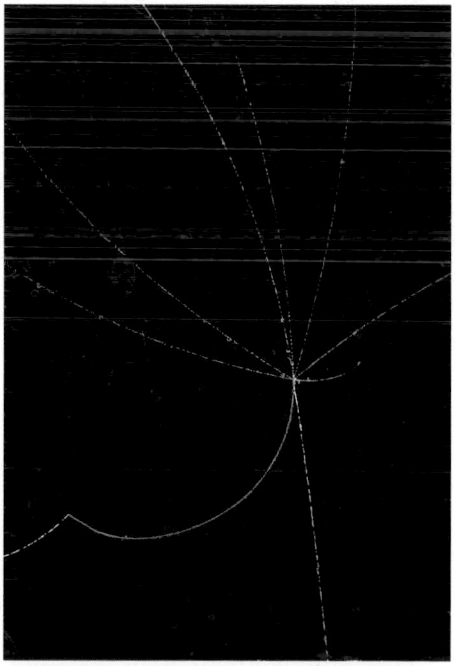

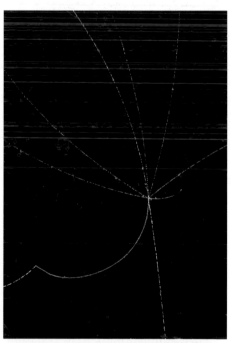

Figure 4.9 An antiproton enters lower right (blue), and collides with a proton in the bubble chamber near the centre of the photograph. The annihilation of the proton–antiproton pair results in the creation of four positive (red) and four negative pions (green).

Antimatter partners for neutral particles

Protons and electrons are charged so there is a clear distinction between these particles and their antiparticles; but what about neutral particles like the neutron and neutrino? These also have antimatter alter egos. They too are neutral and have the same mass (if any) and spin as the particles. However, there is a subtle distinction between the particle and its antiparticle. The relation between the spin of the **antineutron** and its magnetic moment is in the opposite sense to that of the neutron. Similarly neutrinos always spin like a left-handed corkscrew along their trajectories, **antineutrinos** are right-handed.

There are also some particles, like the **neutral pion**, that are their own antiparticle – that is, they are experimentally indistinguishable from their antiparticle. The reason for this will become clearer when we look at the underlying structure of these particles.

Discovery of the antineutron

Once created, antineutrons are easier to detect than neutrons. This is because they annihilate with neutrons and release a great deal of energy. They were discovered by Cork at LBL in 1956. Protons were used to create antiprotons which converted to antineutrons in collisions with target nuclei. The antineutrons passed undetected through two scintillators before annihilating in a Čerenkov counter surrounded by photomultipliers.

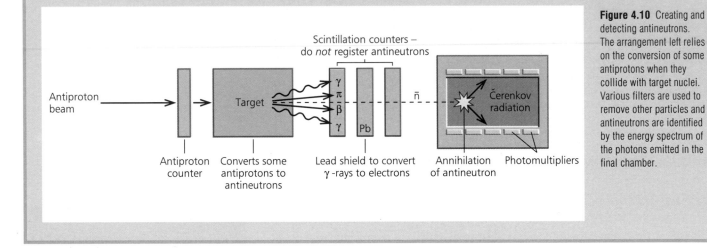

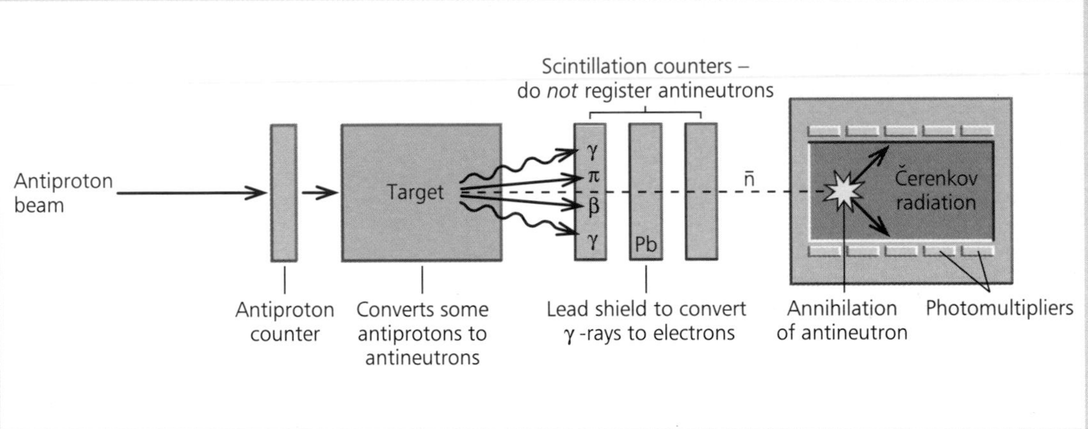

Figure 4.10 Creating and detecting antineutrons. The arrangement left relies on the conversion of some antiprotons when they collide with target nuclei. Various filters are used to remove other particles and antineutrons are identified by the energy spectrum of the photons emitted in the final chamber.

Positronium

Electrons and positrons have opposite charge so they attract one another. This can result in the formation of a light hydrogen-like 'atom' called positronium in which the electron and positron orbit their mutual centre of mass. This lies at a point halfway between the two particles, so the radius of positronium is about double that of the hydrogen atom. (In a hydrogen atom, the electron and proton are kept close together by the same attractive force, but their centre of mass lies close to the centre of the proton, which is much more massive than the electron.) Just like hydrogen, the positronium 'atom' has a well-defined set of allowed energy levels and can absorb and emit radiation as it makes quantum jumps between these levels. Both the electron and positron are spin-half particles (fermions) so positronium can have a total spin of either one or zero. Unlike hydrogen, the ground state of positronium is unstable as the electron can make one further quantum jump to combine and annihilate with the positron. How this occurs depends on what kind of positronium we are dealing with.

For annihilation to occur two things have to happen. The electron and positron must 'come together' and they must emit photons of appropriate energy and momentum to satisfy the conservation laws. The two types of positronium (spin-zero or spin-one) achieve this in different ways.

In both cases the 'coming together' is determined by the uncertainty principle. The wave-like aspects of the electron and positron mean that they do not have precisely defined positions and momenta at each instant. This means that, although the simple planetary atomic model predicts certain specific orbits for each allowed energy level, in reality the two particles may be found with some probability anywhere in the vicinity of the positronium atom. Among these possibilities is the chance that they are both occupying a similar small region of space. The probability of annihilation increases the closer they are, so it is possible to calculate the chance of this happening. If this calculation is combined with the chance that they emit appropriate photons the lifetime of positronium can be calculated.

If the electron and positron have opposite spins then the overall spin is zero and the decay can occur with the emission of a pair of photons of opposite spin. If the spins of electron and positron are parallel the total spin of the positronium atom is one and a third photon is necessary (photons are spin-one particles but the emission of a single photon would not conserve linear momentum). Since this decay requires the creation of more photons it is less likely to occur and so the lifetime of spin-one positronium (1.40×10^{-7} s) is considerably longer than that of spin-zero positronium (1.25×10^{-10} s).

This illustrates an important idea in quantum theory. If there are a number of alternative outcomes to a physical process then the more complicated ones will generally have lower probabilities. Of course, the sum of probabilities for all possible outcomes must be unity (particle physicists say that the probabilities must be **normalised**).

Quantum theory and annihilation

The state of a particle is described by a wavefunction ψ whose 'intensity' ($|\psi|^2$ or mod-ψ-squared) gives the probability per unit volume of finding the particle in a particular small region of space. This probability varies smoothly from one point to another so there is no way that a quantum particle can have a precisely defined trajectory or orbit. There will always be a chance that it is some way off the classical path. This uncertainty in the position and momentum of the particle is defined by the Heisenberg Uncertainty Principle:

$$\Delta x \Delta p \geq h$$

'uncertainty in position × uncertainty in momentum ≥ Planck's constant'

This is not just a measure of our uncertain knowledge; *the particle itself does not have a well-defined position or momentum.*

The annihilation of an electron and positron in positronium occurs because this uncertainty allows two particles which classically never collide to have overlapping wavefunctions. The amount of overlap determines the chance that they will annihilate and the lifetime of the composite state. If we apply the same rule to planets it means there is a finite probability that the Earth and Mars will find themselves on a collision course despite occupying distinct orbits (but don't worry – the overlap of wavefunctions gives a very small probability of this actually happening!).

As a rough guide the probability of annihilation is large once particles come within one Compton wavelength of each other. The Compton wavelength is given by $\lambda_C = \frac{h}{m_o c}$ and is about 2.4×10^{-12} m for positronium.

The anti-Periodic Table

The *Starship Enterprise* in 'Star Trek' generates thrust by combining matter and antimatter and expelling the products at high speed. To do this we would need a supply of matter and antimatter. In January 1996 a team of physicists led by Walter Oelert at CERN announced the creation of the first **antimatter atoms**. All were atoms of **anti-hydrogen** consisting of a single positron in orbit around an antiproton. Each one lasted a mere 40 nanoseconds before being annihilated by ordinary matter.

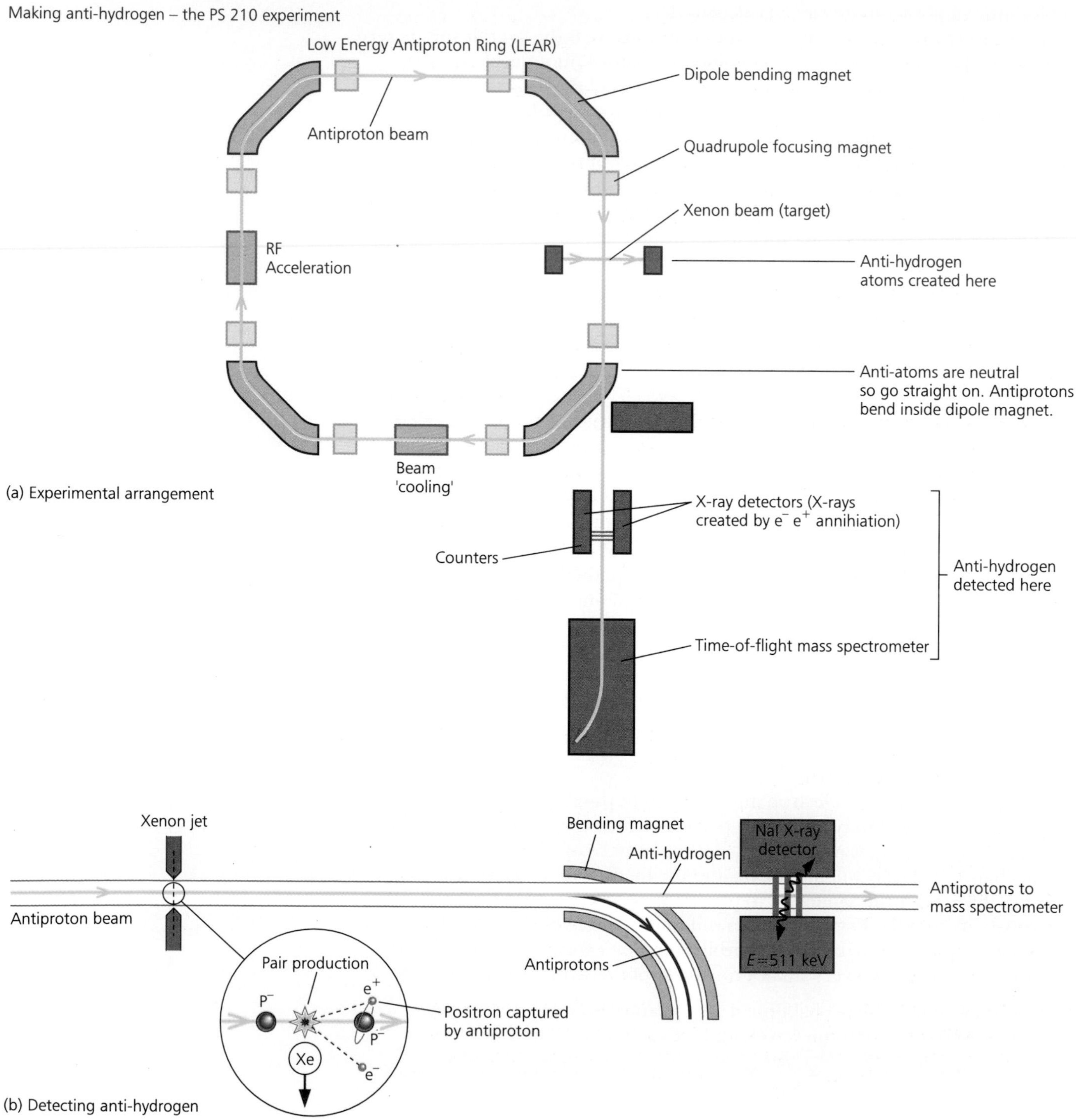

Figure 4.11 Making anti-hydrogen is not easy – the first successful experiments identified just nine atoms and these lasted only a few nanoseconds before they annihilated. We are some way from the technology of 'Star Trek'! It is worth noting that the LEAR (Low Energy Antiproton Ring) at CERN is designed to produce *low-energy* particle beams.

To create anti-hydrogen a gas jet of xenon was fired into the path of a beam of accelerated antiprotons. Occasionally one of the antiprotons would convert a little of its incident energy into an electron/positron pair. Some of the positrons had velocities close to those of the antiprotons and joined them to form anti-atoms. The anti-atoms, which are neutral, continued in a straight line when the rest of the antiproton beam was deflected away by the imposed magnetic field. The presence of the anti-atoms was detected by monitoring the annihilation of the positron and antiproton with matter.

Anti-hydrogen is the first anti-element in the anti-Periodic Table, and there can be little doubt that more massive anti-atoms and anti-molecules will be created in the future. In the meantime, particle physicists hope to catch slow moving anti-hydrogen atoms so that their properties can be investigated. The Standard Model predicts that energy levels in anti-hydrogen are identical to those in hydrogen, so analysing its emission and absorption spectra will be a good test of the theory. It is also proposed to drop anti-atoms to see if they fall with the same acceleration as ordinary matter. This will test Einstein's Equivalence Principle (which requires all objects to fall at the same rate in the same gravitational field) on which he based his theory of gravitation.

Storing antimatter

Antiprotons are produced when high-energy protons smash into a target, but they are rare compared to the pions, muons, electrons, etc. that are also created. Magnetic fields can be used to deflect the antiprotons away from the other particles, but the beam strength is weak and they must be accumulated and stored in a separate ring before experiments like the one described above (to create and study anti-atoms) are possible. This sounds simple, but the original beam of antiprotons is poorly defined and the accumulator has to monitor the beam at one point and use a feedback signal to correct and focus it at another. The condensed beam is stored until a sizeable antiproton stack has accumulated. The antiprotons can then be accelerated in stages and injected into the Super Proton Synchrotron (SPS) where they are made to collide with a counter-rotating beam of protons. Alternatively they can be decelerated in the Proton Synchrotron (PS) and injected into LEAR for low-energy experiments.

SUMMARY

- All particles have antimatter counterparts. Anti-particles resemble their corresponding particles in every respect except the sign of their charge and the handedness of their spin.
- The first anti-particle to be discovered was the antielectron, or **positron**.
- Particles and anti-particles may annihilate if they come together, producing energy.
- **Feynman diagrams** may be used to help understand the interactions between subatomic particles.
- When particles and anti-particles annihilate, the laws of conservation of energy and conservation of momentum are obeyed.
- One electron and one positron can form a light, hydrogen-like atom called **positronium**. Unlike hydrogen, the ground state of positronium is unstable, since the electron and positron may annihilate each other.

QUESTIONS

1 **a** Prove that conservation of energy and momentum forbid the creation of an electron–positron pair from an isolated gamma-ray photon. (*Hint:* consider the conservation laws in the centre of mass frame.)
b In what circumstances can a gamma-ray photon create an electron–positron pair?
c Compare and contrast the positron and the electron.

2 **a** What is positronium?
b Why is positronium unstable?
c How would you expect the energy levels of positronium to compare with those of hydrogen?
d What is anti-hydrogen?
e How would you expect the energy levels of anti-hydrogen to compare with those of hydrogen?

3 **a** Why do free protons not decay to neutrons?
b How is this consistent with the fact that some nuclei decay by beta-plus emission (which involves a nuclear proton changing to a neutron)?

4 In Anderson's first cloud-chamber photograph of the positron the radius of curvature of the track is 140 mm on one side of a 6.0 mm lead plate and 51 mm on the other. The applied magnetic field had a strength of 1.50 T perpendicular to the particle path.
a How could Anderson tell (i) the direction of motion of the particle and (ii) the sign of the charge on it?
b Calculate the energy of the positron before and after passing through the lead plate.
c How did Anderson know he was not dealing with a proton?

5

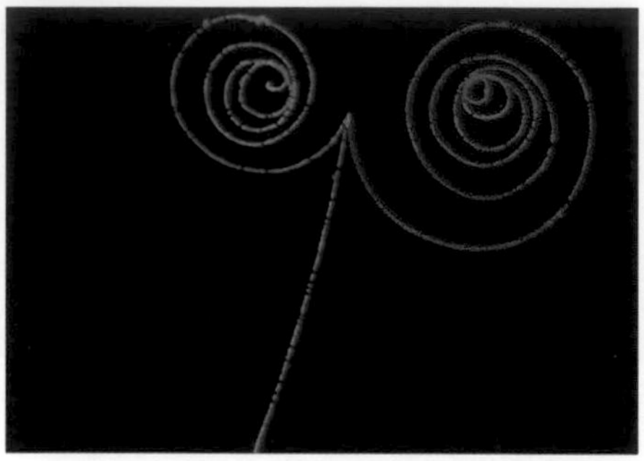

This photograph shows the production of an electron–positron pair by a gamma-ray photon in a bubble chamber.
a What was the probable path of the photon?
b How can you tell that the two particles have opposite charges?
c How can we infer that they have equal mass?

5 The nucleus

Rutherford

Ernest Rutherford was one of the greatest experimental physicists of all time. His discoveries laid the foundation for twentieth century nuclear physics and spanned the revolutionary period from the discovery of radioactivity by Henri Becquerel in 1896 to the discovery of nuclear fission by Otto Hahn and Lise Meitner in 1939.

Rutherford was born in New Zealand and won a scholarship to Cambridge in 1895 where he worked under J.J. Thomson, discoverer of the electron. In 1898 he went to McGill University in Canada as Professor of Physics where he worked with Soddy. In 1899 he distinguished alpha and beta radiation and in 1900 identified gamma rays. In 1905 he and Soddy published their theory of radioactive transformation having also identified half-lives and radioactive series. He returned to England to Manchester University in 1907 and helped invent the Geiger counter in 1908. Geiger and Marsden, under Rutherford's guidance, carried out the famous scattering experiments which led to the discovery of the nucleus in 1910. Trying to explain the structure of the nucleus Rutherford suggested the existence of the neutron (which was finally discovered in 1932 by James Chadwick, another of Rutherford's co-workers). During World War I Rutherford worked for the Admiralty on the sonic detection of submarines and returned to Cambridge in 1919 in time to split the atom. Between 1919 and 1924 he and Chadwick ejected protons from the nuclei of most light elements, confirming the proton as the first nuclear particle.

Ironically, Rutherford was awarded the Nobel Prize *for Chemistry* in 1908. He died in 1937 and is on record as saying that the prospect of obtaining useful amounts of energy from nuclear reactions was 'moonshine'!

Figure 5.1 Rutherford (right) and Geiger (left). 'The two decades, 1895 to 1915, will always be recognised as a period of remarkable scientific activity which has no counterpart in the history of Physical Science…' From Rutherford's address to the Röntgen Society in April 1918.

SCATTERING EXPERIMENTS

Many of Rutherford's discoveries came from **scattering experiments** in which incident particles are deflected by their targets or else cause the targets to recoil or even break apart. This set the agenda for high-energy physics experiments through the rest of the century, the main progress coming from the development of more powerful accelerators and more sensitive detectors (see chapters 1 and 2).

The structure and nature of the atomic nucleus has been revealed by scattering a variety of particles from it, in particular alpha and beta particles. Geiger and Marsden performed the classic scattering experiment in 1910.

Probing the nucleus with alpha particles

Rutherford had noticed as early as 1906 that even a small quantity of air in the path of alpha particles caused some to deflect significantly. He concluded that there must be some very intense electrical charges inside the atom and directed Geiger and Marsden to investigate the scattering of alpha particles through thin gold foil (gold was used because it could be formed into extremely thin sheets and it was known that alpha particles were not very penetrating).

As expected, most alpha particles passed through the foil with little or no deflection. However, a small but significant number **back-scattered** from the foil – Rutherford described it in the following words:

'It was quite the most incredible event that has ever happened to me in my life. It was almost as incredible as if you had fired a fifteen-inch shell at a piece of tissue paper and it came back and hit you.'

This led to three important conclusions:

- the alpha particles are scattered by a very massive object, since anything less massive than an alpha particle could not cause back-scattering
- the object responsible for the scattering is very small, much smaller than the atom. This accounts for the small proportion that back-scatter and the large proportion that barely scatter at all
- the positive charge of the atom is concentrated on the small scattering centres. The sharply rising repulsive force on alpha particles going close to the nucleus causes their deflection.

Putting these together he proposed the 'Rutherford planetary model' of the atom, in which a tiny positive nucleus has nearly all the mass of the atom and all its positive charge, and electrons orbit at relatively great distances. He then used this nuclear model to derive a scattering equation to predict how many alpha particles should deflect at each angle. The predictions fit the data very well and supported the nuclear hypothesis.

Rutherford assumed that the planetary model was correct and used the scattering formula he had derived to calculate the magnitude of the charge on the nucleus. He repeated the scattering experiment using different target materials in the foil in order to determine the nuclear charges for different elements. The pattern of results showed that nuclear charge increases in multiples of the electronic charge as you move through the Periodic Table. This confirmed what Rutherford already suspected, that the amount of positive charge on the nucleus distinguishes one element from another. If hydrogen has unit positive charge on its nucleus, then helium has two units, lithium three, and so on. Atomic number (which determines position in the Periodic Table) is simply the number of units of positive charge on the nucleus. These results made it seem likely that the nuclei of heavier elements are made up of the same subatomic particles as those of lighter elements, they just have more of them.

We can use alpha scattering to estimate nuclear size. If the scattering formula holds for alpha particles with a particular incident energy, then the model of simple electrostatic scattering (on which Rutherford's formula is based) must be valid at this energy. This means that the incident particles are not 'hitting' anything new, so the combined radius of nucleus plus alpha particle must be less than or equal to the closest approach of alpha-particles on a direct collision course (zero **impact parameter**).

Measurements of closest approach suggest that nuclei have diameters of less than 10^{-14} m. This is one ten thousandth (10^{-4}) of a typical atomic diameter so the nucleus occupies only about 1 part in 10^{12} (10^4 cubed) of the atomic volume. Since the electrons that orbit the nucleus are also apparently point-like, our experience of 'solid objects' in the world around us is just a convenient illusion.

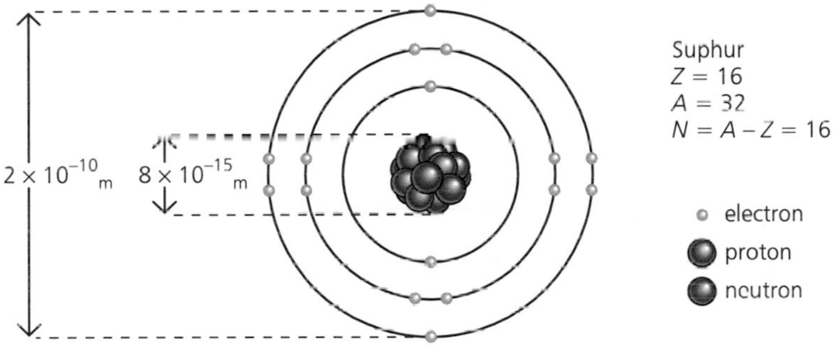

Figure 5.2 In Rutherford's original model the electrons followed circular orbits. This model was extended to elliptical orbits and then quantised by Niels Bohr so that only certain orbits are allowed. It is helpful to visualise the atom as a mini solar system, but it can also be misleading. Modern quantum-mechanical models reject the idea that electrons follow well-defined trajectories inside the atom – the electrons are represented by probability distributions.

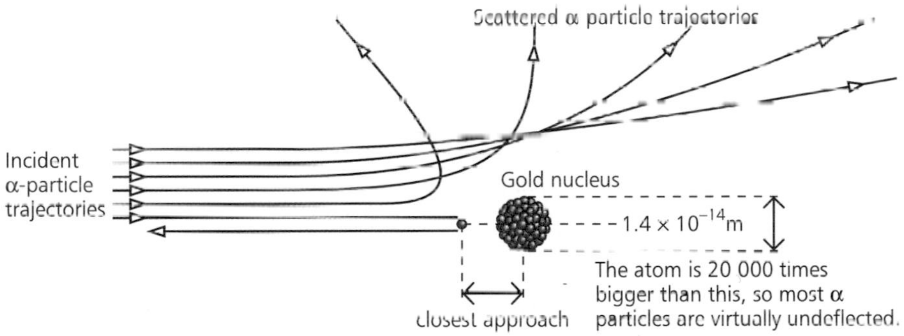

Figure 5.3 Rutherford assumed that alpha scattering was due to electrostatic repulsion between two point-like positively charged particles, the incident alpha particle and the much more massive gold nucleus.

Closest approach

An alpha particle approaching a nucleus along a line passing through the centre of the nucleus will deflect through 180°. It converts KE to EPE as it approaches and momentarily stores all of its incident KE as EPE in the electric field at closest approach. If the nucleus is much more massive than the alpha particle we can simplify the calculations by assuming the nucleus remains at rest throughout the interaction. The closest approach sets an upper limit to the combined radii of the two particles and gives us some idea of the size of nuclei.

Alpha particle energy = E_α = incident KE

Alpha charge Q_α = +2e

Nuclear charge = Q_n = +Ze

EPE of alpha particle in nuclear electric field $= \dfrac{Q_\alpha Q_n}{4\pi\varepsilon_o r} = \dfrac{2Ze^2}{4\pi\varepsilon_o r}$

At closest approach ($r = r_{min}$) the alpha particle's KE = 0 so all incident energy is stored in the field:

$$\frac{2Ze^2}{4\pi\varepsilon_o r_{min}} = E_\alpha$$

$$r_{min} = \frac{Ze^2}{2\pi\varepsilon_o E_\alpha}$$

For a 5 MeV alpha particle incident on a gold nucleus ($Z = 79$):

$$r_{min} = 4.5 \times 10^{-14}\,\text{m}$$

The nucleus must be smaller than this.

N.B. If we include the recoil of the gold nucleus then the calculated closest approach is increased. This is because the momentum of alpha particle and gold nucleus together must equal the initial momentum of the alpha particle. The two particles therefore have some KE at closest approach and so store less potential energy in the electric field.

Conservation of momentum gives:

$(m + M)v = mu$ (M, m are the masses of the nucleus and alpha particle)

$v = \dfrac{mu}{(M + m)}$ (u is the incident velocity of the alpha particle and v the combined velocity)

This result can be used to express the kinetic energy of the alpha particle and nucleus as they move together at closest approach ($KE_{n,\alpha}$) in terms of the initial alpha particle energy E_α:

$$KE_{n,\alpha} = \frac{1}{2}(M + m)v^2 = \frac{1}{2}\frac{m^2u^2}{(M + m)} = \frac{mE_\alpha}{(M + m)}$$

The electrostatic potential energy stored in the field at closest approach is equal to the difference between the initial kinetic energy of the alpha particle and the kinetic energy of the two particles at closest approach. From this we can calculate the separation at closest approach:

$$EPE = \frac{2Ze^2}{4\pi\varepsilon_o r'_{min}} = E_\alpha - KE_{\alpha,n} = E_\alpha - \frac{mE_\alpha}{(M + m)} = \frac{ME_\alpha}{(M + m)}$$

$r'_{min} = \dfrac{(M + m)Ze^2}{2\pi\varepsilon_o ME_\alpha}$ (if $m \ll M$ this reduces to the previous expression)

The early experiments used alpha particles from naturally occurring radioactive sources. Later, higher energy accelerated alpha particles were used. These showed deviations from Rutherford's scattering formula. The deviations were larger for larger angle scattering (which involves a closer approach to the nucleus). These deviations implied that some aspect of the model used to derive the scattering formula must be invalid very close to the nucleus. The alpha scattering was no longer due to a purely electrostatic repulsion, a new force was modifying the interaction, a force that acts only at very short range: **the strong nuclear force**.

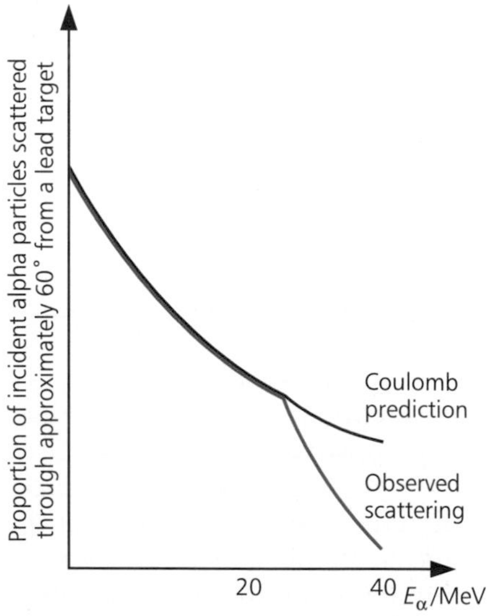

Figure 5.4 For alpha particles with more than about 30 MeV the deviations from simple coulomb scattering from lead at 60° become significant. 30 MeV alpha particle would have a closest approach of about 8×10^{-15} m. This can be used to measure and compare nuclear radii.

Nucleons

As early as 1896 Goldstein observed positive rays in cathode ray tubes. Wien measured their deflection in electric and magnetic fields and showed that they had masses thousands of times greater than the mass of an electron. However, the proton was only identified as a common constituent of all nuclei (a **nucleon**) following the work of Rutherford, Marsden and Chadwick. They systematically bombarded nuclei of different elements with alpha particles and managed to knock protons out of most of the light nuclei. They announced their result in 1919 and Rutherford proposed that the positive charge in a nucleus is entirely due to the protons it contains. Atomic number, Z, is equal to the number of protons in the nucleus.

The ejection of protons from the nucleus changes atomic number and converts one element into another. This transmutation was first achieved in 1919 and is often referred to as 'splitting the atom'. The reaction involved was:

$$^{4}_{2}\alpha + ^{14}_{7}\mathrm{N} \rightarrow ^{17}_{8}\mathrm{O} + ^{1}_{1}\mathrm{p}^{+}$$

A nucleus of nitrogen has been converted to oxygen.

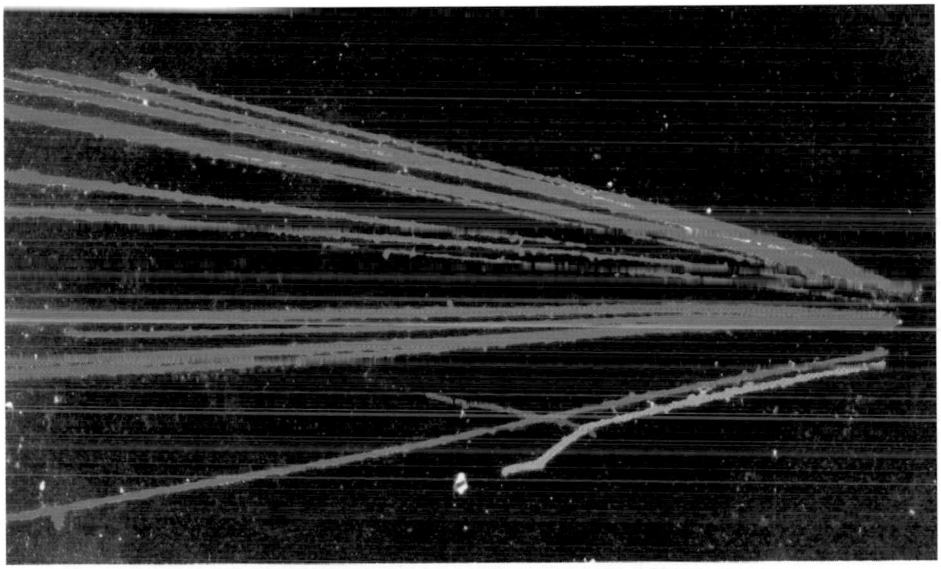

Figure 5.5 'Splitting the atom'. The angle between particle tracks indicates that the ejected particle (red) has a mass about one quarter of that of the alpha particle (yellow). It is a proton.

The need for neutrons

Nuclei cannot be made up simply of protons. This is obvious if we compare the charges and masses of hydrogen and helium nuclei. Helium has four times the mass but only twice the positive charge. This could be explained if the helium nucleus contains four protons and two electrons, but it would raise the question of what prevents other electrons from entering the nucleus and neutralising it.

Also, this hypothesis would not account for the observed spin of the nucleus. Protons and electrons are both fermions with spin $\frac{1}{2}$. Nitrogen has an even spin but would contain fourteen protons and seven electrons (*twenty-one* fermions) on the proton–electron model. It is not possible to combine an odd number of fermions and end up with an even spin. (Remember that spin-half particles can only align parallel or antiparallel to one another.)

Quantum theory raises another problem. If a particle is bound inside the nucleus then the uncertainty in its position is about the same size as the radius of the nucleus. According to the Uncertainty Principle, the smaller the uncertainty in position (δx) the larger the uncertainty in momentum (δp):

$$\delta x \delta p \approx h$$

$$\delta p \approx \frac{h}{\delta x}$$

For an electron trapped in a region of nuclear dimensions the uncertainty in momentum is associated with a kinetic energy large enough to expel the electron, so it cannot be bound there. (Protons and neutrons have much larger masses so although their momentum uncertainties are the same as for an electron in the same volume the associated kinetic energy is much smaller.)

Rutherford proposed the existence of a neutral particle with about the same mass as a proton that would combine with protons to form the nuclei of all elements. His original idea was that the neutron was a kind of composite consisting of a proton and electron very tightly bound together. This is not the modern view of the neutron, since an electron could not be bound in such a small volume for the reasons explained above. The neutron is now regarded as a nucleon in its own right, and when it decays to a proton and electron (also emitting an antineutrino) the electron is *created* in the decay, not released from some previously existing state.

The neutron was observed several times before its 'discovery'. Becker and Bothe noticed that beryllium emits an extremely penetrating radiation when bombarded with alpha particles. Irène and Frédéric Joliot-Curie showed that this radiation could knock protons out of paraffin wax (a hydrocarbon containing much hydrogen) very efficiently. However, none of these scientists had worked with Rutherford. James Chadwick had, and he was following Rutherford's advice to look for the neutron in the same way that you might look for an invisible man in a city street, by watching the effects on those into whom he bumps.

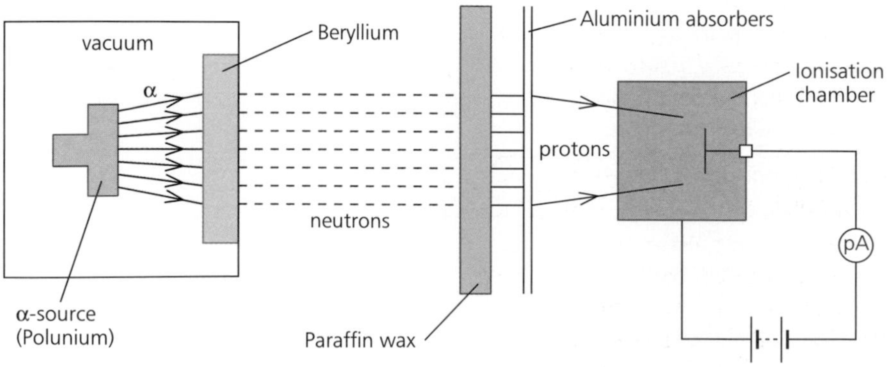

Figure 5.6 Alpha particles knock neutrons out of beryllium. The neutrons knock protons out of paraffin wax. The proton energies are measured and used to calculate the mass of the incident neutrons. (A peculiarity of this experiment is that the rate of detection increases when the paraffin wax is put in place – since it 'converts' undetected neutrons into detectable protons.)

Chadwick's experiments were simple and decisive. He used alpha particles to knock neutrons out of a nucleus and detected them by measuring the energy spectrum of protons ejected from paraffin wax by the neutrons.

Chadwick chose polonium as the alpha source because it does not emit gamma rays. Gamma rays would confuse things because they too can eject protons. The alpha particles knock neutrons out of beryllium nuclei. The reaction taking place in the beryllium is:

$$^{4}_{2}\alpha + {}^{9}_{4}\mathbf{Be} \rightarrow {}^{12}_{6}\mathbf{C} + {}^{1}_{0}\mathbf{n}$$

The neutrons themselves are neutral and so do not show up in most detectors, which rely on electromagnetic interactions to cause ionisation or electrical pulses. However, they collide with protons in the hydrogen of paraffin wax and eject them. This is like a collision between two snooker balls where the particles have similar mass and size. In a head-on collision the neutron stops and the proton flies off with a velocity equal to that of the incident neutron. These protons confirm the existence of the neutrons.

The energy of the protons is measured using various thicknesses of aluminium absorbers, and then an ionisation chamber measures their rate of arrival. Putting these two pieces of information together we can work out the energy spectrum of the protons (that is the number arriving in each energy range). This tells us the energy and mass of the incident neutrons.

Chadwick concluded that neutrons have a similar mass to protons and no charge. He supported his conclusion by measuring the recoil velocities after collisions between the neutrons and hydrogen or nitrogen in a cloud chamber. This gave a way of checking the mass of the neutron.

The model of the nucleus now has protons and neutrons (nucleons) bound together by the strong nuclear force. The **proton number, or atomic number** ***Z*** determines the element and the **mass or nucleon number** ***A*** determines the mass of the nucleus (it is *not equal* to the atomic mass, but related to it). **Isotopes** of an element differ only in the number of neutrons in the nucleus. For example,

$^{238}_{92}$U is the most common isotope of uranium. Its nucleus contains 92 protons and 238 − 92 = 146 neutrons.

$^{235}_{92}$U, the rarer fissionable isotope of uranium also has 92 protons in its nucleus but only 143 neutrons.

Both have 92 orbital electrons in the neutral atom.

Probing the nucleus with electrons

There is one major drawback in using alpha particles to investigate the nucleus – they consist of nucleons and so are affected by the strong nuclear force. Electrons, on the other hand, are leptons. Leptons do not interact by the strong force, so electrons can be used to look at the charge distribution in the nucleus. To do this we use the wave-like property of diffraction and measure the diffraction pattern for electrons scattered from the nucleus.

Wave–particle duality

Discoveries by Planck, Einstein and Compton (among others) led to the conclusion that the most appropriate model for light is sometimes a wave (e.g. when explaining interference and diffraction) and sometimes a stream of particles (e.g. the photoelectric effect or Compton scattering). This introduced the idea of 'wave–particle duality' which is a little misleading since it applies to *our description of light* rather than light itself.

The wave-like character of light is represented by its wavelength, λ.

Momentum, p, represents its particle-like character.

In 1919 Prince Louis de Broglie used Einstein's mass–energy equivalence to relate these two characteristics.

For a photon: $E = hf = \dfrac{hc}{\lambda} = mc^2$

$$\therefore \lambda = \frac{h}{mc}$$

But mc is the photon momentum, p, so:

$$\lambda = \frac{h}{p} \quad \text{or} \quad \textbf{wave-like property} = \frac{\textbf{Planck's constant}}{\textbf{particle-like property}}$$

The equation above is known as the 'de Broglie relation'.

De Broglie suggested that this relation might hold for *everything*, not just light. The consequence is that electrons, protons, atoms (and all other material things), classically considered to be particles, would also show wave-like properties of diffraction and interference.

The effects of diffraction and interference are only noticeable if the wavelength involved is comparable to the dimensions of the object or aperture used. A quick calculation shows that even low-energy electrons have very short '**de Broglie wavelengths**'.

$$E = \frac{p^2}{2m} \quad \therefore p = \sqrt{2mE} \quad \text{so} \quad \lambda = \frac{h}{\sqrt{2mE}}$$

For 1 keV electrons $\lambda = 3.9 \times 10^{-11}$ m.

This is a bit smaller than an atomic radius.

Diffraction of electron beams passing through holes or slits in the electron gun of a TV is negligible because the aperture is enormous compared to the de Broglie wavelength. However, when electron beams pass through crystals or past a nucleus the object may well be comparable to the de Broglie wavelength and so diffraction effects are important.

Diffraction of electrons by atoms was first demonstrated by Davisson and Germer in 1926. They used the regular planes of atoms in a crystal like the parallel slits of a diffraction grating. Scattered electrons formed a pattern similar to an X-ray diffraction pattern and they used this to calculate the wavelength associated with the electrons. The calculated wavelengths agreed with de Broglie's prediction.

Nuclei are much smaller than atoms. Their radii are measured in femtometres (1 fm = 10^{-15} m). This means the electrons used to form diffraction patterns from nuclei will have to have wavelengths in the same range. Since wavelength is inversely related to particle momentum the electrons will need to have a large momentum and energy. We can control electron wavelength by controlling their energy in an accelerator. High-energy electron beams can then be directed at targets containing the nuclei of interest and the scattered electrons will form a diffraction pattern from which we can determine the radius of the nuclei.

Measuring the nucleus with electrons

Electrons of 190 MeV from the Stanford Linear Accelerator were used to measure nuclear radii. When calculating the de Broglie wavelength of these electrons we must treat them as relativistic particles. This is obvious if we recall that the rest mass of an electron is equivalent to a rest energy E_o of about 0.5 MeV. These electrons have a gamma factor of 380 and their kinetic energy dwarfs their rest energy.

$$E^2 = p^2c^2 + E_o^2 \approx p^2c^2$$

E is the total energy and is approximately equal to the kinetic energy.

$$\therefore p \approx \frac{E}{c}$$

This relation is the same for a photon and gives:

$$\lambda = \frac{h}{p} \approx \frac{hc}{E}$$

This is a very useful approximation for relativistic particles.

$$\textbf{If } E = 190\,\textbf{MeV} \qquad \lambda \approx 6.5 \times 10^{-15}\,\textbf{m}$$

The diffraction pattern for plane waves passing a circular object of diameter D is the same as if they passed through a circular aperture of the same size. This is sketched below. The essential point is that the angle at which the first minimum occurs is given by:

$$\sin\theta = \frac{1.22\lambda}{D}$$

If we can measure the angular position of the first minimum then we can calculate the diameter of the scattering object. This method is used to calculate nuclear radii by the elastic scattering of electrons.

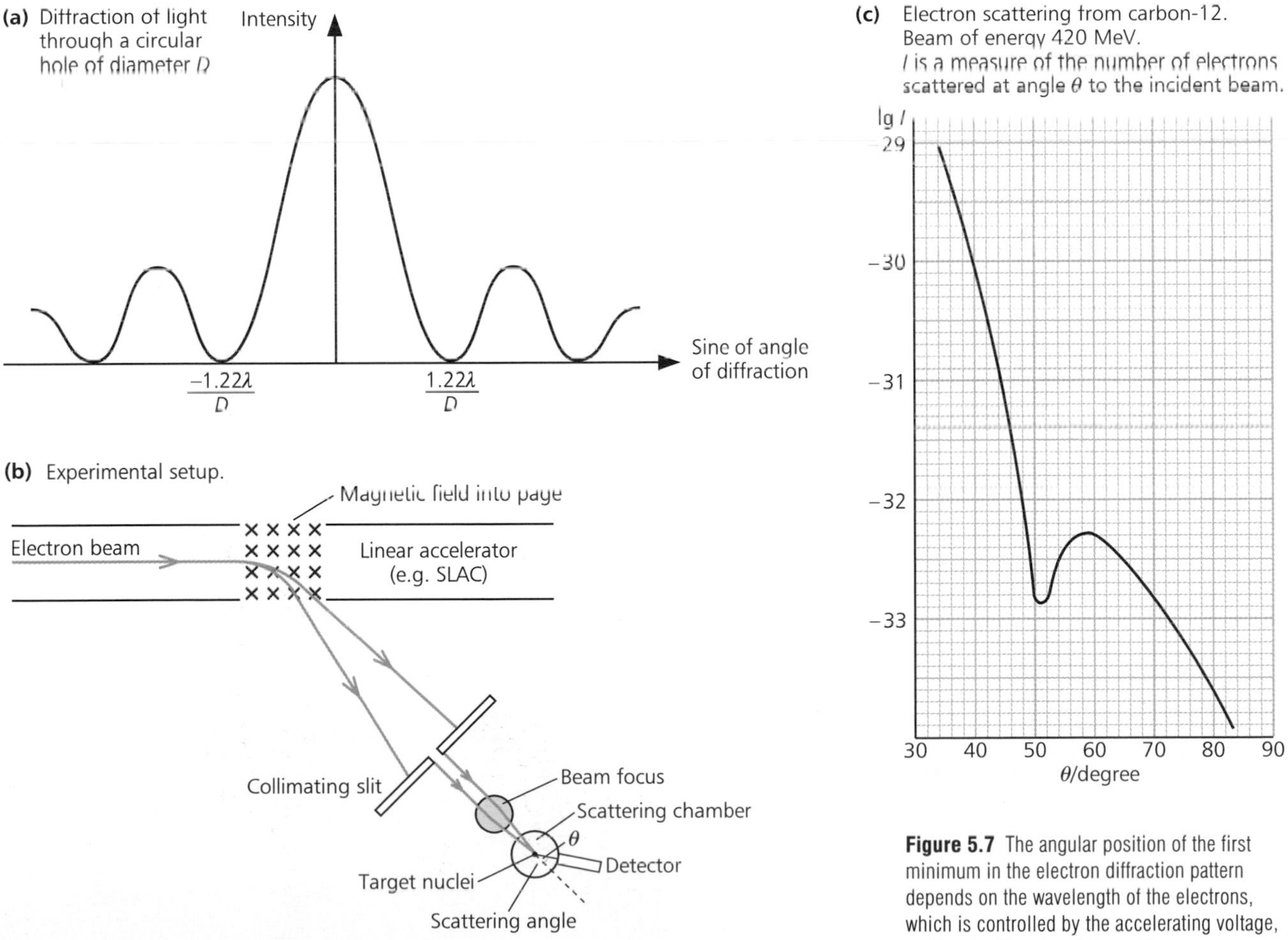

Figure 5.7 The angular position of the first minimum in the electron diffraction pattern depends on the wavelength of the electrons, which is controlled by the accelerating voltage, and by the diameter of the nucleus.

Table 5.1 Nuclear radii derived from electron scattering experiments.

Nucleus	A	$R/10^{-15}$ m	$\sqrt[3]{A}$
H	1	1.00	1.0
He	4	2.08	1.6
C	12	3.04	2.3
O	16	3.41	2.5
Si	28	3.92	3.0
S	32	3.02	3.2
Ca	40	4.54	3.4
V	51	4.63	3.7
Co	59	4.94	3.9
Sr	88	5.34	4.4
In	115	5.8	4.9
Sb	122	5.97	5.0
Au	197	6.87	5.8

It is obvious from the data above that the radius increases as the number of nucleons in the nucleus (A) goes up. This tells us that the nucleons occupy space, as more are added the nucleus gets larger. What is much more interesting is that the radius increases roughly as the cube root of the nucleon number (the light nuclei are exceptions to this), or the nucleon number is proportional to the radius cubed.

$$r \propto A^{\frac{1}{3}} \qquad \text{or} \qquad A \propto r^3$$

Why should this be? Assume the nucleus is spherical. Its volume would be $\frac{4}{3}\pi r^3$ which is also proportional to the cube of the radius. This means the number of nucleons is proportional to the volume of the nucleus, so the volume occupied by a single nucleon in any nucleus is more or less the same. This would be the case if the nucleons close-packed in some way – perhaps nuclei are made up of close-packed nucleons? It also tells us that the density of nuclear matter is about the same in all nuclei.

Experimental data gives: $r = r_0 A^{\frac{1}{3}}$ **with** $r_0 \approx 1.2 \times 10^{-15}$ **m**

For carbon $A = 12$ **so** $r \approx 3.3 \times 10^{-15}$ **m**

The density of a nucleus is enormous, about 10^{17} kg m^{-3}! A teaspoonful of this nuclear matter would have a mass of about 500 million tonnes. This may seem like science fiction, but such matter exists, in bulk, in neutron stars. These form when the core of a supernova continues to collapse – eventually gravitational attraction forces all atomic electrons to combine with protons to form neutrons. Rapidly spinning neutron stars signal their presence by pulses of electromagnetic radiation that are so regular they may one day be used as a standard time signal against which to compare terrestrial clocks.

Figure 5.8 The weak regular radio signals she discovered in 1968 were such a surprise to Jocelyn Bell Burnell that she labelled them LGM (for 'little green men'). More detailed work showed that the signals had a period of 1.337 301 13 seconds with an accuracy better than one part in 10^8! She had discovered the first pulsar, a rapidly rotating neutron star. She is shown with Anthony Hewish who won the Nobel prize for this work in 1974.

MODELS OF THE NUCLEUS

The strong force

The neutron–proton model explains nuclear charge and mass. However the protons repel one another with an electrostatic repulsion which produces enormous forces on the nuclear scale and which falls off as an inverse-square law with distance. To hold a nucleus together there must be a new nuclear force which:

- binds nucleons to each other
- is stronger than electromagnetism on the scale of the nucleus
- is weaker than electromagnetism on the scale of the atom (otherwise all nuclei would clump together)
- is repulsive at very short range (to prevent the protons and neutrons collapsing still further).

The **strong nuclear force** acts on protons and neutrons equally but does not affect leptons. The limited range of the strong force means it only exerts a significant force between adjacent nucleons. This explains why very heavy nuclei are not stable – as more protons are added they are repelled by *all* the other protons already present but only attracted by the nucleons adjacent to them. Eventually the electrostatic repulsion will be too great for the strong force to overcome.

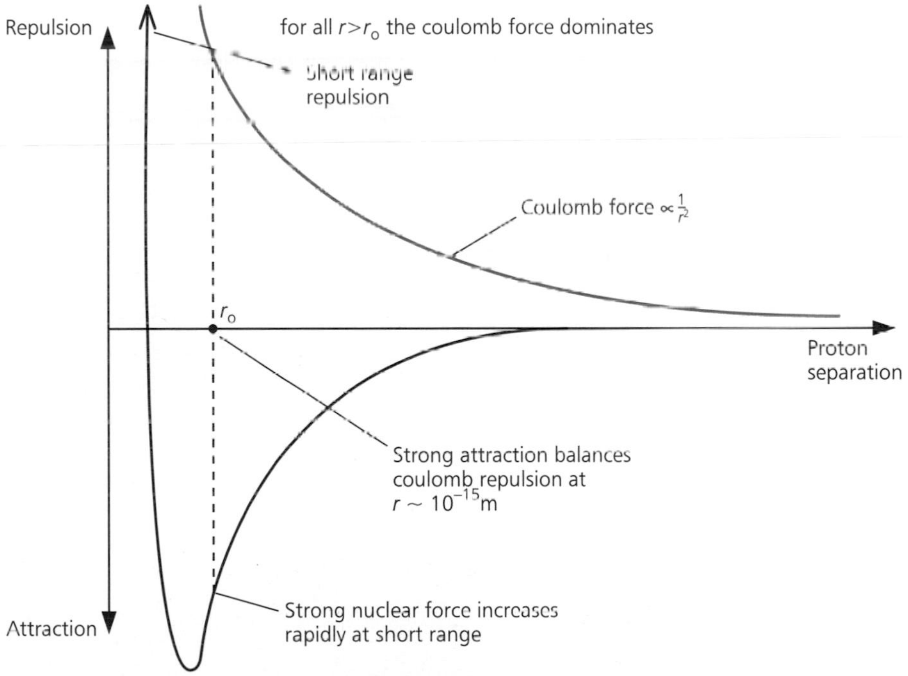

Figure 5.9 The strong nuclear force.

The way the strong force varies with nucleon separation is very similar to the way the forces vary between molecules in a liquid (Van der Waals forces). Niels Bohr suggested that the nucleus would therefore behave a bit like a charged liquid drop. The **liquid drop model** is particularly useful to explain fission (a drop is disturbed and eventually splits into two parts which repel one another because of their positive charge). It is interesting that the forces between nucleons arise as a kind of residual force from the interactions between quarks (see chapter 6 for more details) just as the Van der Waals force arises as a residual force from the electromagnetic forces that bind atoms into molecules.

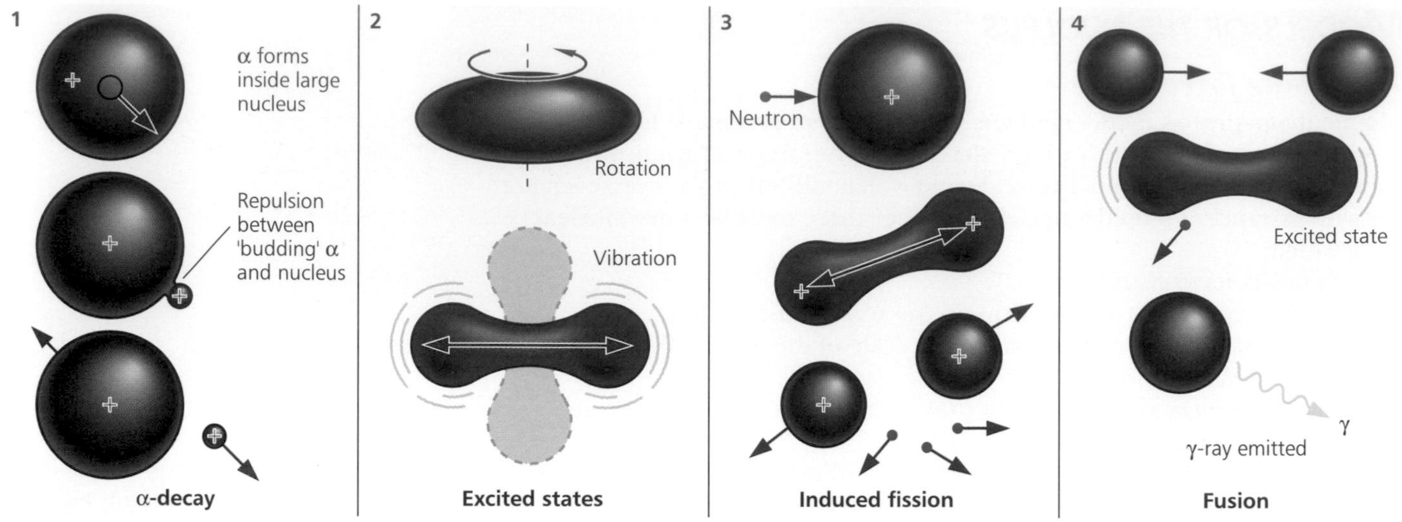

Figure 5.10 Many aspects of nuclear behaviour can be described by imagining the nucleus behaves like a charged liquid drop.

The **close-packed model** or crystalline model suggested by the constant nuclear density is also sometimes useful. For example, rapidly rotating nuclei behave as if the nucleons stretched out in a line along the axis of rotation.

In the **shell model** nucleons move in discrete orbits inside the nucleus rather like the electrons in an atom. The allowed orbits are quantised so the nucleus can make energy jumps between excited states by absorbing or emitting photons. The forces in the nucleus are much larger than those on orbital electrons in an atom so nucleon quantum jumps are much larger than electronic quantum jumps – nuclei tend to absorb or emit gamma rays rather than visible (or near-visible) light.

The noble or inert gases are particularly stable because their outer electron shells are full. A similar situation can arise if nucleon shells are full, and this explains the existence of 'magic numbers' – nucleon numbers that are particularly common for the stable nuclei. These are: 2, 8, 20, 28, 50, 82 and 126. Oxygen-16, for example, is a doubly magic nucleus since it has 8 protons and 8 neutrons. It is also particularly stable and abundant.

A survey of the stable nuclei reveals a preference for particular combinations of neutrons and protons.

Figure 5.11 Lise Meitner (left) made major contributions to nuclear physics. In 1918, with Otto Hahn (right), she discovered protactinium. In 1939, with her nephew Otto Frisch, she correctly identified nuclear fission. She made these discoveries despite being banned from laboratories for being a woman (by Emil Fischer in Berlin) and later having to flee Germany because of the persecution of Jewish scientists.

Table 5.2

Proton number Z	Neutron number $N = A - Z$	Number of stable nuclei
even	even	160
even	odd	56
odd	even	52
odd	odd	4

This suggests that protons and neutrons tend to pair up in stable nuclei. Unpaired protons or neutrons destabilise the nucleus.

Neutron-rich nuclei?

One thing that often puzzles people is why neutral nuclei made entirely from neutrons do not occur. This is because neutrons are unstable and would tend to beta decay to protons. In stable nuclei neutrons are prevented from decaying to protons by energy conservation. Protons and neutrons are distinguishable fermions and so separately obey the Pauli Exclusion Principle. This means that if we build up a nucleus by adding the nucleons one by one then the first ones will drop into low energy levels and later ones will be in successively higher energy levels. Eventually we will have two 'stacks', one of neutrons and one of protons. The proton stack will start from a slightly higher level than the neutron stack because of their electrostatic potential energy. Now imagine a nucleus with a great surplus of neutrons – the neutron stack will rise far above the proton stack and the nucleus can lose energy by converting a neutron to a proton and dropping the proton onto the top of the proton stack (beta decay).

However, if the neutron stack is below the proton stack then for a neutron to convert to a proton it must have enough additional energy to 'climb' to the top of the proton 'stack'. If this energy requirement is too big (that is, if it is greater than the energy released when a neutron decays) the nucleus will not undergo beta decay. On the other hand, if the proton stack is too high there may be an energy advantage in positron emission (beta-plus decay) or in breaking a heavier nucleus by alpha decay or fission. This occurs because the electrostatic potential energy of the protons in a smaller nucleus is less than in a large nucleus. In stable nuclei the tops of the neutron and proton 'stacks' are usually similar in energy.

The core of a neutron star *is* a large group of neutrons, but this is stabilised by an intense gravitational field which prevents neutron decay (too much work would have to be done against gravitational forces to emit the electron created in the decay).

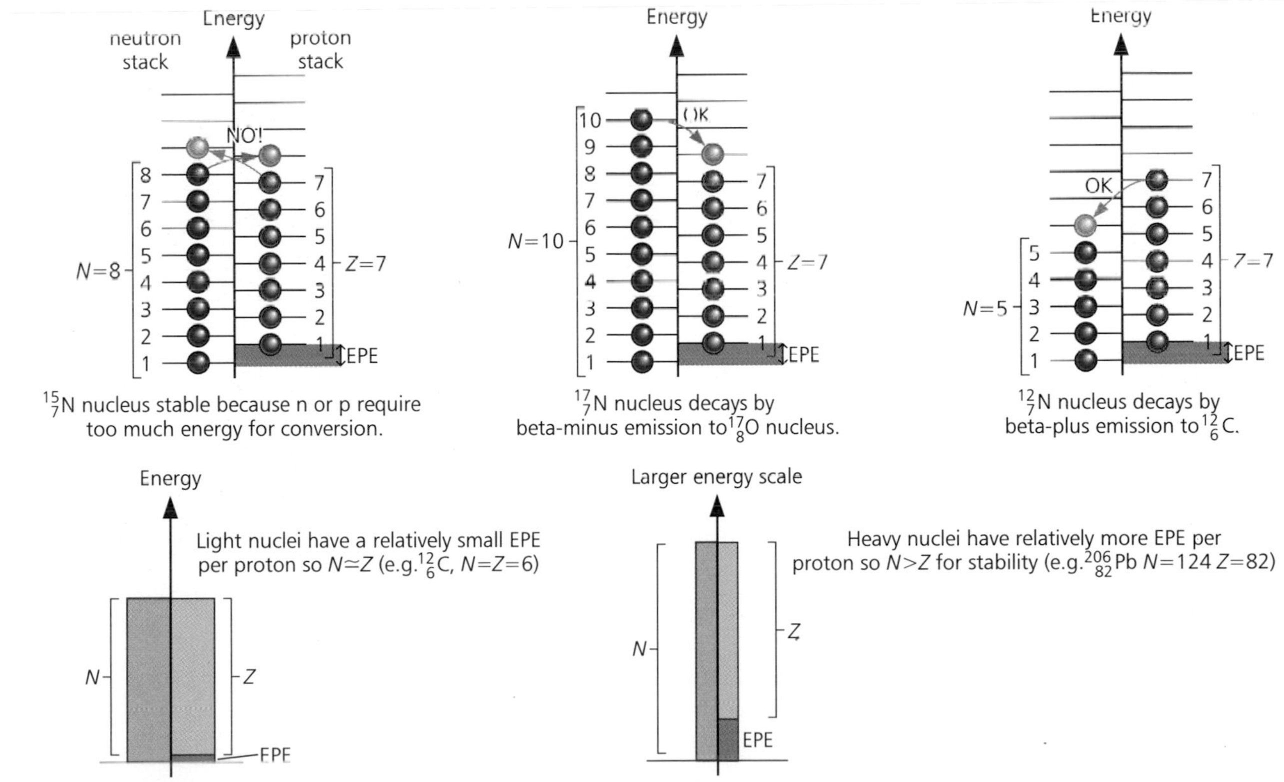

Figure 5.12 Neutron and proton 'stacks' in nuclei.

Using neutrons

What can you do with a neutral particle about 10^{-15} m across? Quite a lot actually. For a start slow neutrons can be used to induce fission and ignite a chain reaction. This is the case, uncontrollably, in fission bombs (like the bombs dropped on Hiroshima and Nagasaki). Nuclear reactors use fission reactions to generate electricity, but here control rods are inserted into the core to control the chain reaction by absorbing some of the neutrons. This prevents the reaction rate from growing too far or too fast.

We can use the intense flux of neutrons inside a nuclear reactor to create artificial radioisotopes for use in medicine. The neutrons are absorbed by stable nuclei and make them unstable, often as beta emitters. The artificial radioisotopes can then be used as tracers to follow metabolic pathways or the physical transport of particular chemicals around the body.

The fact that neutrons are neutral can be a great advantage as they can 'sneak up' on a nucleus even at low speeds (unlike protons or alpha particles which can only get close to a nucleus if they have enough kinetic energy to 'climb' the potential hill caused by electrostatic repulsion). **Neutron activation** techniques can be used in the study and renovation of paintings. If a painting is irradiated by neutrons then some of the atoms in the pigments will become temporarily radioactive. The half-lives for decay of these isotopes will differ depending on the element involved. If we monitor the activity of the painting for some time after neutron irradiation then the contributions from each element will die away at a different rate. From this it is often possible to build up images of the painting at different stages in its history. This can be useful in deciding what is original and what has been changed over the years. It can also be used to reveal early sketches and alternative compositions.

Neutrons have also been used as an alternative to gamma rays in radiotherapy to kill cancer cells.

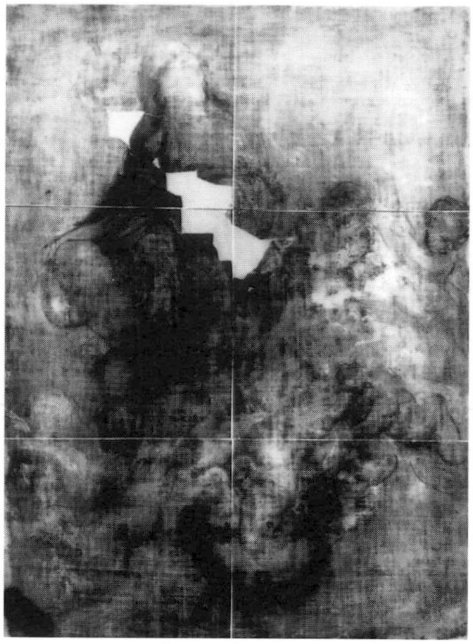

Figure 5.13 Neutron-activation analysis reveals a hidden self-portrait of Anthony Van Dyck. Turn the photograph upside down to see it.

SUMMARY

- Evidence for the existence of the nuclear atom came from experiments in which alpha particles were fired at sheets of gold foil. Most of the particles went straight through the foil, while a small number were scattered through angles > 90°.
- At low energies, alpha particles scattering from a massive nucleus obey a simple relationship. At high energies, alpha particles show deviations from this relationship due to the **strong nuclear force**.
- Experiments by Rutherford and others in which alpha particles were used to knock protons out of light nuclei led to the conclusion that the positive charge on the nucleus is due entirely to the protons it contains.
- Work by Chadwick confirmed that the nucleus also contains neutrons, with a mass very similar to that of the proton, but no charge.
- The **de Broglie relation**, $\lambda = \frac{h}{p}$, relates a wave-like property (λ) to a particle-like property (p). Matter (e.g. electrons) and radiation (e.g. light) show both wave-like and particle-like characteristics. This is called **wave–particle duality**.
- Because electrons are leptons, and do not experience the strong force, they can be used to probe the interior of the nucleus, making use of their wave-like behaviour.

- The radius of the nucleus is proportional to the cube root of nucleon number, $r \propto A^{\frac{1}{3}}$. This suggests that the nucleons in the nucleus are close packed.
- The nucleus behaves like a charged liquid drop, the strong force balancing the electrostatic repulsion of the protons.
- The existence of discrete energy levels that the nucleus may occupy suggests that the nucleons may occupy shells within the nucleus, rather like the shells occupied by orbital electrons.

QUESTIONS

1 a In the Rutherford scattering experiment the gold ($Z = 79$) foil was several hundred atoms thick. Why can it still be assumed that the back-scattered alpha particles have only interacted with a single gold nucleus?

b Use the closest approach of 8 MeV alpha particles to estimate an upper limit for the radius of the gold nucleus. Why is this only an upper limit?

2 Explain why a proton–electron model of the nucleus is untenable and was replaced by the proton–neutron model.

3 The track coming in from the bottom was made by an alpha particle entering a cloud chamber filled with nitrogen. What can be deduced from the photograph?

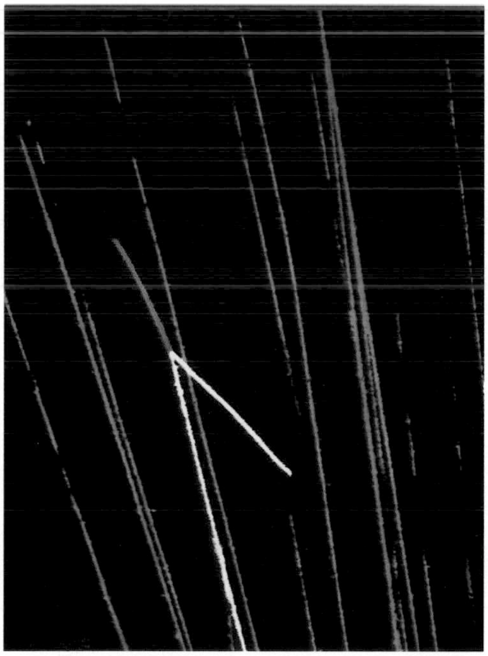

4 a Why is there a limit to the nucleon number of stable nuclei?

b Data from elastic scattering of high-energy electrons suggests that the number of nucleons in a nucleus is proportional to the radius of the nucleus to the power one third. What is the significance of this?

c The scattering of 420 MeV electrons from carbon-12 produces a first minimum at about 51° from the incident direction. Use this to estimate the radius of a carbon-12 nucleus (see figure 5.7c, page 69).

5 a Why is the expression 'wave–particle duality' often used when describing electrons?

b What is the de Broglie wavelength of an electron accelerated through (i) 1 kV, (ii) 1 MV, (iii) 1 GV?

6 In what ways does the information gained by scattering electrons from nuclei differ from that obtained when alpha particles are scattered from nuclei?

7 a Nuclear diameters are of the order 10^{-14} m and atomic diameters are of the order of 10^{-10} m. Use these rough figures to estimate the ratio of the density of nuclear matter to that of ordinary solid matter (e.g. steel or diamond).

b Where in the Universe do we find large quantities of matter with nuclear density?

8 a If the strong force can hold neutrons and protons together in a nucleus why don't we find stable nuclei that consist only of neutrons?

b Why do stable heavy nuclei contain more neutrons than protons?

c Why is there a limit to the size of stable nuclei?

9 a What features of induced nuclear fission can be explained by assuming that the nucleus behaves like a charged liquid drop?

b In what ways does the strong nuclear force resemble the force between molecules of a liquid?

6 Hadrons and quarks

WHAT IS A FUNDAMENTAL PARTICLE?

The ancient Greeks were the first people we know to suggest the existence of fundamental particles. Leucippus and his pupil Democritus came up with this idea in the fifth century BC in order to simplify the explanation of material properties. They coined the term 'atomos', meaning indivisible, and suggested that different substances were composed of different types of atom. In the nineteenth century John Dalton used the atomic hypothesis to explain how elements combine to form compounds. The modern atom began life as the smallest part of an element that retains the properties of that element. It was also supposed to be indivisible.

Mendeleev's discovery of periodic properties among the elements suggested some kind of periodic *structure* in these atoms. The developments in particle physics from Thomson's discovery of the electron in 1897 to Chadwick's discovery of the neutron in 1932 unravelled and explained this structure. However, even in 1932 it was realised that the journey into matter had not ended. Pauli had proposed the neutrino to explain beta decay, and Dirac had predicted the existence of antimatter. Where would it all end? Actually it was just beginning.

We have already described the discovery of new particles related to the electron. This was unexpected, but at least the leptons had an obvious family resemblance and are limited to three generations of particles. This is more than could be said for the host of strongly interacting particles (the **hadrons**) produced by ever more energetic accelerators in the second half of the twentieth century. Hundreds of new particles were discovered, and by the early 1960s the situation seemed almost hopeless – there were no obvious patterns or relationships between the particles and no unifying theory to relate them to one another.

In this chapter we look at the properties of some of these particles and the broad categories into which they seem to fit. What appears more and more obvious is that the hadrons are not fundamental particles and the patterns which link them are produced by a deeper, simpler level of organisation. The problem is to find the simplest set of fundamental particles that can reproduce these patterns.

HADRONS

Hadrons and leptons

These two major classes of particles are distinguished by the way they interact. Gravity (as far as we know) affects everything. Electromagnetism affects anything with charge. However, the strong force which holds nucleons together in the nucleus does not affect electrons and neutrinos (or any of the other leptons). The strong force divides particles into two classes, those which are affected by it, the hadrons, and those which are not, everything else.

The **weak interaction**, which is responsible for beta decay, acts on both leptons and hadrons.

Both strong and weak nuclear forces can cause particle decays. The difference in their strength shows itself in the typical **lifetimes** of the decaying particles. Something that decays by the strong interaction tends to have a very short life, typically 10^{-23} s – the time it takes for light to cross a proton. On the other hand, particles decaying by the weak interaction are relatively long-lived, having lifetimes around 10^{-9} s or longer (the neutron itself has a half-life for decay to a proton of about 15 minutes). Particles that decay by the electromagnetic interaction lie somewhere between these two extremes, having lifetimes around 10^{-18} s or more.

The **lifetime** of a particle is the average time for a particle of a particular type to decay. This is not the same as the **half-life** for decay which is the time taken for half of a large number of unstable particles to decay.

The pi-mesons

In quantum field theory the forces between particles are explained by an exchange of 'force-carrying particles'(see chapter 7). The force-carrier for electromagnetism is the photon and in 1935 Hideki Yukawa predicted the existence of the **pi-meson**, or **pion** to carry the strong nuclear force between nucleons. Charged pions were eventually discovered in cosmic rays by Powell in 1947. The **neutral pion** (or **pi-zero**) was discovered in 1949 by Bjorkland at the Lawrence Berkeley Laboratories (LBL) in California – the first unstable particle to be discovered using an accelerator.

Pions are created in large numbers at the top of the atmosphere as cosmic rays collide with nuclei. Pions have a mass about 15% of the mass of a proton or neutron and are the lightest hadrons. If their only means of decay was by the strong force they would be stable (because there are no lighter strongly interacting particles into which they can decay). However, they also interact by the weak force so most charged pions decay to muons:

$${}^{0}_{1}\pi^{+} \rightarrow {}^{0}_{1}\mu^{+} + {}^{0}_{0}\bar{\nu}_{\mu}$$
$${}^{0}_{-1}\pi^{-} \rightarrow {}^{0}_{-1}\mu^{-} + {}^{0}_{0}\nu_{\mu}$$

the lifetime for these decays is 2.6×10^{-8} s.

The pi-zero, being uncharged, can decay directly to gamma rays (via the electromagnetic interaction).

$${}^{0}_{0}\pi^{0} \rightarrow 2\,{}^{0}_{0}\gamma$$

the lifetime for this is much shorter, 8×10^{-17} s.

High-energy cosmic ray collisions generate large numbers of pi-zeros. The gamma rays they produce as they decay give them away. If the gamma rays strike a lead plate this induces them to create electron–positron pairs which generate a characteristic fan-shaped shower in a magnetic field.

Pions have a mass between that of nucleons and electrons. They were soon grouped with other 'light' hadrons and called **mesons**. Later it was realised that the essential difference between mesons and nucleons is related to structure, not mass – mesons that are more massive than nucleons do exist.

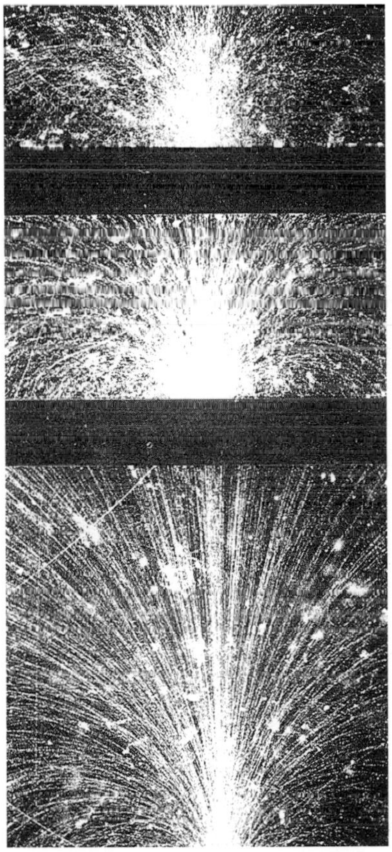

Figure 6.1 The pi-zeros created when cosmic rays collide with nuclei high in the atmosphere soon decay to high-energy gamma rays. The gamma rays create cascades of electron–positron pairs when they interact with matter. In this photograph a shower has been captured in a cloud chamber. There is a magnetic field perpendicular to the page and this makes electrons and positrons curve away from each other. The two dark horizontal bars are lead sheets and the shower regenerates itself when the gamma rays formed from electron–positron annihilation continue into the next sheet.

Mesons and baryons

As more and more new hadrons were discovered they formed two natural sub-groups within the hadron family.

Baryons These are heavy particles, like the proton and neutron.
They are fermions (i.e. they have half-integer spin).
The lightest baryon is the proton, which is stable.

Mesons The first mesons to be discovered had masses between those of nucleons and electrons.
They are bosons (i.e. they have integer spin).
The lightest meson is the pion.

Baryons and mesons are both affected by the strong force.

To explain the decays and transformations that do and do not occur in nature we give a **baryon number** ***B*** to all hadrons. The total baryon number is conserved in all interactions.

Mesons have $B = 0$.

Baryons have $B = 1$, anti-baryons have $B = -1$

Collisions between pi-minus particles and protons can produce pi-zeroes and neutrons. This is allowed because baryon number and charge (Q) are conserved:

$$^{0}_{-1}\pi^- + {}^{1}_{1}\mathbf{p}^+ \rightarrow {}^{0}_{0}\pi^0 + {}^{1}_{0}\mathbf{n}$$

B	0	+	1	=	0	+	1
Q	−1	+	1	=	0	+	0

However, the decay of a proton to a positron and a pi-zero is not allowed (even though it conserves charge) because it violates conservation of baryon number (+1 would become 0).

A plague of hadrons

From the late 1940s to the 1960s cosmic rays and proton synchrotrons (at laboratories such as Brookhaven, Berkeley and CERN) revealed the existence of many more mesons and baryons. Initially these were distinguished by their masses, the mesons being less massive than protons and all the baryons being more massive. However, there *are* very massive mesons so a better way to distinguish them is by the way they decay. When mesons decay the final stable particles are leptons and photons. Baryon decay always produces protons as well. Compare the decay of a neutron with that of a pi-plus:

$$\mathbf{n} \rightarrow \mathbf{p}^+ + \mathbf{e}^- + \bar{\nu}_e$$
$$\pi^+ \rightarrow \mu^+ + \nu_\mu$$

This distinction between mesons and baryons prevents protons from decaying to pions. Since the proton is the lightest baryon it is stable. *Conservation of baryon number* can explain this. All the baryons have baryon number 1 and mesons have baryon number 0. The decay of protons to pions could be:

$$\mathbf{p}^+ \rightarrow \pi^+ + \gamma$$

Q	1	=	1	+	0
L	0	=	0	+	0
B	1	≠	0	+	0

This decay conserves charge (Q), lepton number (L) and can conserve energy and momentum if a suitable gamma-ray photon is emitted, but it does not conserve baryon number. If protons decayed to pions the baryon number of the Universe would change, which is forbidden! In fact no decay has ever been observed in which baryon number is not conserved.

(Some recent unified theories predict that protons may decay and baryon number may not be conserved. However experiments looking for proton decays have not yet detected them and the absence of evidence allows us to put a lower limit on the lifetime of the proton – at least 10^{32} years! This is more than 10^{21} times the age of the Universe.)

Among the hundreds of hadrons we shall look in more detail at just three – the kaons, the omega-minus and the J-psi particle. Each of these has a special significance either because it forced physicists to introduce new quantities and conservation laws or (with the omega-minus) because it confirmed a prediction based on a new theory.

The strange particles

In 1946 Rochester and Butler noticed a 'V' shaped track in their cloud chamber at Manchester University. The angle between the two tracks making the V was too great for it to be an electron–positron pair. The two tracks were caused by a π^+/π^- pair formed by the decay of a heavier hadron. The distinctive shape of the decay meant the new hadron was first named a 'V-particle' but later it became known as the **kaon**.

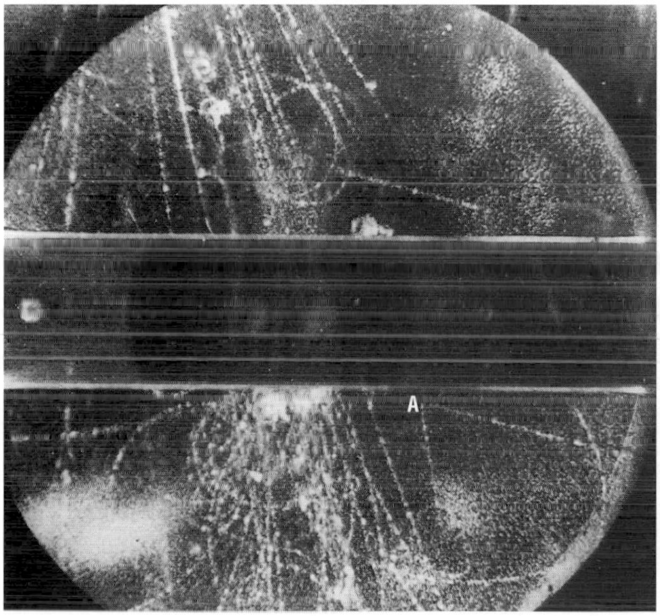

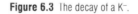

Figure 6.2 The first observation of the decay of a neutral kaon. The kaon decays at point A into a pi-plus and a pi-minus.

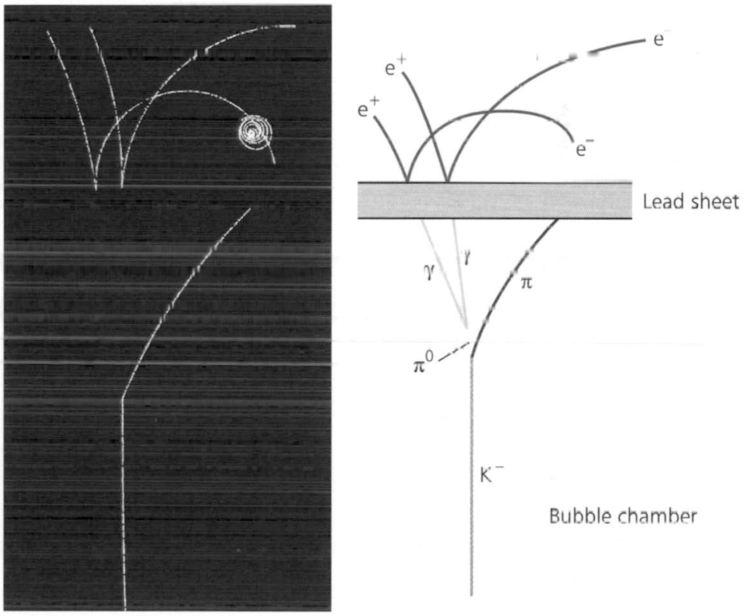

Figure 6.3 The decay of a K⁻.

Four kaons were discovered in cosmic ray experiments: two neutral kaons (K^0, and $\overline{K}^0$ or 'K^0-bar'), and two charged kaons (K^+ and K^-). However, they have a variety of decay modes so it was not until they could be produced to order by accelerators that they were really grouped together as a family – but this family didn't seem to behave itself.

Kaons are produced, like pions, from strong interactions between colliding hadrons (e.g. when pions collide with protons or protons collide with nuclei) and so were expected to decay by the same interaction. This has a characteristic decay time of about 10^{-23} s, so the kaons should disappear pretty rapidly, probably forming pions. In fact they have a lifetime of about 10^{-8} to 10^{-15} times longer. Although this is still incredibly short to us, if 'human time' was made 10^{15} times longer, one second would last 10 million years! This is why kaons came as such a shock to particle physicists, and because of this unexpected behaviour the kaons were soon referred to as **strange particles**.

However, their long lifetime was a clue – *weak interactions* have lifetimes of this order. Could it be that kaons are created by the strong force but decay by the weak force?

Evidence to support this hypothesis came from the reactions in which kaons are created. If kaons are produced in a reaction involving pions or protons they are always paired with another strange hadron. For example, the Σ^+ (sigma-plus) is a baryon that is often created with kaons in reactions like:

$$\pi^- + p^+ \rightarrow K^- + \Sigma^+$$

$$\begin{array}{lcccccc} Q & -1 & + & 1 & = & -1 & + & 1 \\ L & 0 & + & 0 & = & 0 & + & 0 \\ B & 0 & + & 1 & = & 0 & + & 1 \end{array}$$

This is fine, it conserves charge, lepton number and baryon number, but so does the reaction:

$$\pi^- + p^+ \rightarrow \pi^- + \Sigma^+$$

$$\begin{array}{lcccccc} Q & -1 & + & 1 & = & -1 & + & 1 \\ L & 0 & + & 0 & = & 0 & + & 0 \\ B & 0 & + & 1 & = & 0 & + & 1 \end{array}$$

and this reaction *never* happens. This is very strange because we would expect the second reaction to be *more common* than the first because the pions are less massive than kaons and so more likely to be produced.

The problem was solved by introducing a new property possessed by particles like the kaons and sigmas, known as **strangeness, S**. This must be conserved in the strong interactions that form the strange particles but is not conserved (strangeness is violated) when they decay (unless of course they decay to other strange particles). Since the kaon is the lightest strange meson it must violate strangeness when it decays. The K^+ is defined to have strangeness S = +1.

Once we define the strangeness of one of these particles the appropriate values for all others can be determined from the reactions that link them to the defined particle. For example, to conserve strangeness when a K^+, K^- pair are created the K^- must have strangeness –1. The creation of a Σ^+ with a K^- in the equation above gives the Σ^+ strangeness +1, and so on. The fact that this scheme could be carried out *and agreed with all observed creation and decay reactions* gives us great confidence that, however abstract the idea and peculiar the name, strangeness really is a genuine particle property like charge or spin.

Heavy hadrons and resonances

The discovery of kaons was followed quite quickly by the discovery of many more mesons and baryons. As accelerator energies increased, so increasingly massive hadrons were discovered. The first strange baryon was the lambda particle, so called because the track it leaves when it decays to a proton and pi-minus looks like the Greek λ. It is more massive than the proton but has a lifetime of 2.6×10^{-10} s, far longer than if it decayed by the strong interaction. It has to decay by the weak interaction because this *does not conserve strangeness* and so allows a particle with S = –1 (determined from the reactions that form it) to decay to products with total strangeness zero:

$$\Lambda^0 \rightarrow p^+ + \pi^-$$

$$\begin{array}{lcccccc} Q & 0 & = & 1 & + & -1 \\ L & 0 & = & 0 & + & 0 \\ B & 1 & = & 1 & + & 0 \\ S & -1 & \neq & 0 & + & 0 \end{array}$$

Many of the new particles decay by the strong interaction to less massive hadrons and so their lifetimes are very short, typically 10^{-23} s. Existing for such a short time means the presence of these particles can only be inferred from the behaviour of their decay products and the conservation laws. They are often called '**resonances**' because there is a sudden 'absorption' of the colliding particles when the accelerator producing them is 'tuned' to an appropriate energy. The first resonance to be discovered was the Δ (delta) resonance in 1953 at Brookhaven. We cannot measure its lifetime directly but it is calculated using the energy–time uncertainty principle. A long-lived particle has a greater uncertainty in time and so produces a sharp energy resonance. On the other hand, if the particle exists for a very short time the uncertainty in its energy is greater and the resonance curve will be broader.

Energy–time uncertainty

The Heisenberg Uncertainty Principle tells us that certain pairs of properties are linked so that a measurement of one unavoidably and uncontrollably disturbs the value of the other. Momentum and position form one such pair, energy and time form another. If the energy E of a particular event is known to an accuracy of $\pm\delta E$ then the uncertainty in the time of the event is at least $\pm\delta t$ where these uncertainties are linked by:

$\delta E \delta t \geq h/2\pi$ where h is Planck's constant. ($h/2\pi$ is such an important quantity that it has its own symbol $\hbar$).

Figure 6.4 This bubble chamber photograph shows the shower of particles produced in a high-energy proton–proton collision. A proton enters from the bottom (yellow), collides with a proton at rest in the bubble chamber to create seven negative pions (blue), nine positive particles (red) and the lambda. The lambda is neutral so leaves no track but it decays to a proton (yellow) and pi-minus (purple) at (A) which are distinguished by the direction and curvature of their tracks in the magnetic field.

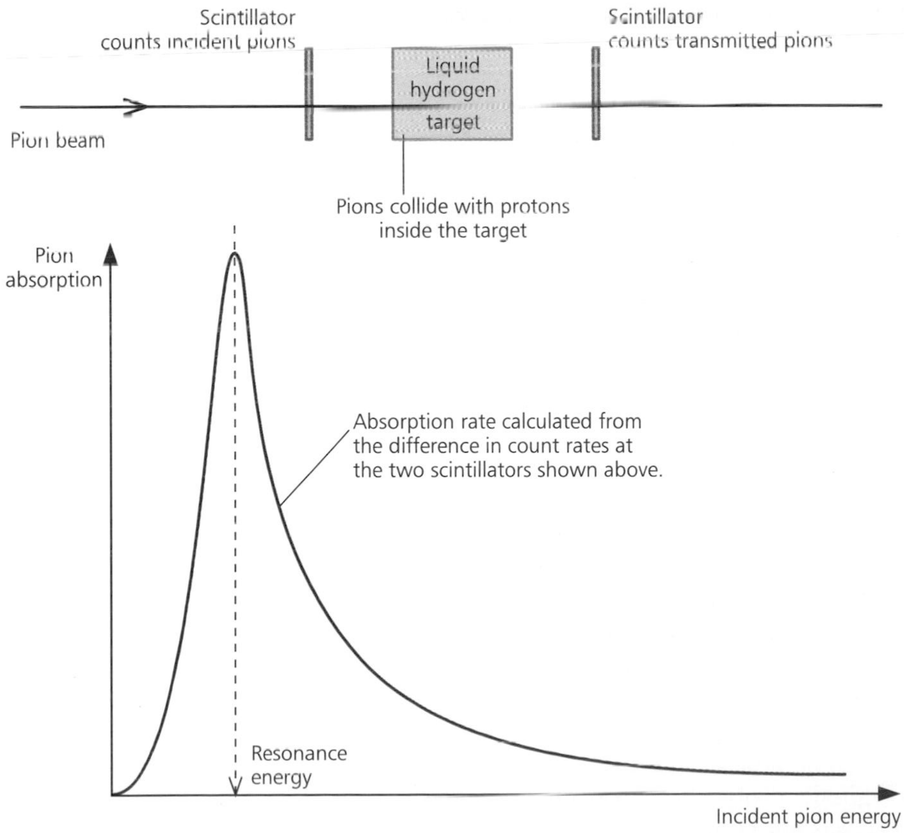

Figure 6.5 Resonances are so short-lived that the excited states themselves cannot be directly detected. However, when pions collide with protons the proportion absorbed rises sharply at resonance. The energy of the resonance is a measure of the energy of the 'particle' produced and the width of the resonance peak is inversely related to the particle lifetime.

What is the status of these extremely short-lived resonances? One way to think of them is as excitations of more familiar particles such as protons, pions, lambdas and kaons (the lightest non-strange and strange baryons and mesons respectively). These resonant states are easier to understand if we think of the hadrons as composite particles made up of smaller more fundamental parts which can rearrange themselves in different ways according to the available energy.

THE QUARK MODEL OF HADRONS

The eightfold way

By 1960 the number of known hadrons was large enough to make physicists look for patterns and try to reduce the apparent plague of particles to a simpler scheme.

Table 6.1 Properties of hadrons known by about 1960.

Particle	Charge	Relative mass	Baryon number	Strangeness	Lifetime	Spin
proton (p^+)	1	1	1	0	stable(?)	$\frac{1}{2}$
neutron (n^0)	0	1	1	0	15 min	$\frac{1}{2}$
lambda (Λ^0)	0	1.1	1	−1	10^{-10} s	$\frac{1}{2}$
sigma ($\Sigma^\pm$)	±1	1.2	1	−1	10^{-10} s	$\frac{1}{2}$
sigma (Σ^0)	0	1.2	1	−1	10^{-20} s	$\frac{1}{2}$
delta-2-plus (Δ^{++})	2	1.2	1	0	10^{-23} s	$\frac{3}{2}$
delta ($\Delta^\pm$)	±1	1.2	1	0	10^{-23} s	$\frac{3}{2}$
delta-zero (Δ^0)	0	1.2	1	0	10^{-23} s	$\frac{3}{2}$
xi-zero (Ξ^0)	0	1.3	1	−2	10^{-10} s	$\frac{1}{2}$
xi-minus (Ξ^-)	−1	1.3	1	−2	10^{-10} s	$\frac{1}{2}$
sigma-star ($\Sigma^{\pm *}$)	±1	1.4	1	−1	10^{-23} s	$\frac{3}{2}$
sigma-zero-star (Σ^{0*})	0	1.4	1	−1	10^{-23} s	$\frac{3}{2}$
xi-zero-star (Ξ^{0*})	0	1.5	1	−2	10^{-23} s	$\frac{3}{2}$
xi-minus-star (Ξ^{-*})	−1	1.5	1	−2	10^{-23} s	$\frac{3}{2}$
pion (π^+)	±1	0.14	0	0	10^{-8} s	0
pi-zero (π^0)	0	0.14	0	0	10^{-16} s	0
eta (η^0)	0	0.5	0	0	10^{-19} s	0
kaon ($K^\pm$)	±1	0.5	0	±1	10^{-8} s	0
neutral kaons (K^0 and $\overline{K^0}$)	0	0.5	0	±1	10^{-8} s and 10^{-10} s	0

Murray Gell-Mann and Yuval Ne'eman proposed grouping the particles according to their strangeness and charge. When they did this the known particles formed incomplete but convincing geometric patterns. They treated the gaps in these patterns in exactly the same way as Mendeleev had treated the gaps in the Periodic Table in the previous century. They used them to predict the existence of as yet undiscovered particles. The mesons and baryons formed similar patterns of eight particles which became known as the 'Eightfold Way'. When the patterns were originally proposed the eighth meson, which fits at the centre of the pattern was not known. However, its properties could be predicted from the gap in the existing pattern, and when the **eta meson** turned up with all the right properties (in 1961) it gave physicists confidence that they were onto something.

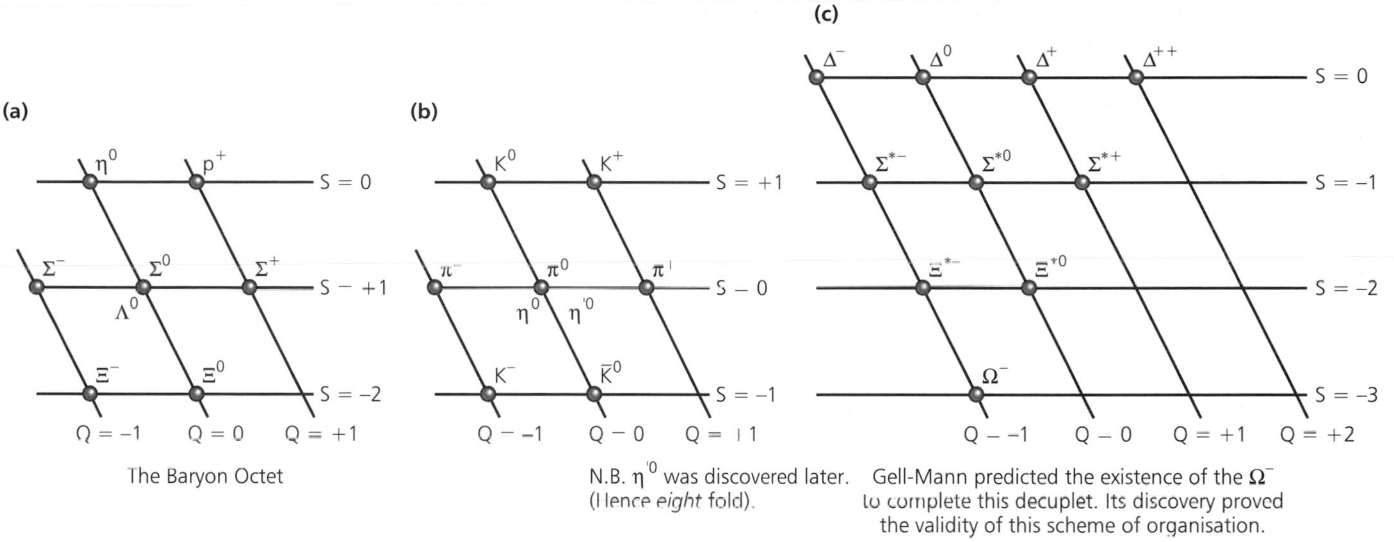

Figure 6.6 The eightfold way. The charge axis is inclined as shown for historical reasons. In this way the geometric symmetry of the hexagon emphasises the symmetric relation between the particles. (**a**) The baryon octet. (**b**) The first meson nonet. (**c**) The baryon decuplet.

In a similar way the **delta** Δ, **sigma-star** Σ* and **xi-star** Ξ* resonances (nine particles) form a triangle whose vertex is very obviously missing. Gell-Mann predicted the existence and properties of a new particle to complete the 'decuplet' of particles. It should have negative charge, strangeness minus three, and a mass of about 1680 MeV. The mass prediction was possible because each additional unit of strangeness seemed to result in an increase of about 150 MeV. According to these predictions the omega-minus (as he called it) should have a mass 150 MeV greater than the Ξ* (about 1530 MeV).

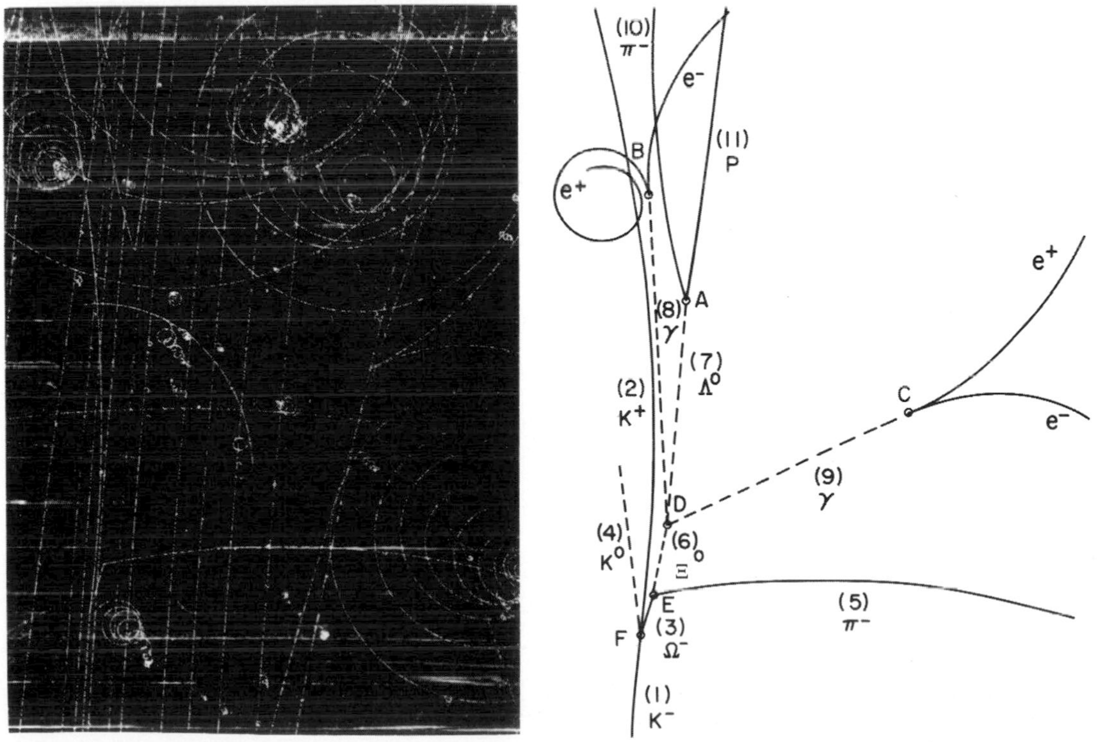

Figure 6.7 The discovery of the omega minus particle at Brookhaven in 1964 confirmed the eightfold way as a 'Periodic Table' of hadron properties. This photograph, from the 80 inch bubble chamber, was the first to show the creation and decay of an omega minus.

The discovery of the omega minus showed that the Gell-Mann and Ne'eman classification scheme was a valid and useful way to group hadrons, but it didn't explain *why* they form these patterns.The Periodic Table of the elements is only *explained* when we get inside the atom and see how electrons form shells whose patterns repeat periodically (e.g. the lone electrons in the s-shells of the alkali metals or the closed shells of the inert gases). Similarly, the patterns of the eightfold way can be explained by getting inside hadrons to smaller, simpler building blocks, the **quarks**.

Quarks

Murray Gell-Mann and George Zweig both noticed that the eightfold way patterns could be explained if all hadrons were made from just three distinct types of particle (and their associated antiparticles). We call these particles quarks, although the names 'ace' and 'parton' were also suggested by physicists at the time.

Table 6.2 Properties of the three quarks.

Quark flavour	Charge/*e*	Strangeness	Spin/$\hbar$
up (u)	$+\frac{2}{3}$	0	$\frac{1}{2}$
down (d)	$-\frac{1}{3}$	0	$\frac{1}{2}$
strange (s)	$-\frac{1}{3}$	−1	$\frac{1}{2}$
anti-up ($\bar{u}$)	$-\frac{2}{3}$	0	$\frac{1}{2}$
anti-down ($\bar{d}$)	$+\frac{1}{3}$	0	$\frac{1}{2}$
anti-strange ($\bar{s}$)	$+\frac{1}{3}$	+1	$\frac{1}{2}$

In this model baryons consist of quark triplets. For example, the proton is a combination of two up and one down quark (uud) and the neutron is two down and one up quark (ddu). Check this in the table of quark properties and you will see that the charges come out right, and so does the strangeness. The spin also works. Three fermions can produce either spin $\frac{1}{2}$ or spin $\frac{3}{2}$ – the proton and neutron have spin $\frac{1}{2}$. If we excite these particles into a higher energy state in which the spins are parallel and the particle has spin $\frac{3}{2}$ we get the delta-plus and delta-zero resonances. Add in the strange quark and out pop the strange baryons. The strange quark has an extra mass of about 150 MeV so this also explains the baryon masses. Combinations of these three basic quarks produce all the hadrons just as they appear in the eightfold way pattern.

Mesons are spin-zero particles. These are made of a quark/antiquark pair. Once again all the eightfold way mesons can be generated by combining quarks and their antiquarks. If you write down all possible quark/antiquark pairs using up, down and strange quarks you will find nine possibilities, not eight. The eta η'^0 meson was duly discovered.

On the quark model baryons naturally form groups of 8 or 10 particles, mesons form groups of 9. The baryon octet is formed by quark triplets with total spin $\frac{1}{2}$ whereas the resonances all have spin $\frac{3}{2}$ and form a decuplet.

Flavour

This is a term used to distinguish different types of quark. Up quarks and down quarks are different flavours, just as electrons and muons are different flavours of lepton. Flavour should not be confused with colour. Colour is more like charge, so up or down quarks, for example, can come in any of the three quark colours.

(i) Baryons (B = 1)

Table 6.3 Eightfold way hadrons and their quarks.

Quark triplet	Strangeness	Charge	Spin $\frac{1}{2}$	Spin $\frac{3}{2}$
ddd	0	–1		Δ^-
udd	0	0	n^0	Δ^0
uud	0	1	p^+	Δ^+
uuu	0	2		Δ^{++}
dds	–1	–1	Σ^-	Σ^{-*}
uds	–1	0	Σ^0, Λ^0	Σ^{0*}
uus	–1	1	Σ^+	Σ^{+*}
dss	–2	–1	Ξ^-	Ξ^{-*}
uss	–2	0	Ξ^0	Ξ *
sss	–3	–1		Ω^-

The difference between the proton and the delta-plus particle is in the way quark spins combine. A quark triplet can have only $\frac{1}{2}$ or $\frac{3}{2}$ units of spin depending on whether two or all three spins are aligned parallel. In the proton one pair of quarks spin parallel and the third quark is antiparallel to them. In the delta plus all three are parallel, which is a more energetic and so less stable arrangement.

N.B. There is a subtle point here. If two electrons occupy the same energy level in an atom the Pauli Exclusion Principle compels them to spin in opposite directions (otherwise identical particles would have the same quantum states of energy and spin). The quarks in hadrons are not identical, since they have different 'colours' (see chapter 7) so two quarks with the same flavour must spin *parallel* to one another. This means that quark triplets where one quark has a different flavour (e.g. uud) can have spin $\frac{1}{2}$ with the d quark spinning opposite to the pair of up-quarks, or spin $\frac{3}{2}$ where all three quarks spin in the same direction. If all three quarks are different (uds) there are three possibilities – if the ud pair spin parallel (spin 1) then s can be parallel to these (Σ^{0*}, spin $\frac{3}{2}$) or antiparallel to them (Σ^0, spin $\frac{1}{2}$). If the ud pair are antiparallel (spin 0) then the spin of the s-quark can be in either direction and a Λ^0 is formed. When all three quarks have the same flavour (e.g. ddd) they are all distinct so must have parallel spins. In this case there will be no spin $\frac{1}{2}$ particle.

(ii) Mesons (B = 0)

Table 6.4

Quark pair	Strangeness	Charge/*e*	Meson (spin 0)
d anti-u or $d\bar{u}$	0	–1	π^-
u anti-u or $u\bar{u}$	0	0	π^0 *
d anti-d or $d\bar{d}$	0	0	
s anti-s or $s\bar{s}$	0	0	$\eta^0\eta'^0$
u anti-d or $u\bar{d}$	0	1	π^+
s anti-d or $s\bar{d}$	–1	0	$\bar{K}^0$
s anti-u or $s\bar{u}$	–1	–1	K^-
d anti-s or $d\bar{s}$	1	0	K^0
u anti-s or $u\bar{s}$	1	1	K^+

*N.B. Where the quark/antiquark pair have the same flavour they do not correspond directly to the mesons in the final column. These mesons are made from a mixture of the quark/antiquark combinations.

The π^0 is a mixture of up/anti-up and down/anti-down quarks. The η^0, η'^0 are mixtures of all three quark/antiquark pairs.

Mesons can also be formed with spin 1, if the quark/antiquark pair have parallel spin. Mesons with even higher spin states are formed when the quarks and antiquarks move in energetic orbits around one another.

Deep inelastic scattering

Early in the twentieth century many scientists were still sceptical about the reality of atoms. They thought that atoms might simply be a mathematical fiction that is useful in simplifying our explanation of matter but with no physical reality. When Einstein published his papers on special relativity and the photoelectric effect in 1905 he was also writing about the statistics of Brownian motion showing how atomic collisions could be related to these tiny visible disturbances of suspended particles (e.g. smoke particles in air buffeted by air molecules). Nowadays few people doubt the existence of atoms.

Gell-Mann and Zweig's quark theory was even more abstract than the theory of atoms. It originated as a mathematical model of a pattern among hadrons, and despite its successes at predicting new hadrons it was not supported by any direct physical observations. No one had ever 'seen' a quark.

We have already seen how to measure the radius of a nucleus using the scattering of high-energy electron beams. The ability to resolve such fine detail comes from the short de Broglie wavelength of the incident electrons. This in turn is controlled by the electron energy (see page 68). If we increase the energy sufficiently the de Broglie wavelength becomes smaller than the size of a nucleon and we can use electrons to probe *inside* the neutron and proton.

When we do this the results are reminiscent of those obtained in the Rutherford scattering experiments. Some electrons scatter violently as if they have encountered tiny dense charged particles inside the proton. If the results of electron scattering are compared with those obtained by scattering neutrinos (which do not interact electromagnetically, only by the weak force) the difference can tell us the size of charges inside the nucleons. They are $\frac{2}{3}$ and $-\frac{1}{3}$ of the electronic charge, as predicted by the quark model.

This is called **deep inelastic scattering** because the incident leptons penetrate the hadrons and transfer energy to the quarks with which they collide. One of the consequences of this energy transfer is that quarks are expelled from the hadron and 'jets' of new particles are created. In addition to providing direct evidence for the existence of quarks, deep inelastic scattering also reveals the presence of gluons (force-carrying particles) inside the nucleons and shows that the quarks and gluons act like 'free' particles confined in the hadron.

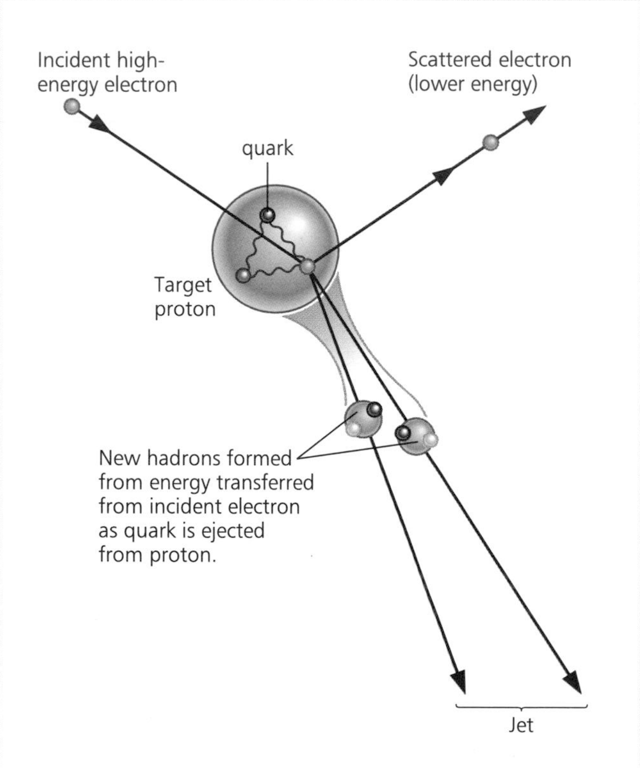

Figure 6.8 Deep inelastic scattering – a high-energy electron knocks a quark out of a proton. However, the energy required to do this is sufficient to create new quark-antiquark pairs, so new hadrons emerge in a 'jet'.

Charm and the lepton–quark symmetry

In beta-minus decay a neutron is converted to a proton. If we look at this from the point of view of quarks it becomes clear that the decay converts an udd baryon into an uud baryon and creates an electron and antineutrino in the process. The weak interaction responsible for the decay has *changed the nature* of one of the fundamental particles involved in it – a down quark has converted to an up quark. No other interaction is able to do this. In the 1960s Sheldon Glashow, Steven Weinberg and Abdus Salam developed a unified theory of the electromagnetic and weak interactions that groups the leptons and quarks into 'doublets'. In particular the up and down quarks seemed to correspond in some way to the electron and electron neutrino:

$$\begin{pmatrix}\mathbf{d}\\ \mathbf{u}\end{pmatrix} \Leftrightarrow \begin{pmatrix}\mathbf{e}\\ \nu_{\mathbf{e}}\end{pmatrix}$$

The muon, a second generation lepton, was discovered in 1936, and forms a second lepton doublet with the muon-neutrino. Is there a corresponding quark doublet? If so the strange quark would have another new type of quark as a partner, a **charmed quark**.

$$\begin{pmatrix}\mathbf{s}\\ \mathbf{?}\end{pmatrix} \Leftrightarrow \begin{pmatrix}\mu\\ \nu_{\mu}\end{pmatrix}$$

Glashow predicted the properties of the required fourth quark – it must have charge 2/3 and be much more massive than any of the other quarks. The reason for the high mass is because it had not been observed in any of the collision experiments going on at the time (around 1970). If its mass had been comparable to that of the strange quark then many charmed hadrons would have been produced and observed in experiments around the world.

The search for charmed mesons used electron–positron storage rings at various laboratories. Here the electrons and positrons orbit in a circular accelerator and are brought together in head-on collisions. If the collision energy is greater than or equal to the rest energy of the particle then it may be produced. When charmed hadrons were first predicted their expected mass (>3 GeV) was just above the energy available in accelerators. As accelerator energy increased so the charmed particles began to appear. The first to be discovered was the J/ψ meson, a combination of a charmed quark and a charmed antiquark with a rest energy of 3.095 MeV. In 1974 this charmed meson was discovered independently by Goldhaber, Perl and Richter in the SPEAR (Stanford positron–electron asymmetric rings) at SLAC and by Ting at Brookhaven. The Stanford experiment used electron–positron collisions, the Brookhaven experiment looked at the debris of proton collisions with nuclei. The meson was called a 'J-particle' at Stanford and a 'ψ-particle' at Brookhaven.

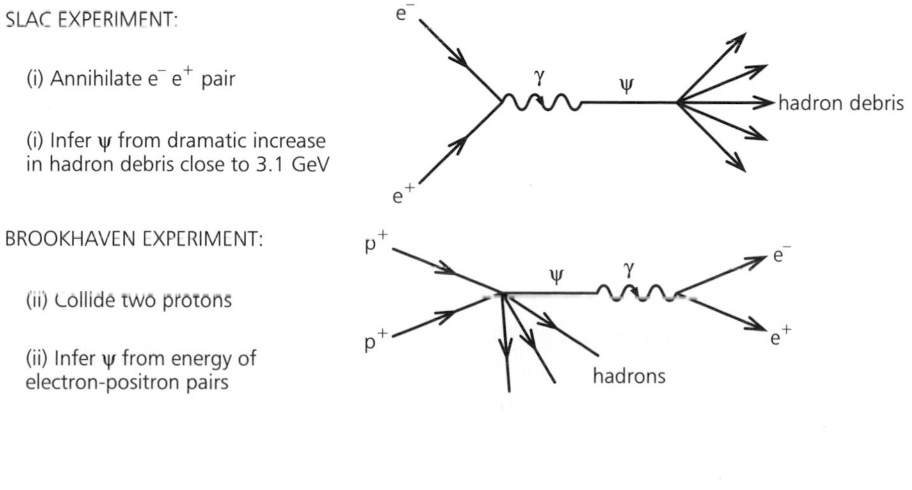
SLAC EXPERIMENT:
(i) Annihilate e⁻ e⁺ pair
(i) Infer ψ from dramatic increase in hadron debris close to 3.1 GeV
e⁻
e⁺
γ
ψ
hadron debris
BROOKHAVEN EXPERIMENT:
(ii) Collide two protons
(ii) Infer ψ from energy of electron-positron pairs
p⁺
p⁺
ψ
γ
e⁻
e⁺
hadrons

Figure 6.9 Experimental techniques used to discover the J-psi particle. Notice that if either of the two diagrams above is reversed it closely resembles the other.

The J/ψ resonance spike was unexpectedly sharp. This suggests a long lifetime (see page 95–6). In this context 'long' is 10^{-20} s, about a thousand times longer than for other known resonances. This is similar to the discovery of long-lived kaons that led to the discovery of strangeness; once again the lifetime is extended because of a new particle property whose conservation laws prevent a rapid decay, *charm*.

The J/ψ discovery was rapidly followed by new charmed particles, the first being the ψ' meson with a mass of 3.7 MeV (almost four times the mass of the proton). This is an excited state of the ψ in which the quark/antiquark pair orbit one another with higher energy (and therefore greater mass) and have total spin 1 rather than spin 0. The excited states of the ψ mesons are analogous to the excited states of a hydrogen atom and the system is called **charmonium**. When it de-excites and the quarks drop back to lower energy states the excess energy is 'radiated' as pions, muons, electrons or photons.

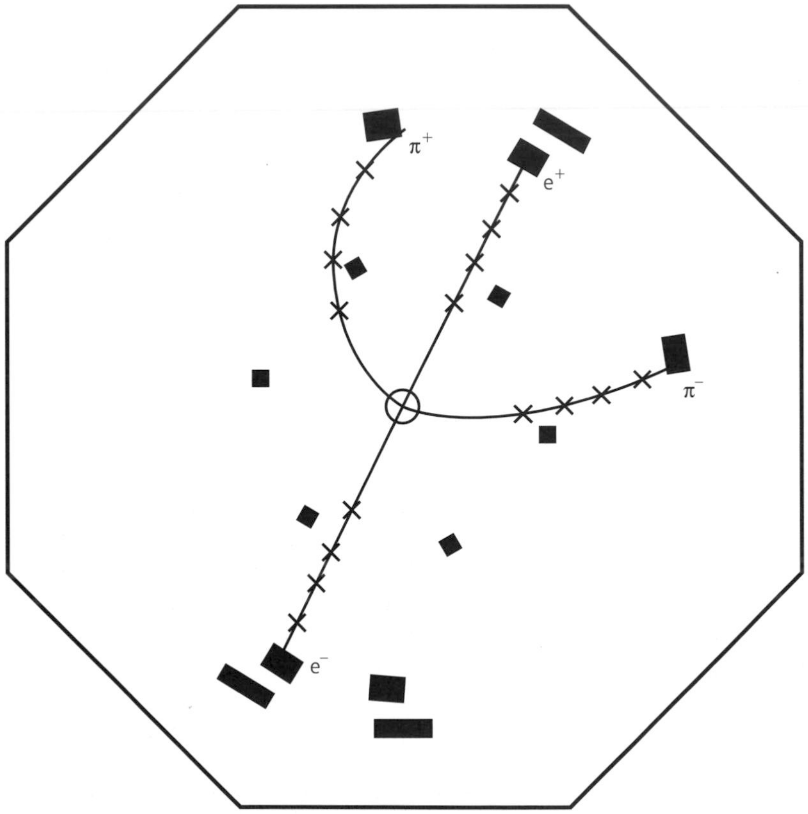

Figure 6.10 The ψ' particle writes its own signature when it decays!

The third generation

The discovery of the tau particle in 1974 was rather upsetting for particle physicists. Here was a third generation lepton with a mass about 4000 times greater than the electron. Together with its expected tau-neutrino it would form a third and more massive lepton doublet. Should we therefore expect a third quark doublet? Will Nature continue repeating the same patterns at ever higher energies?

By now you will not be at all surprised that the answer to the first question is 'yes'. The third generation of quarks consists of the **bottom** and **top** quarks. Their existence was confirmed in 1977 with the discovery of the **upsilon** particle (a bottom and anti-bottom pair forming the 'ground state' of 'bottomonium'!) and in 1995 with the discovery of the top quark decay at Fermilab.

Evidence for the top quark

Beta decay of the neutron (udd) to a proton (uud) involves the weak interaction and converts a down quark into an up quark. The down quark emits a W^- particle as it converts to an up quark and that W^- decays rapidly to an electron and antielectron-neutrino.

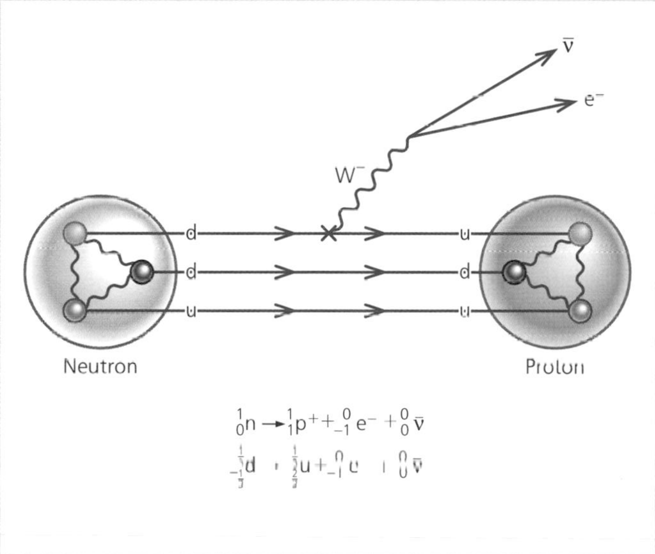

Figure 6.11 Beta decay of a neutron occurs when a down quark changes to an up quark by emitting a W^- particle.

The W^- is one of the 'force-carrying particles' involved in electroweak interactions (see chapter 7).

By analogy, a top quark is expected to decay rapidly to its lighter partner the bottom quark. It does this by emitting a W^+ which can decay to a number of other particles. One particular decay mode is to either a positron or positive muon with their associated neutrinos. The bottom quark will also decay to a jet of particles, so the creation of a top and anti-top in a proton–antiproton collision experiment should produce a very characteristic pattern of decays. However, because these events will be very rare they have to be sifted from a vast quantity of data and must then be shown to be statistically significant.

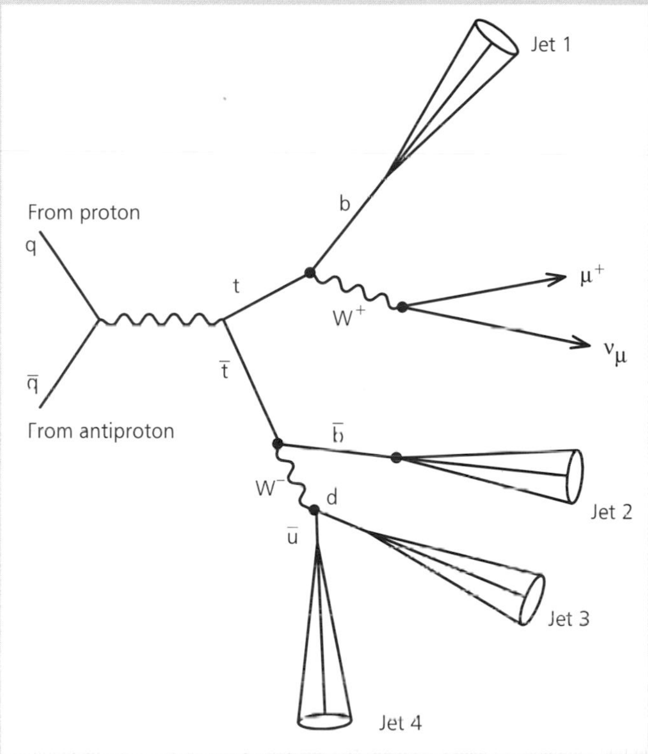

Figure 6.12 The characteristic 'signature' of the top quark.

The first convincing evidence for this particle 'signature' came from the CDF (Collider Detector at Fermilab) in 1995. Figure 6.12 shows the creation of a top/anti-top pair from quarks in a colliding proton and antiproton. The top quark immediately decays to a bottom by emitting a W^+, which decays to a positive muon and its neutrino. The bottom survives a short while before decaying to produce a jet of particles. The decay of the anti-top is similar but here the W^- decays to a pair of down and anti-up quarks which in turn decay to produce two jets of particles. This particular decay scheme is called a 'lepton plus four jets' mode because these are all detected by CDF. The neutrino's existence is inferred from conservation of energy. Note that this diagram does not imply the existence of free quarks, these transformations take place inside hadrons and the jets will consist of baryons and mesons.

We have neglected the second question. Will Nature repeat these particle patterns at ever higher energies? It looks like the answer to this is 'no', and there are probably only three generations of particles. The evidence for this comes from both particle physics and cosmology.

In the hot early Universe energy was distributed mainly between photons and neutrinos, the few hadrons and leptons contributing an insignificant amount to the total. The proportion of energy going to each group depends upon the number of generations of leptons. If there are three generations then the proportions would be 51% to photons and 49% to neutrinos. The more lepton generations the more neutrinos would share in the energy and the more this ratio would tip in favour of neutrinos. In particular, if there are four generations of leptons the proportions would have been 44% to photons and 56% to neutrinos. This ratio determines the ratio of abundances of deuterium and helium as the Universe expands and cools, abundances that can be estimated from astronomical evidence. The observed abundances are consistent with just *three* lepton generations.

There is another way to get at this number. The Z^0 particle (another force-carrying boson in the electroweak theory) decays to hadrons and leptons. This is a massive particle (the rest energy of the Z^0 is 93 GeV, about 100 times the rest energy of the proton) so it should be able to decay into a wide range of lighter particles. The lifetime of the Z^0 will depend on how many decay options are available, the more options the more rapidly it will decay. An accurate measurement of Z^0 lifetime is therefore a measure of the number of generations of leptons and quarks (if there are more generations there will be more alternative decays and hence a shorter lifetime). Measurements of Z^0 decay at CERN also suggest that there are only three generations.

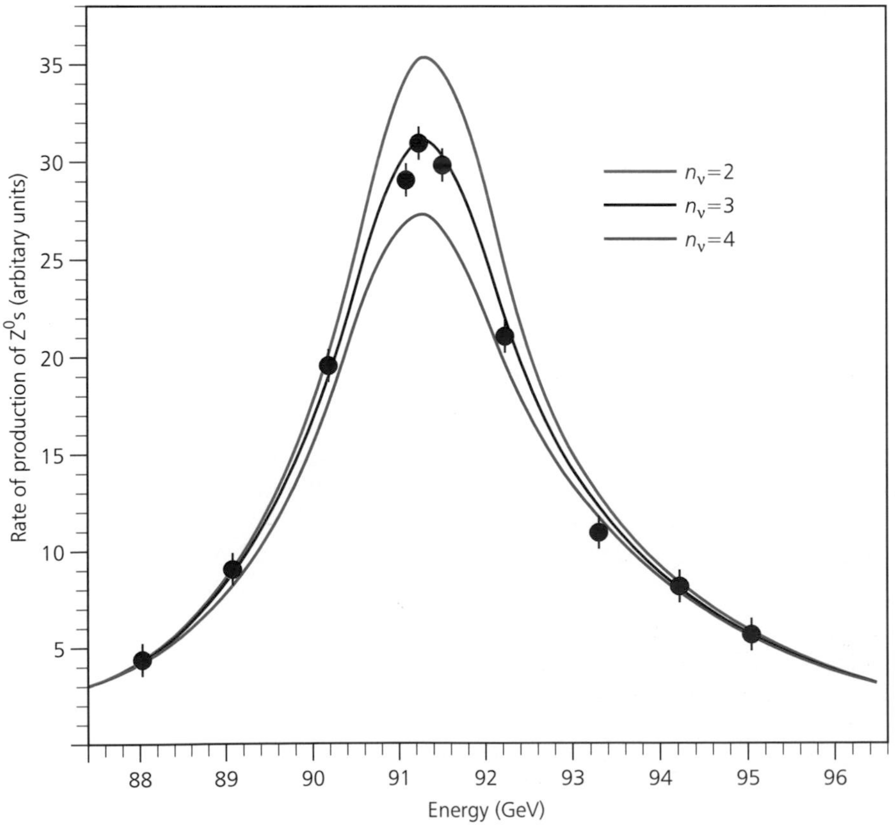

Figure 6.13 The theoretical predictions for the rate of Z^0 creation when electrons and positrons collide at LEP depend on the number of lepton generations (n_v). The experimental data closely agree with the curve for just three generations. The close symmetry between lepton and quark doublets suggests that there will also be only three generations of quarks.

All the quarks and all the leptons

Table 6.5

Generation	Quark	Charge/*e*	E_0/GeV	Spin/$\hbar$	Lepton	Charge/*e*	E_0/GeV	Spin/$\hbar$
1	d	$-\frac{1}{3}$	0.008	$\frac{1}{2}$	e	–1	0.511	$\frac{1}{2}$
1	u	$+\frac{2}{3}$	0.004	$\frac{1}{2}$	ν_e	0	0?	$\frac{1}{2}$
2	s	$-\frac{1}{3}$	0.150	$\frac{1}{2}$	μ	–1	106	$\frac{1}{2}$
2	c	$+\frac{2}{3}$	1 200	$\frac{1}{2}$	ν_μ	0	0?	$\frac{1}{2}$
3	b	$-\frac{1}{3}$	4 700	$\frac{1}{2}$	τ	–1	1780	$\frac{1}{2}$
3	t	$+\frac{2}{3}$	~93 000	$\frac{1}{2}$	ν_τ	0	0?	$\frac{1}{2}$

N.B. (1) Anti-particles have the same mass but opposite charge to their matter counterparts.
(2) All these particles are fermions.
(3) Although the Standard Model takes the neutrino mass to be zero most unified theories require a mass for the neutrino. There is some evidence to support the idea of non-zero neutrino mass and this would also help to solve the solar neutrino problem (see chapter 8 – the measured flux of neutrinos arriving at the Earth is significantly less than that predicted from models of nuclear reactions in the Sun).
(4) All quarks have baryon number $\frac{1}{3}$ and antiquarks have baryon number $-\frac{1}{3}$.
(5) It is worth reflecting on the fact that all the matter we see around us is made from quarks and leptons belonging to the *first* generation of this scheme.
(6) Notice that the sum of uud or udd quark masses is much less than the mass of a proton or neutron (each of mass about 1 GeV/c^2). There is still a great deal we do not understand about the way quarks interact inside the nucleus.

Stop press

The discovery of the top quark at Fermilab was a confirmation of the Standard Model, but this was followed in early 1996 by some disturbing news. Results from the Collider Detector at Fermilab (CDF) showed that *very* high energy collisions between protons and antiprotons produced far more scattering than was predicted. This could be because the energy and momentum of the quarks and gluons inside the colliding hadrons is different from our present model (which works well at lower energies) but it also raises the possibility that there may be another layer of structure inside the quarks.

SUMMARY

- There are two major classes of particles. **Hadrons** are those particles which are affected by the strong nuclear force, while **leptons** are unaffected by the strong force.
- Hadrons can be divided into two groups. The **baryons** are heavy particles, like the proton and neutron, and have half-integer spin. The **mesons** have integer spin and got their name because the first ones to be discovered had a mass half way between that of nucleons and electrons.
- All hadrons have a **baryon number**, *B*, which must be conserved in all particle interactions. *B* for all baryons is 1, anti-baryons have $B = -1$, while all mesons have $B = 0$.

- The Heisenberg Uncertainty Principle tells us that certain properties such as momentum and position, and energy and time are inextricably linked. The smaller the uncertainty of one member of the pair the greater the uncertainty in the other. For energy and time we can write $\delta E \delta t \geq h/2\pi$.
- Grouping the hadrons in a pattern known as the **eightfold way**, in a similar way to the grouping of elements in the Periodic Table, provided physicists with a way of predicting the existence of as yet undiscovered particles.
- The pattern of the hadrons in the eightfold way can be explained if all the hadrons are made from three types of particles and their antiparticles. These particles are the **quarks**.
- Baryons are made up of three quarks (a **quark triplet**), while mesons consist of a quark/antiquark pair.
- There are three **generations** of quarks, in the same way as there are three generations of leptons. Each generation contains two types of quark – up/down; strange/charmed; top/bottom.
- Evidence from the energy distribution in the early Universe, and from the lifetime of the Z^0 particle, suggests that there are no more than three generations of quarks and leptons.

QUESTIONS

1 How many leptons, hadrons, baryons and quarks are contained in a carbon-12 nucleus (omit force-carrying particles)? Which of these are fermions and which are bosons?

This is a challenging question.

2 A stationary pi-plus decays to an anti-muon and a muon-neutrino:

$$\pi^+ \rightarrow \mu^+ + \nu_\mu$$

a How is lepton number conserved in this decay?
b The rest masses of the pi-plus and anti-muon are 139.6 MeV/c^2 and 105.7 MeV/c^2 respectively. Calculate the kinetic energies of the anti-muon and muon-neutrino. (*Hint*: use $E^2 = E_0^2 + p^2c^2$ for both particles with $E_0 = 0$ for the neutrino.)
c What can be said about the directions in which the two new particles are emitted?

3 a When mesons decay the final products are leptons and photons. How is this possible if the Standard Model forbids quarks changing to leptons?
b How do the properties of hadrons relate to the quarks they contain?

4 What are the essential characteristics that distinguish:
a fermions from bosons
b hadrons from leptons
c baryons from mesons?

5 What was the significance of each of the following discoveries:
a the muon
b the omega-minus
c the J/ψ particle
d the Z^0
e the top quark?

6 a What is the difference between the elastic scattering of high-energy electrons used to measure nuclear diameters and the deep inelastic scattering of very high-energy electrons used to probe nucleons?
b Explain why the de Broglie equation implies that we need higher energies to resolve finer details.

7 The first strange baryons and mesons, like the lambda and the kaon, had unexpectedly long lifetimes – in fact these lifetimes first alerted physicists to the new property. However, strange resonances have very short lifetimes of around 10^{-23} s.
a What is meant by a 'resonance'?
b Explain why it is possible for a strange resonance to have such a short lifetime.
c Why are there no strange leptons?

7 The forces of nature

EXPLAINING FORCE

What is a force?

There is something we need to get clear right from the start: *forces always come in pairs*.

Think of a grasshopper leaping into the air; it rapidly extends its powerful back legs and presses very hard on the ground for a short period of time. During the same time the ground, which is compressed ever so slightly by the force exerted on it, pushes back on the grasshopper's feet with an equal and opposite force. The grasshopper accelerates upwards gaining energy (force times distance) and momentum (force times time). When it leaves the ground the forces on it and on the ground stop at the same instant. Now it is moving vertically and the only force acting on it (ignoring friction) is from gravity, its own weight pulling it down.

The Earth too is moving, it gained an equal and opposite momentum as the grasshopper jumped. Small though it is, each atom of the grasshopper's body is attracted to every atom of the Earth and as its upward motion slows so does the 'downward' motion of the Earth. For one frozen instant the two objects are relatively at rest with the grasshopper poised at its maximum height above the ground, but gravitational forces still act on both of them. The grasshopper accelerates downwards and the Earth accelerates up to meet it at a tiny rate. When they collide the downward force on the Earth is again equal and opposite to the upward force on the grasshopper and the two forces are exactly the right strength and act for exactly the right time to bring the two bodies to rest once again!

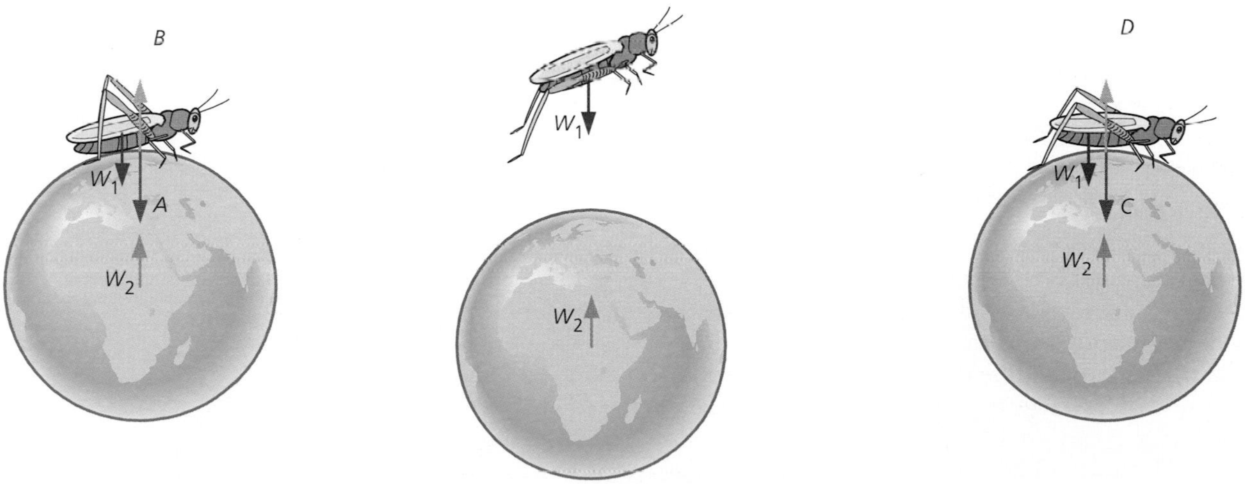

W_1 = weight of grasshopper in Earth's gravitational field
W_2 = weight of Earth in grasshopper's gravitational field
A = force of grasshopper pushing down on Earth at take-off
B = reaction of Earth pushing up on grasshopper at take-off

C = impact force of grasshopper on Earth as it lands
D = impact force of Earth on grasshopper as it lands
$W_1 = W_2$ $A = B$ $C = D$ (magnitudes).

Figure 7.1 What we call a force is just one end of an interaction.

This little story illustrates several important ideas. First it shows how momentum is conserved because the two bodies *interact*. If the Earth had not been moved by forces from the grasshopper then the only momentum involved would have been that of the grasshopper which changed continually throughout the jump. Secondly it shows that at every stage in the motion any force from the Earth on the grasshopper results in a corresponding force from the grasshopper on the Earth. There is no such thing as a force that arises in isolation – all forces arise from **interactions**.

This is the point of Newton's third law of motion (the 'action/reaction' one) and it is extremely important for understanding the forces between subatomic particles. If forces arise from *interactions between pairs of particles* then any explanation of forces must involve the behaviour of *both* particles.

Forces and fields

Force has been described in various ways in physics. The starting point is the idea of two things colliding with one another and exerting forces by contact. This works well for most of our own actions where we push or pull things we are touching but it doesn't work so well for gravity, magnetism or electrostatics where the same effects can be produced without contact. For a while these interactions were described as an **instantaneous action-at-a-distance**, but this is difficult to comprehend. How can two things affect one another if there is nothing passed between them to indicate their presence?

Faraday introduced the idea of an electric and magnetic **field** spreading through space through which charged or magnetised bodies could pass their influence. A similar idea was developed for gravitation and all action-at-a-distance models were recast in this form. Fields have been one of the most successful models in physics and explain forces in the following way (electrostatics and gravitation are used as an example):

- charges/*masses* create electric/*gravitational* fields which spread through space
- electric/*gravitational* fields can exert forces on charges/*masses*
- a charge/*mass* placed in the electric/*gravitational* field experiences a local force from the field determined by the field strength at that point in space.

Quantum field theories

The fundamental theory of the forces between particles is based on the quantum theory of fields. Electromagnetism was the first successful quantum field theory and a glance at its development will help us to understand what quantum field theories are about.

Think of two electrons some distance apart. They will exert a force on one another because of their electrostatic fields. If one particle is waved backwards and forwards (e.g. by an a.c. voltage in an aerial) the field it creates will also wave backwards and forwards. This distortion in the field will take time to travel to the other electron. Maxwell calculated that the rate at which these electromagnetic disturbances travel outwards is the speed of light (and so confirmed that light is electromagnetic). When the waves arrive at the second electron the forces on it will fluctuate causing it too to oscillate. This is the principle behind radio and TV transmission systems. It also tells us that electromagnetic interactions are linked to the transmission of electromagnetic waves between charges.

The next step is to bring in wave–particle duality. The waves that transmit between interacting electrons also have a particle-like nature. The minimum energy that can be transferred by electromagnetic radiation is one photon. In our experience light does not seem 'granular' because we receive an enormous number of photons per second on our retinas. For interacting electrons however, the quantisation or 'graininess' of light is likely to be *very* important. The quantum theory of forces explains interactions as an exchange of particles; for these two electrons this would be an exchange of photons.

Figure 7.2 The forces of an interaction can be transmitted by exchanging particles.

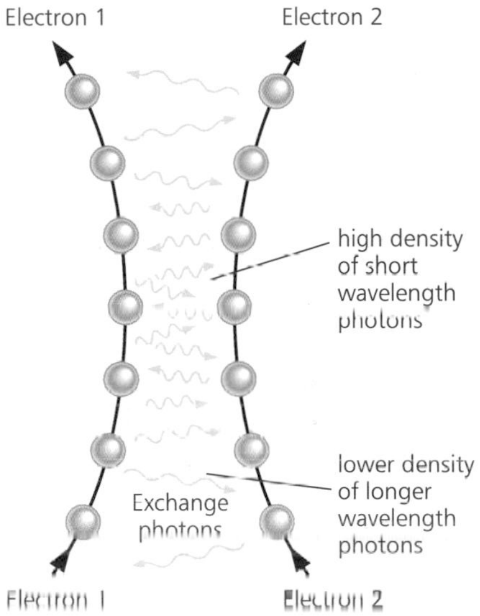

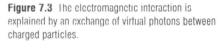

Figure 7.3 The electromagnetic interaction is explained by an exchange of virtual photons between charged particles.

There is a rather subtle distinction to be made here. The electromagnetic interaction taking place in a TV transmission involves electromagnetic waves radiated from one electron affecting another as they pass. This radiation is real in the sense that it carries energy away from the transmitting electron and could be detected and absorbed by a receiving electron anywhere else. On the other hand, the electromagnetic interaction taking place when two electrons repel one another is explained by the exchange of *virtual particles*, in this case, **virtual photons**. A virtual particle owes its existence to energy it has 'borrowed' from the system and which must be paid back within a certain time. The more energy that is borrowed, the shorter the lifetime of the virtual particle. This peculiar behaviour is another consequence of the Heisenberg Uncertainty Principle (see below). Two electrons interact by a continual exchange of virtual photons created and annihilated by electrons.

Virtual particles

Energy conservation is not violated by quantum mechanics but on the subatomic scale the precise time and energy of an event is indeterminate. For example, if an atom emits a photon at a precise time then the energy of the photon has a large uncertainty; on the other hand if the photon energy is determined then the exact time of emission is uncertain. This uncertainty obeys a mathematical relation called the Heisenberg Uncertainty Principle:

$$\delta E \delta t \approx \frac{h}{2\pi}$$

where δE means 'uncertainty in energy' etc.

When two particles interact the energy of the system has an uncertainty over short time intervals which can be large enough to create virtual particles. They are called virtual because they must be reabsorbed within a short time, δt, they do not radiate off as particles in their own right. The link between interacting particles is in this exchange process.

Virtual particles are important in many physical processes. We have already seen that a sufficiently energetic gamma-ray photon has a probability of creating an electron–positron pair. A photon which is just short of this energy may be able to 'borrow' enough energy to create a virtual electron–positron pair which will then recombine to form the gamma ray a little later. In calculating the probabilities of particular events we have to include the probabilities of exotic events like this.

An isolated electron has an indeterminate energy over short times so it will be surrounded by a cloud of virtual photons emitted and reabsorbed by the electron. Since photons have no rest mass there is no lower limit to the energy of the virtual photons and so no upper limit to the time for which a virtual photon can exist. The lower the energy of the photon the longer it can exist and so the longer the range over which it might affect other particles (its range is $c\delta t$, where δt is the time it exists for). Detailed calculations based on this idea show that the force exerted on other charges diminishes as an inverse square law with distance. This is in complete agreement with Coulomb's law of electrostatics. The electrostatic field is therefore generated by the exchange of virtual photons whereas the radiation field of a charged particle is conveyed by real photons.

Even empty space is full of activity. The vacuum itself obeys the Uncertainty Principle so that virtual particles of all kinds are continually created and annihilated everywhere. The interaction of orbital electrons with virtual particles created in the vacuum between the electron and the nucleus causes a slight shift in the orbit of the electron that affects the frequency of spectral lines emitted by the atom. This **Lamb Shift** was first measured by Willis Lamb in 1947.

THE FOUR FUNDAMENTAL INTERACTIONS

The four interactions

We have already begun to generalise the idea of a force. When we talk about the 'forces of nature' what we really mean are the distinct types of interaction between particles. These are distinguished from one another by the types of particle which are involved and the conservation laws that are obeyed by the interaction. Each type of interaction involves the exchange of different kinds of force-carrying particles. There are four interactions.

Gravitational interaction

This affects particles with mass. It is very weak but has an infinite range and is purely attractive so it governs the structure of matter in bulk (e.g. stars and galaxies).

Electromagnetic interaction

This affects particles with charge. It is much stronger than gravity but tends to cancel in bulk matter because atoms are neutral. It too is of infinite range and governs the structure of atoms and thereby the behaviour of materials and all chemical processes.

Strong interaction

Particles affected by the strong force are called hadrons, and are all made from quarks. The strong force itself is really a residual force from the interaction between quarks (the 'colour force', discussed later). The force between hadrons is very short range but much stronger than electromagnetism and it determines the structure of the nucleus.

Weak interaction

In beta decay a neutron decays to a proton and creates an electron and antineutrino in the process. This nuclear interaction creates a particle, the antineutrino, that is not affected by electromagnetism or the strong force. A new short range interaction must be involved. The weak interaction is the most difficult to grasp because it really involves the decay of quarks inside nucleons, so looking at it from the point of view of beta decay makes it look more complicated. Quarks and leptons are both affected by the weak interaction. If you are in any doubt about the weakness of the weak interaction you should reflect on the fact that several thousand billion neutrinos passed through your body while you read this sentence.

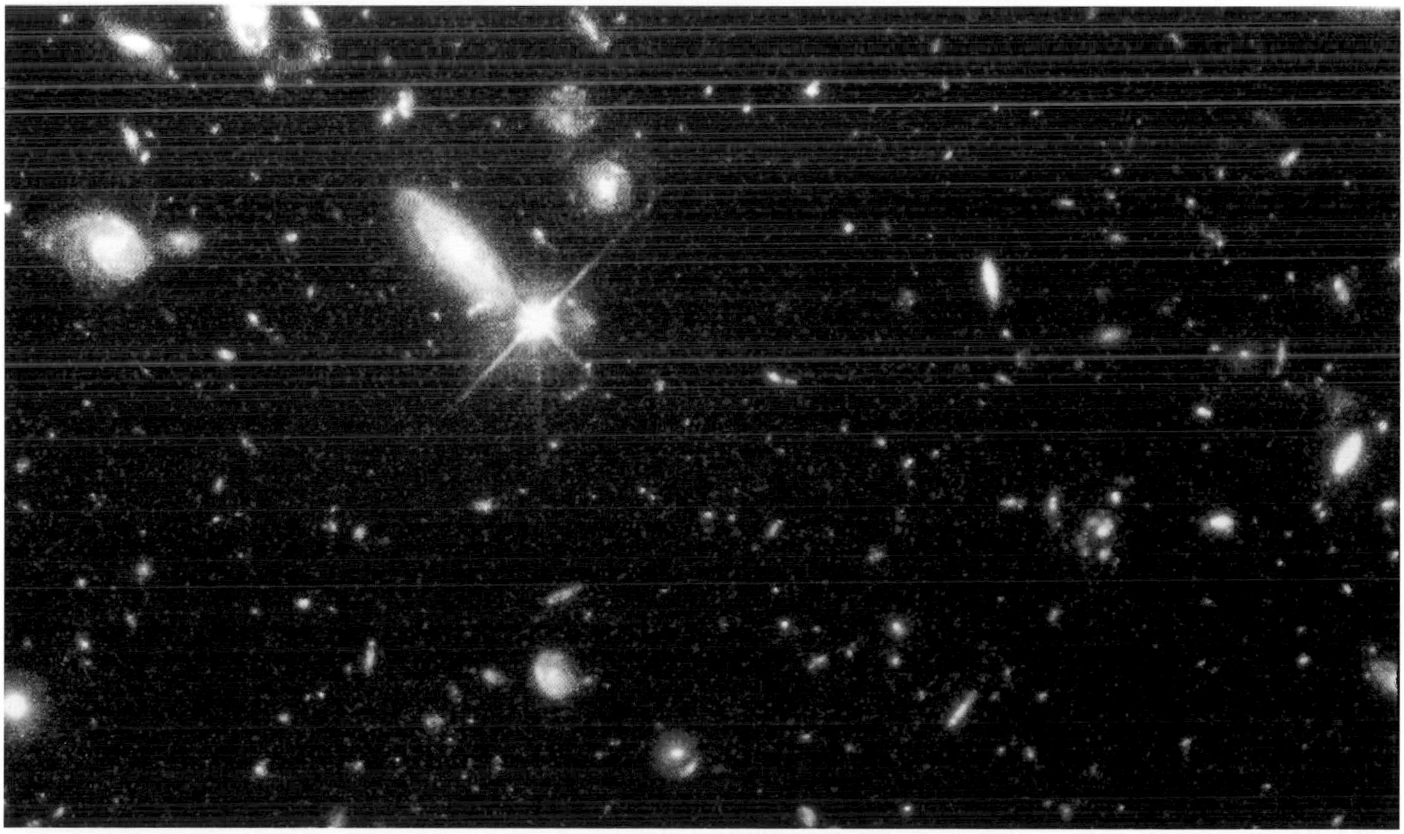

Figure 7.4 The galaxies shown here are all in a region of space that might be covered by a grain of sand held at arm's length. The diversity of galactic forms is created by the weakest force of nature, gravity. On the other hand the electromagnetic energy of light by which we see these galaxies comes from nuclear fusion reactions in stars brought about by the strong force.

Feynman diagrams and exchange forces

Richard Feynman showed how to draw pictures of particle interactions. These pictures were extremely useful in the development of quantum field theories because they can help to construct equations to predict the outcome of experiments. They are also a great help in trying to understand what is happening and why certain transformations occur and others are forbidden.

A *few words of warning*. Feynman diagrams are *not* pictures of the trajectories of the interacting particles in space and time. What is important are the relationships between particles that are shown in the diagrams, particularly at the vertices where quantities such as charge must be conserved (exactly what conservation laws apply depends upon the type of interaction involved). The mechanical analogue of particle exchange is where two skaters throw a heavy ball backwards and forwards and get pushed apart as a result of the impulses. This seems to explain repulsion by exchange, but makes attraction harder to understand. All that is important is that the particles are linked in an interaction by the exchange of virtual particles; whether or not the result is attraction depends on the interaction energy between the two particles and is not obvious simply from the shape of the diagram.

The diagrams below show examples of electromagnetic scattering, the strong force, and a weak decay. In all cases charge is conserved at each vertex and a virtual particle is exchanged. Note that the wavy line representing the virtual particle starts and ends in the diagram – this particle has no long term existence. On the other hand the lines representing electrons, protons and neutrons do not end in the diagram but extend beyond it. These are real particles.

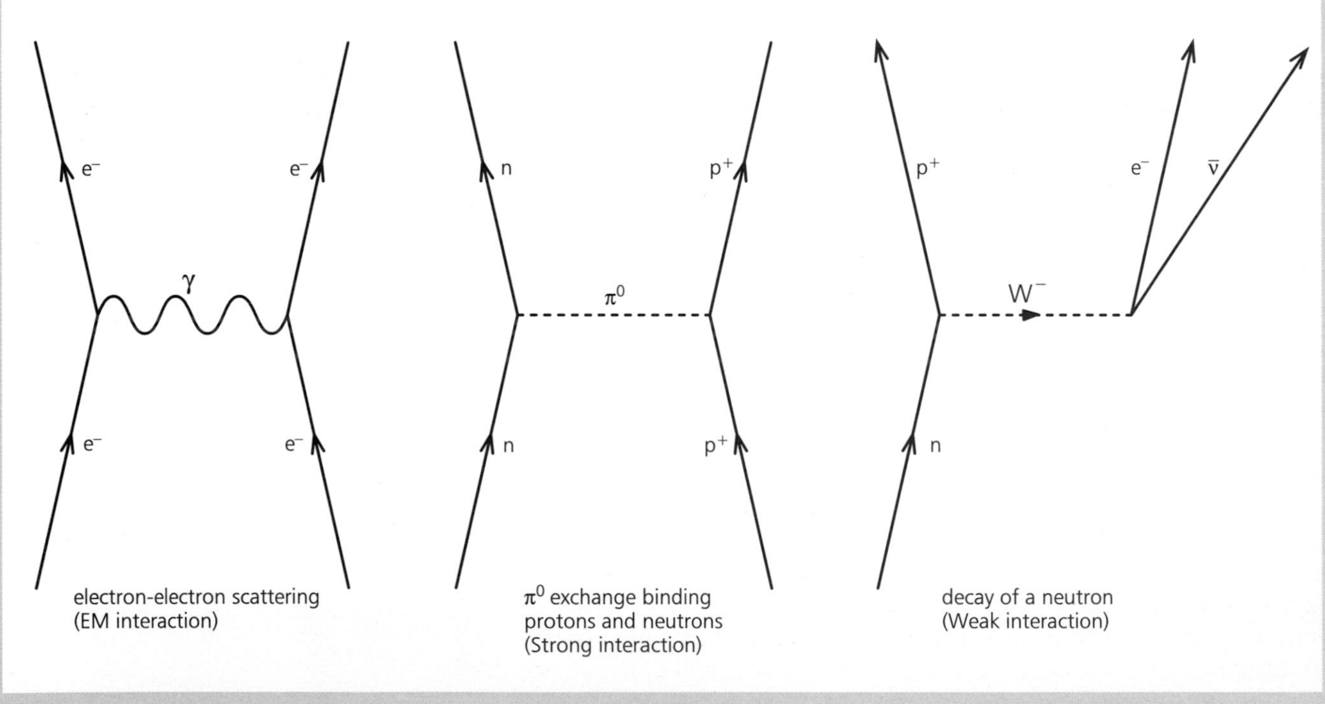

Figure 7.5 Three examples of Feynman diagrams – notice that the first is a repulsion, the second an attraction and the third fits neither simple description.

All the fundamental interactions involve virtual particle exchange. The particles exchanged determine the nature of the interaction and are different in each case. All of them have integer spin and are called **bosons** (after Satyendra Nath Bose the Indian physicist who, with Einstein, developed the mathematical theory of how integer spin particles behave). They are described as **'gauge' bosons** because they derive from a mathematical theory involving a certain kind of symmetry that goes by this name.

Fermions, bosons and the Exclusion Principle

We have classified particles in terms of their interactions, but there are other ways to divide them into groups. Perhaps the most important way of all is by spin. All particles have either integer or half-integer spins and are called bosons and fermions respectively. The reason this is important is because it determines how the particles behave in complex systems.

For example, atoms are built up by filling energy levels with electrons from the smallest, tightest-bound orbital (1s) out to the very edge of the atom. There are well-known rules for this and chemists regularly record the electronic structure of particular elements and use this to explain their behaviour. Sodium, for example is written as:

$1s^2\ 2s^2\ 2p^6\ 3s^1$

(This means there are 2 electrons in the 1s state, 2 more in the higher energy 2s state, 6 in 2p etc. The single electron in the 3s state is easily lost and accounts for sodium's reactivity.)

Why can't the electron in the 3s state lose energy by making a quantum jump down to the lower energy 2p, 2s, or 1s states? The answer is that these states are already full and the **Pauli Exclusion Principle** forbids more than one fermion from occupying exactly the same quantum state (s-orbitals have two distinct states and p-orbitals have six). *Why* does the Pauli principle apply? It applies because the quantum mechanical description of a particle is as a mathematical '**wavefunction**' and the wavefunction for a *pair* of fermions is always zero if they are in the same state. This makes the probability (which is related to the intensity of the wavefunction) of two electrons occupying the same quantum state become zero.

The wavefunction for a pair of bosons is actually enhanced if they are in the same state, so the probability of finding groups of bosons in the same state is increased. This has important physical and technological applications. **Laser** light consists of large numbers of identical coherent photons. **Superconductivity** works because electrons form 'Cooper pairs' that act as bosons and move through the structure without interacting with the lattice. **Superfluids** are also explained by groups of bosons occupying a single macroscopic quantum state and flowing without friction. It is thought that the neutrons inside a neutron star may be subject to such incredible forces that they too form pairs and act as a superfluid **Bose condensate**.

- Fermions have half-integer spins and are always subject to the Pauli Exclusion Principle so they cannot all condense into the lowest available energy state.
- Bosons are not subject to the Pauli Exclusion Principle so they tend to fall into the lowest energy state to form extended quantum states called Bose condensates.

Gravity

The gauge bosons for gravitation are called **gravitons** but their existence is predicted only by analogy with the other forces. There is no successful quantum field theory of gravitation at the moment and there are no experiments designed to look for gravitons.

Stephen Hawking has made some progress in combining gravity and quantum theory in the vicinity of a black hole where the intense gravitational field would be sufficient to induce the creation and annihilation of large numbers of particle and antiparticle pairs. He showed that if one of the pair falls into the black hole the other can be radiated and the whole process is like the radiation of a black body. This led to the idea that black holes have a temperature, radiate their energy and mass and will eventually explode in a puff of radiation. The radiation from a black hole is called **Hawking radiation** but has not yet been observed.

Electromagnetism and Quantum Electrodynamics (QED)

The gauge bosons for electromagnetism are **photons**. Photons are uncharged so this interaction leaves the charges of the interacting particles unchanged. They are spin 1 particles (all force-carrying particles are bosons) so their emission from a spin $\frac{1}{2}$ particle such as an electron can leave it as a spin $\frac{1}{2}$ particle (with its spin inverted: if a spin $\frac{1}{2}$ particle emits a spin 1 particle it becomes a spin $-\frac{1}{2}$ particle).

The quantum theory of the interaction of light with matter is called **quantum electrodynamics** or **QED** for short. It is the most successful theory ever formulated by human beings and can predict the outcomes of some experiments to an accuracy better than 1 part in 10^{11}. The theory and its method have been copied as models for all the other interactions (with varying degrees of success). You may be surprised to be told that this method is a method of successive approximation. This is best explained using an example. Imagine you had to calculate the probability that an electron–electron collision resulted in a particular outcome. How would you go about it?

First of all you must start with the simplest scattering, an exchange of one photon, and draw a Feynman diagram for this. Then complicate it a bit, by assuming that a second photon is exchanged soon after the first, and draw a second diagram. Now add in more complicated possibilities – exchange photons that convert to electron–positron pairs en route or electrons that emit and reabsorb the same virtual photon. Draw a Feynman diagram for each alternative way that the desired outcome can be achieved until the scenario is too weird and unlikely to make a significant contribution. Now you have set of possibilities, or *possible histories* for the scattering event. Use the rules of QED to convert each diagram into a calculation and sum the probabilities of each process. This should give the probability of the outcome represented by each of these different processes. If the accuracy is not good enough add a few more terms.

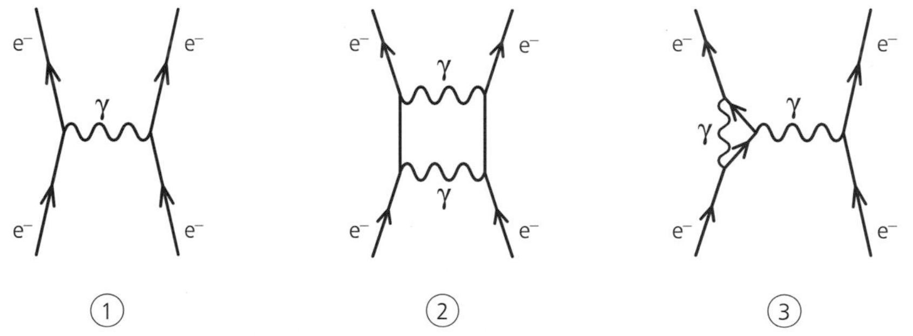

Figure 7.6 To calculate the probability of a particular event we must add contributions from all the different possible ways that event might occur. In this case an electron scatters from another electron by the electromagnetic interaction. The three diagrams are successively more complex but all contribute to the scattering. In the second one, two photons are exchanged, in the third the first electron emits two photons and reabsorbs one of them.

This approach, where we consider all the different ways an event might occur and use them all to calculate the probability of that event is sometimes called a **sum over histories**.

The strong interaction

The strong interaction is more complicated than electromagnetism because the hadrons affected by this force are themselves composite particles (made of quarks) and the strong force is a residual effect of the colour force between quarks. Nevertheless in 1935 Hideki Yukawa, a Japanese physicist, developed a theory of the strong interaction involving the exchange of **pi-mesons**. Whereas electromagnetic forces are transmitted by a single gauge boson, the photon, the strong force has three: pi-mesons can be positive, negative or neutral and their exchange can alter the charge as well as the energy and momentum of the particles. Pi-mesons do not have zero rest mass so there is a lower limit to the energy that must be borrowed to create them. This implies an upper limit to their range before they must be reabsorbed (since their velocity cannot exceed the speed of light). This explains the short range of the strong interaction.

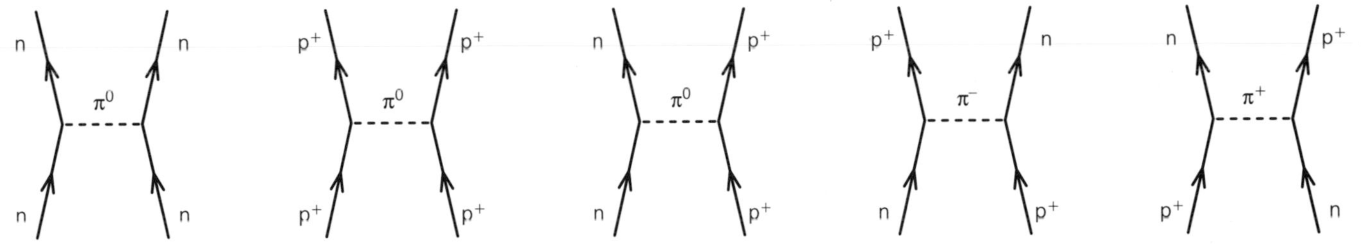

Figure 7.7 Protons and neutrons are bound together by the exchange of virtual pions. This gives many first order possibilities. All the usual conservation laws must apply at each vertex in the diagram. For example, if a proton emits a pi-plus it must turn into a neutral particle, in this case a neutron.

The range of the strong interaction

Electromagnetism and gravitation are long range forces because the gauge bosons (force-carrying particles) have zero rest mass. The energy–time uncertainty principle allows a small amount of energy to be borrowed for a long time so low-energy, long wavelength photons can be exchanged over long distances. There is no limit to the distance, although the energy and momentum of the photon exchanged will obviously diminish as the distance is increased. This accounts for the inverse square law in both cases.

The strong force is different. It is extremely strong over a very short range and then drops off rapidly to zero. Yukawa proposed that this short range was because the force carrying particle involved had a non-zero rest mass. He then used the known range of the strong force to predict the mass of the exchange particle, which is called a pi-meson or pion. Energetic pions would only be exchanged over a short distance because they would have to pay back their borrowed energy too soon. The longest lived and so longest range pions would be those which borrowed just enough energy to create them. If their calculated lifetime is multiplied by the speed of light this will give an upper limit to the range of the strong force.

Range of strong interaction $R \approx 10^{-15}$ m

Speed of light $c = 3.0 \times 10^{8}$ m s^{-1}

Maximum lifetime for pion $\Delta t \approx \frac{R}{c} = 3.3 \times 10^{-24}$ s

Uncertainty principle: $\Delta E \Delta t \approx \frac{h}{2\pi}$

$$\Delta E \approx \frac{h}{2\pi \Delta t} = 3.2 \times 10^{-11}\,\text{J} = 200\,\text{MeV}$$

Taking this as a rough measure of the rest energy of a pion gives:

$$m_\pi \approx \frac{\Delta E}{c^2} = 3.5 \times 10^{-28}\,\text{kg}$$

Yukawa's prediction was for a rest energy around 140 MeV. This is between the mass of a nucleon and an electron which is why the particle is called a meson (meaning 'middle'). Charged pions were discovered in 1947 and their rest energy was indeed 140 MeV (the neutral pion is slightly less massive, at 135 MeV). Yukawa was awarded the Nobel Prize for this work in 1949.

(This model of the strong force has been drastically revised. It is now thought to be a vestige of the 'colour force' that binds quarks together to form mesons or baryons. When pions are exchanged between nucleons the strong force arises from the 'colour charge' on the quarks they contain.)

Quantum chromodynamics

The strong interaction between nucleons is a residual effect of the force between quarks. All the hadrons (strongly interacting particles) are made of quarks. Mesons are quark pairs and baryons are quark triplets. The omega-minus particle that confirmed the quark model of baryons consists of *three* strange quarks. Since the quarks are fermions this poses a problem. Like electrons in the atom they must obey the Pauli exclusion principle and occupy distinct quantum states. A pair of similar quarks can do this by having opposite spins, but a triplet must be distinguished by some additional property.

This led Oscar Greenberg to propose a new property of quarks called '**colour**'. This has a role analogous to that of charge in electromagnetism, but with one major difference. Instead of just positive or negative charge there are three colours each of which can be positive or negative. Quarks carry the positive colour 'charges' and antiquarks carry the negative colour 'charges'. The colours have been labelled red, blue or yellow (sometimes green) – all hadrons are made from 'colourless' combinations of these (colour plus anti-colour in mesons and one red, one yellow and one blue quark in baryons – red plus yellow plus blue makes white, which is colourless!).

Quarks attract or repel one another according to the relationship between their colours. The colour force is carried by **gluons**. These gluons are spin-one gauge bosons that transmit the interaction between quarks. There are eight varieties of gluon and these carry colour differences (e.g. red-minus-blue) between the quarks and so change the nature of the quarks with which they interact. A quark interaction is shown in figure 7.8 (as the quarks involved are always inside mesons and baryons the Feynman diagrams include the other quarks in the hadron).

The theory of **quantum chromodynamics** (**QCD**) was modelled on QED but is different in several important ways. Firstly the photon in QED is uncharged so it cannot interact with other photons (e.g. emit another photon or absorb one) on its way between charged particles. The gluons, however, all carry colour so they can interact with gluons and may well emit or absorb gluons between quarks. Whereas the electromagnetic interaction falls off as an inverse square law the colour interaction gets *stronger* with distance (but does have a maximum range since gluons have a large rest mass). On the other hand, if quarks come very close together the colour force becomes very weak and the quarks act like free particles. This is called **asymptotic freedom** and means that quarks inside a hadron are free within the bounds of their confinement.

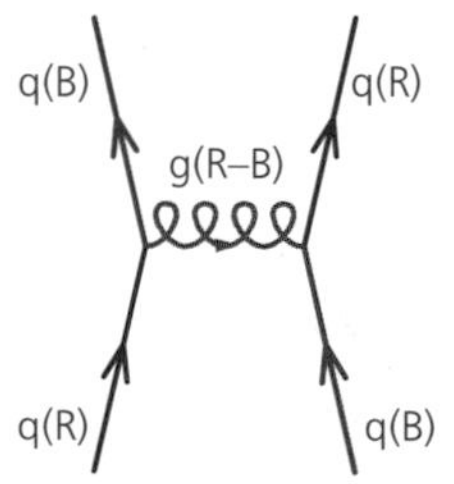

Figure 7.8 If a red quark emits a 'red-minus-blue' gluon it turns into a blue quark. If the red minus blue gluon is absorbed by a blue quark this one becomes a red quark. The exchange of gluons is responsible for the colour force between quarks.

Evidence for gluons

Deep inelastic scattering of high-energy electrons revealed the inner structure of the proton and neutron. In the 1960s at SLAC high energy electrons were fired at targets containing neutrons and protons. The de Broglie wavelength of the electrons was small compared to the radius of these hadrons and the results of the experiment were as surprising as Rutherford's scattering experiment half a century earlier. The electrons scattered as if the neutron or proton contained small dense particles.

The results showed that, even though the neutron is neutral it contains charge, which helps to explain its magnetic moment. Detailed analysis showed that, even if the neutrons and protons are constructed from triplets of quarks these do not have enough energy and momentum to account for the electron scattering. The rest must be carried by other particles, presumably the gluons.

The nucleons may be fundamental building blocks of all atomic nuclei, but they are far from being fundamental particles.

Further evidence for the substructure of nucleons came from electron–positron collision experiments at various accelerators in the 1970s and 1980s. When the electron and positron annihilate the products often include hadrons. This is because the annihilation produces high-energy quark–antiquark pairs which generate jets of hadrons as they separate. Three or four jet events are rare but can occur if the quark and/or antiquark emit a gluon before they separate. The gluon also produces a jet of hadrons as it decays and these betray their origin by having a total angular momentum equal to that of a spin 1 particle rather than a spin $\frac{1}{2}$ particle (gluons, like all gauge bosons, are spin 1).

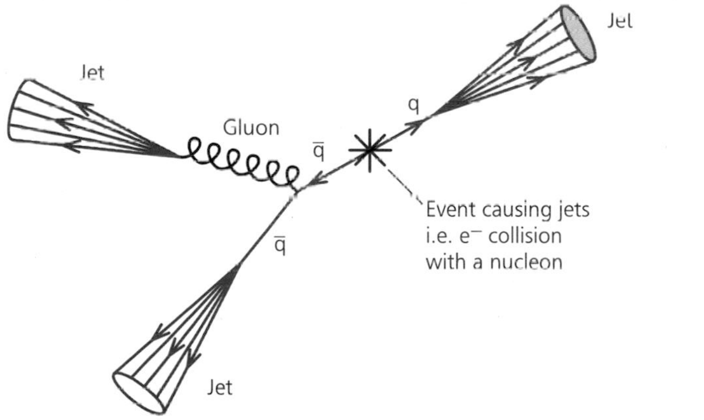

Figure 7.9 If the quark–antiquark pair emits a gluon a third jet of hadrons will be produced. Sometimes this is so close to one of the quark jets that it is not separately resolved.

Neither quarks nor gluons can exist as single particles because they would not be colourless. One way to understand this is in terms of the colour force (see page 102). As quarks and antiquarks separate the force between them becomes larger and larger until so much energy is stored in the colour field that new quarks are created which bind to the quark–antiquark pair to make new mesons and baryons. This is sometimes referred to as the theory of **quark confinement**.

The weak interaction

The weak force converts neutrons to protons in beta decay. This involves changing the nature of a quark in the neutron and creating a lepton–antilepton pair. A related process converts neutrons to protons and emits an electron when neutrinos are fired at neutrons. In both cases the sign of the particle has been changed by the interaction, so the gauge boson must carry charge. These force-carrying particles are called $W^{\pm}$ particles and their interactions are shown below.

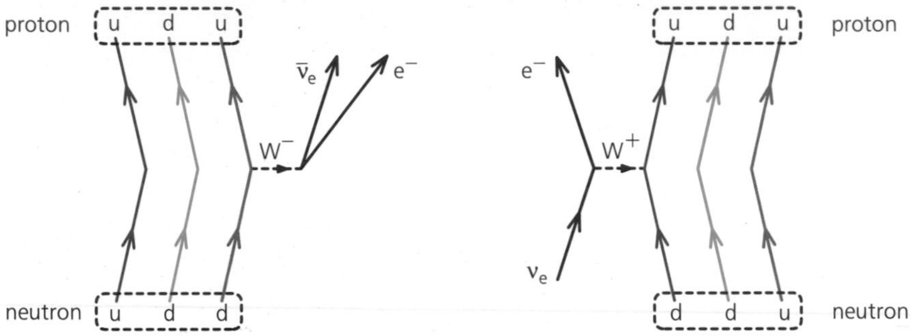

$^1_0n \longrightarrow {}^1_1p + {}^0_{-1}e^- + {}^0_0\bar{\nu}_e$

beta decay

${}^0_0\nu_e + {}^1_0n \longrightarrow {}^1_1p + {}^0_{-1}e^-$

an inverse beta process

Figure 7.10 Feynman diagrams for charged weak interactions.

The weak interactions described above all involve a transfer of charge. Can a neutral weak interaction take place? This would be an event in which something like a neutrino collides with a proton and deflects it but does not change the nature of either particle. The interaction could not be mediated by the exchange of a virtual photon because the neutrino is unaffected by the electromagnetic interaction – it would need a new gauge boson. The Z^0 boson was predicted for the job and this type of interaction was called a neutral current interaction because no charge is transferred.

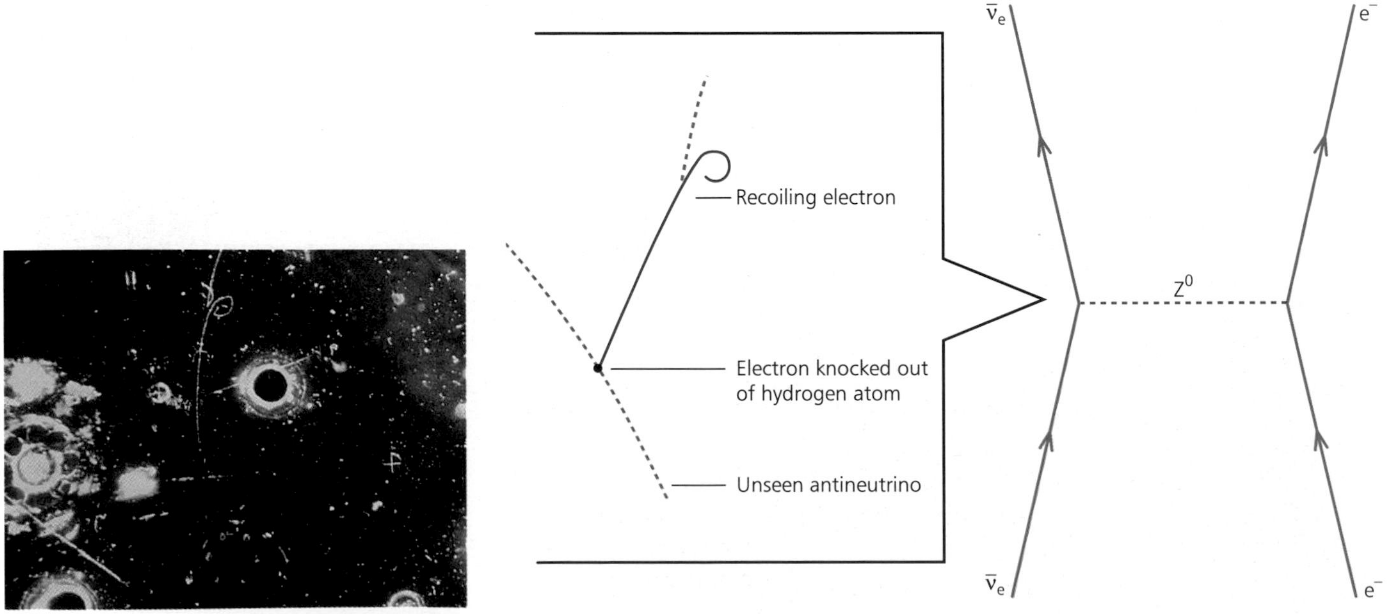

Figure 7.11 The photograph shows an electron knocked out of an atom by an antineutrino passing through a chamber filled with liquid hydrogen – a neutral current interaction.

The discovery of the W and Z particles

The W and Z particles were predicted from the unification of weak and electromagnetic interactions into the electroweak theory of Glashow, Salam and Weinberg (who shared the Nobel Prize in 1979). The calculated masses of 83 GeV/c^2 and 93 GeV/c^2 respectively (almost double the mass of an iron nucleus) meant the particles could only be produced by a high-energy accelerator. CERN's large proton synchrotron (SPS) was converted to a proton/antiproton collider in an attempt to produce collisions of sufficient energy to create them.

How would they show themselves? They both have extremely short lifetimes, about 10^{-25} seconds each, so they can only be detected by their decay products. Both decay to leptons by the weak interaction, so for example they could decay by:

$$W^+ \rightarrow e^- + \bar{\nu}_e$$

$$Z^0 \rightarrow \mu^+ + \mu^-$$

Two huge detectors, UA1 (underground area 1) and UA2 (underground area 2), were built to look for these characteristic decays. UA1 and UA2 are layered detectors (see chapter 2) and each layer yields different information. When the responses of all layers are considered and compared a picture of the particles emitted in the proton/antiproton decay can be built up.

(a)

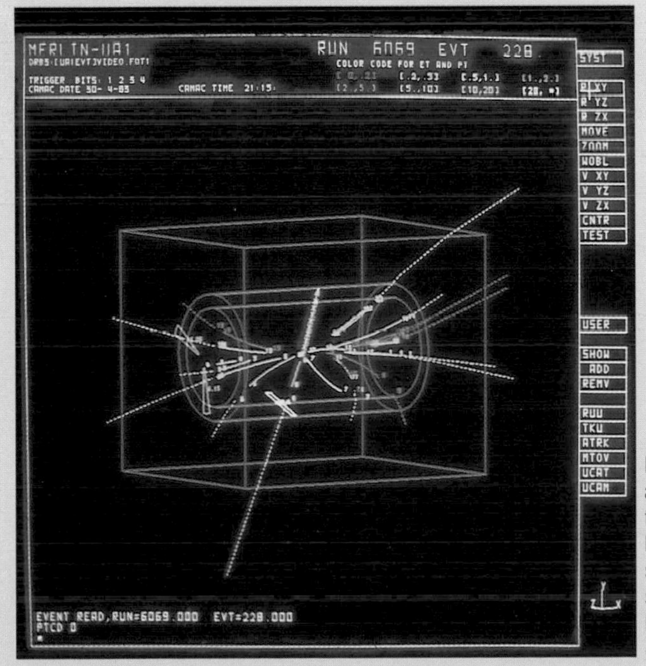

(b)

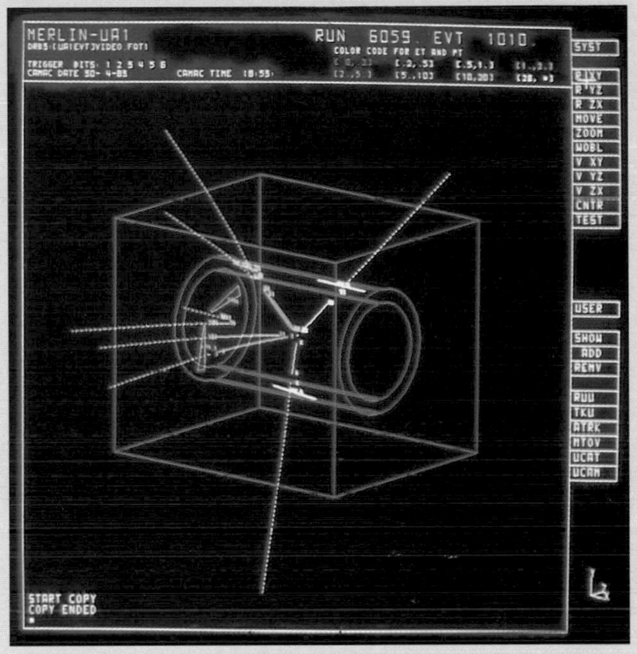

(c)

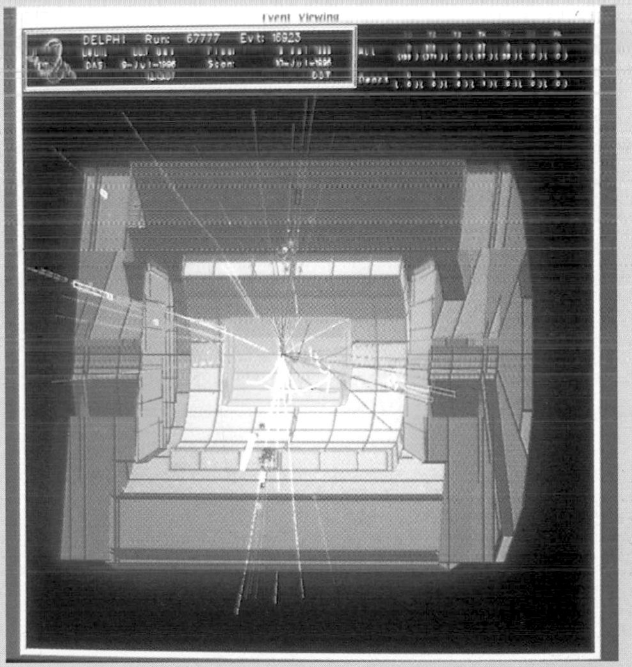

Figure 7.12 Computer reconstructions of **(a)** a W⁻ decay and **(b)** a Z^0 decay. A proton and an antiproton have annihilated in the centre of the detector. The computer calculates the paths and momenta of the emitted particles. In (a) the energetic particle exiting bottom left (blue) is an electron. It was created with a neutrino (blue) which is also shown moving in the opposite direction. Their combined energy is about 83 GeV, which suggests that they were formed in the decay of a W^-. In (b) a Z^0 has decayed to two high-energy electrons (white and purple) and a number of other particles (green.) Their combined energy is about 93 GeV, the rest energy of a Z^0. **(c)** Decay of the W^+ W^- pair.

UNIFICATION

TOEs and the Holy Grail

There is a sub-plot running through the history of physics. It is an attempt to explain everything with a single elegant mathematical theory. This is the 'Holy Grail' of physics and there are rumours that some theoreticians are close to finding this 'Theory of Everything'. It is worth looking back to see how far we have already come in simplifying the complexity of the world.

Gravity, electrostatics and magnetism were well known to the ancients, but it wasn't until the nineteenth century that physicists such as Faraday and Maxwell showed that both electricity and magnetism arise from the same source – electric charges. In the process they showed that light was also an electromagnetic effect. This work, which culminated in the Maxwell Equations describing the electromagnetic field, unified optics, electrostatics and magnetism into a single discipline: electromagnetism.

In the twentieth century Glashow, Weinberg and Salam showed that a mathematical model of the weak interaction predicted the existence of a fourth gauge boson in addition to the W^+, W^-, and Z^0. Rather than being a new particle this turned out to be the familiar photon. The significance of this is that electromagnetism and the weak interaction are not distinct interactions but different aspects of the same interaction. This was the birth of **electroweak theory** and unified the weak nuclear force with electromagnetism.

The theory of the colour force between quarks is based on the theory of QED but is not as successful, mainly because the mathematical series used in calculations do not converge so quickly as those in QED. **Grand Unified Theorie**s (**GUTs**) of the strong and electroweak forces have been proposed but none is entirely satisfactory.

The ultimate theory would be a **Theory of Everything** (**TOE**) that includes gravity, the strong force and the electroweak force in a single set of equations. Recently this has begun to look possible and the leading contender is **Superstring Theory** which describes the Universe in ten spatial dimensions!

The main stumbling block to constructing a TOE has been gravity. Whereas the other forces of nature are described by quantum field theories gravity is described by Einstein's **General Theory of Relativity** as a distortion of spacetime geometry. This is a beautiful and convincing mathematical theory but seems worlds away from the uncertainties of the quantum world. This was a view held by Einstein who spent the last years of his life isolated from the mainstream of physics as he tried in vain to create a unified theory based on geometrical considerations. The exciting prospect of modern physics is that superstring theories may succeed where Einstein failed and produce a TOE

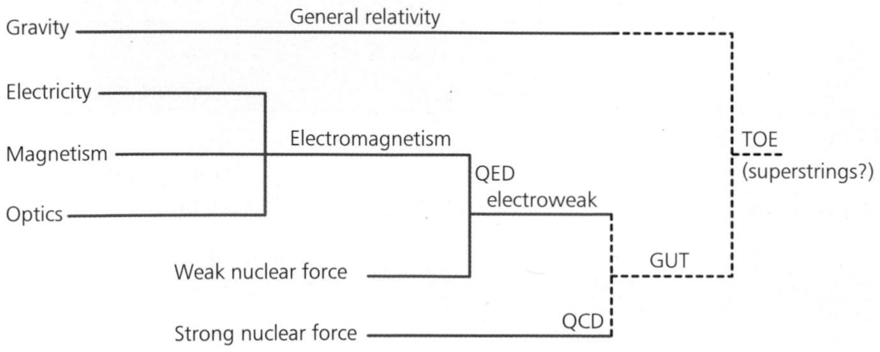

Figure 7.13 Unification.

based on higher dimensional geometries which is also consistent with quantum field theory. Edward Witten described string theory as 'twenty-first century physics that fell accidentally into the twentieth century'.

Of course, calling something a 'Theory of Everything' is misleading. In principle the behaviour of everything derives from fundamental particle interactions, but complex systems very often seem more than the sum of their parts. For example, the behaviour of the stock market must be based, ultimately, on quantum physics, but quantum theory is not much use in planning where to invest. Science will not end with a TOE, but such a theory would be the greatest human achievement in understanding the ultimate nature of the world around us.

The Standard Model

The model of particles and forces we have developed in the previous chapters is called the Standard Model. We know it is not complete, we know it is not final, but it gives a concise summary of the fundamental constituents of matter and their interactions. It is summarised below.

Matter

- Three generations of quarks and leptons.
- All quarks and leptons are fermions (with spin $\frac{1}{2}$).
- All have corresponding antiparticles.

Table 7.1

	Leptons		Quarks		Where found
first generation	electron (e^-)	electron-neutrino (ν_e)	up (u)	down (d)	ordinary matter
second generation	muon (μ^-)	muon-neutrino (ν_μ)	charm (c)	strange (s)	only found in cosmic
third generation	tau or tauon (τ^-)	tau-neutrino (ν_τ)	top (t)	bottom (b)	rays and accelerators

Interactions

- All interactions are either gravitational, electromagnetic or by the strong or weak nuclear forces.
- All interactions are transmitted by gauge bosons.

Table 7.2

Interaction	Gauge bosons	Acts on	Conservation laws	Typical lifetime	Typical range
gravity	graviton zero rest mass	everything	*Q*, *B*, *S*, *L*	no gravitational decays	infinite inverse square law
electromagnetism	photon zero rest mass	charged quarks and leptons	*Q*, *B*, *S*, *L*	10^{-18} s	infinite inverse square law
weak	W^+, W^-, Z^0 83 GeV/c^2, 93 GeV/c^2	quarks and leptons	*Q*, *B*, *L* but not *S*	10^{-10} s	10^{-18} m
colour (strong)	8 different gluons zero rest mass?	quarks	*Q*, *B*, *S* (leptons not involved so $L = 0$)	10^{-23}	10^{-15} m

Key: *Q* = charge, *B* = baryon number, *S* = strangeness, *L* = lepton number.

Epilogue: the mystery of mass

The ratio of the mass of a proton to the mass of an electron is about 1836. This number is independent of the units in which we choose to measure mass. It is a dimensionless number that tells us a fundamental relationship in the universe, but why does it have this value? Why do any of the particles we observe have the values we measure for them? What is mass? This is the most important unresolved problem in particle physics.

Peter Higgs of Edinburgh University has proposed a possible solution. He thinks that the mass of a particle is determined by the way it interacts with a new type of particle called a **Higgs boson**. In April 1993 William Waldegrave, then Minister for Science issued the following challenge to particle physicists:

'I will offer a bottle of vintage champagne – at my own expense – to anyone who can write down on a single sheet of A4 paper, in a way that my constituent Michael Berry says is scientifically correct, what the Higgs boson is and why you would like to find it.'

The authors of five entries (out of 117) were awarded a bottle of champagne each. One of these, by Roger Cashmore of Oxford University, is below.

The need to understand mass

What determines the size of objects that we see around us or even the size of ourselves? The answer is the size of the molecules and in turn the size of the atoms that compose these molecules. But what determines the size of the atoms themselves? Quantum theory and atomic physics provide an answer. The size of the atom is determined by the paths of the electrons orbiting the nucleus. The size of those orbits, however, is determined by the mass of the electron. Were the electron's mass larger, the orbits (and hence all atoms) would be smaller, and consequently everything we see would be smaller. So understanding the mass of the electron is essential to understanding the size and dimensions of everything around us.

It might be very hard to understand the origin of one quantity, that one being the mass of the electron. Fortunately nature has given us more than one elementary particle and they come with a wide variety of masses. The lightest particle is the electron and the heaviest is believed to be the particle called the top quark, which weighs at least 200 000 times as much as an electron. With this variety of particles and masses we should have a clue to the individual masses of the particles.

Unfortunately, if you try to write down a theory of particles and their interactions then the simplest version requires all the masses of the particles to be zero. So on the one hand we have a whole variety of masses and on the other a theory in which all masses should be zero. Such conundrums provide the excitement and the challenges of science.

There is, however, one very clever and very elegant solution to this problem, a solution first proposed by Peter Higgs. He proposed that the whole of space is permeated by a field, similar in some ways to the electromagnetic field. As particles move through space they interact with this field, and if they interact with it they acquire what appears to be mass. This is similar to the action of viscous forces felt by particles moving through any thick liquid. The larger the interaction of the particles with the field the the more mass they appear to have. Thus the existence of this field is essential in Higgs' hypothesis for the production of the mass of particles.

We know from quantum theory that fields have particles associated with them, the particle for the electromagnetic field being the photon. So there must be a particle associated with the Higgs field, and this is the Higgs boson. Finding the Higgs boson is thus the key to discovering whether the Higgs field does exist and whether our best hypothesis for the origin of mass is indeed correct.

If the Higgs boson does exist it should show itself in collision experiments at energies in excess of about 1 TeV (10^{12} eV). We are just at the threshold of these energies with colliders like CDF at Fermilab and some rumours have suggested that the Higgs boson may already have been seen there. LEP2 might also provide evidence for the Higgs mechanism; and if they still have not been found, the Large Hadron Collider at CERN will be available early next century to search for them.

Summary

- Forces always exist in pairs, as described by Newton's third law of motion.
- A **field** is a model which can be used to explain how one body can influence another body even though the two are not in contact with one another. For example, one oscillating electron influences another by radiating waves through the electromagnetic field which connects them.
- On a subatomic scale, fields can be thought of as having particle properties, through wave–particle duality. In this way of thinking, two electrons interact through an exchange of virtual photons.
- The energy and lifetime of virtual particles involved in interactions are related through Heisenberg's Uncertainty Principle: $\delta E \delta t \approx h/2\pi$.
- The Uncertainty Principle leads to the continuous creation of **virtual particles** and their annihilation, even in deep space.
- There are four interactions: gravitational, electromagnetic, strong and weak. Each of these interactions has its own type of virtual particle, or **gauge boson**.
- The **gravitational interaction** affects particles with mass. It is very weak, but has an infinite range. Its gauge boson is the **graviton**.
- The **electromagnetic interaction** affects particles with charge and has an infinite range. It is much stronger than gravity, although it tends to cancel in bulk matter because atoms are electrically neutral. Its gauge boson is the **photon**.
- The **strong interaction** affects hadrons. Although it is much stronger than the electromagnetic interaction, it has a much shorter range. Its gauge boson is the **gluon**, responsible primarily for the interaction between quarks.
- The **weak interaction** affects quarks and leptons, and acts over a distance much smaller than the diameter of the nucleus. Its has three gauge bosons, the W^+, W^- and Z^0 particles.
- To account for the structure of the omega-minus particle, quarks must possess a property known as **colour**. There are three 'colours' of quark – red, blue and yellow (or sometimes green).
- To account for the mass of particles, a field called the **Higgs field** has been proposed. This field would have a gauge boson called the **Higgs boson** associated with it. The existence of the Higgs field could be shown through the discovery of the Higgs boson.

QUESTIONS

1 Compare how electrons are bound to nuclei in atoms with the way neutrons and protons are bound together in the nucleus.
  a Name the force involved in each case.
  b What are the ranges of these forces?
  c Name the particles acting as force carriers in each case.

2 **a** What is the ratio of the electrostatic repulsion to the gravitational attraction between two protons a distance r apart?
  b How does this ratio depend on the proton separation?
  c Suggest some of the cosmological consequences of a slight imbalance between the magnitude of charge on electrons and protons.
  d How is it possible, given your answers to (a) and (b) that gravity dominates the structure of the Universe on the large scale?

3 **a** Why is it not possible for pions to decay by the strong interaction?
  b How do they decay?
  c Why is the pi-zero lifetime about a billion times shorter than that of the charged pions?
  d What quarks form the pi-plus, pi-minus and pi-zero mesons?
  e Are pions bosons or fermions? Justify your answer.
  f Why are the following proposed proton decays never observed?
  (i) $p^+ \rightarrow \pi^+ + \gamma$
  (ii) $p^+ \rightarrow e^+ + \pi^0$

4 Show how charge, lepton number and baryon number are all conserved in the following transformations:
  a $\pi^- + p^+ \rightarrow \pi^0 + n$
  b $\pi^+ \rightarrow \mu^+ + \nu_\mu$
  c $K^- \rightarrow \mu^- + \bar{\nu}_\mu$
  d Is strangeness conserved in each of (a), (b) and (c)?

5 Kaons are mesons with greater mass than pions and so might reasonably be expected to decay by the strong interaction to pions.
  a What is the characteristic lifetime for a particle that decays by the strong interaction?
  b The lifetime of the charged kaons is actually close to 10^{-8} s. What does this suggest about how charged kaons decay?
  c What prevents kaons from decaying by the strong interaction?
  d Write down an equation for the decay of a K^- and explain what conservation laws are obeyed or violated by the decay.

6 Strange particles are often produced in collisions between pions and protons. The equations below are suggested as mechanisms for the production of the Σ^+ baryon:
  (i) $\pi^- + p^+ \rightarrow K^- + \Sigma^+$
  (ii) $\pi^- + p^+ \rightarrow \pi^- + \Sigma^+$
  a Give a reason why it might be expected that the second reaction occurs far more frequently than the first.
  b In fact the second reaction is never observed, why is this?
  c What do you understand by the term 'strangeness'?

7 The first strange baryon to be discovered was the lambda-zero, Λ^0. This has a mass of 1.115 GeV/c^2 compared to the proton mass of 0.9383 GeV/c^2 and decays by the weak interaction to a proton, an electron and an antineutrino. (The electron has a mass of 0.511 MeV/c^2.)
  a Why does it decay by the weak interaction?
  b Write an equation for the decay and show how charge, lepton number and baryon number are all conserved in the decay.
  c What is the total energy released in the decay?
  d Compare the quark structure of the proton and the lambda-zero. What happens in the decay?
  e Compare this decay with the decay of free neutrons.

8 Summarise the evidence that suggests there are no more than three generations of quarks and leptons.

9 Explain why protons are absolutely stable in the Standard Model, but might be expected to decay in a unified theory.

10 Which of the proposed reactions listed below are allowed and which are forbidden by conservation laws in the Standard Model? For those which do not occur, explain why.
  a $p^+ + p^+ \rightarrow \Delta^+ + \Delta^+$
  b $e^+ + p^+ \rightarrow e^- + \Sigma^0 + K^+$
  c $K^+ + n \rightarrow \pi^0 + \Delta^+$
  d $\pi^+ + n \rightarrow \Lambda^0 + K^+$
  e $\mu^+ \rightarrow e^+ + \nu_e$
  f $\pi^- + p^+ \rightarrow \pi^- + \pi^+ + n$
  g $\nu_e + p^+ \rightarrow e^+ + n$
  h $K^- + p^+ \rightarrow \Omega^- + K^+ + K^0$

11 In the Standard Model total baryon number is always conserved. How can this be interpreted in terms of quarks? Is the same thing true of leptons?

12 What are the exchange particles that carry each of the following forces:
  a electromagnetism
  b the weak interaction
  c the strong nuclear force
  d gravitation
  e the colour force?
  f There are five forces listed above, why then do we often refer to the 'four forces of nature'?

QUESTIONS

13 **a** What is the difference between a real particle and a virtual particle?
b How does the energy–time uncertainty principle limit the range of forces transmitted by virtual particles with non-zero rest mass?

14 Draw a Feynman diagram to show the decay of a free neutron.

15 Why is electromagnetism a long range interaction whereas the strong nuclear interaction is very short range?

16 Many unified theories predict that protons are unstable and could decay by the mechanism below:

$$p^+ \rightarrow e^+ + \pi^0$$

a What 'conservation laws' are violated in this decay?
b The force-carrying gauge boson that changes a quark to a lepton inside the proton is extremely massive. What does this imply about (i) the range of this interaction, (ii) the probability that it occurs, and (iii) the lifetime of the proton?

17 The Pauli Exclusion principle applies to all fermions, so it must apply to quarks. This helps to explain why 'colour' was introduced as a new property to distinguish quarks of the same 'flavour' in baryons.
a What does the spin of all fermions have in common?
b Give examples of quark 'flavours'.
c Why is the omega minus (which contains three strange quarks) a problem for the quark model if it lacks the property of colour?
d How does colour solve the problem?
e In what sense are all hadrons colourless?

18 **a** Suggest why mesons consisting of two up quarks or two down quarks do not exist.
b Write down all possible combinations of quark–antiquark pairs involving up, down or strange quarks.
c Identify these mesons and state the charge, baryon number and strangeness of each one.
d How can all of these be 'colourless'?

19 Draw Feynman diagrams to show:
a how two electrons interact and repel one another
b how a neutron and a proton may be bound together by exchanging charged or neutral pions
c how red and blue quarks can be bound together by the exchange of a virtual gluon.

8 Particle physics and cosmology

Opposites are complementary

Niels Bohr thought that quantum theory teaches us an important lesson about the physical world: opposites are sometimes complementary to one another. He developed this way of looking at things to explain how an electron might be viewed sometimes as a particle and sometimes as a wave even though the two models seem mutually exclusive. We come across a similar complementarity with particle physics and cosmology. At first sight it might seem that the fundamental nature of matter and its interactions (on a scale of 10^{-18} m or less) could not be farther removed from the large scale structure of the Universe (10^{26} m and more), but this is not so. The types of particles which are abundant in the Universe today were determined in the time immediately following the Big Bang, and the fate of the Universe may well be decided by the properties and varieties of these particles. Astronomical observations can help solve problems in particle physics (e.g. the number of particle generations) and measurements in particle physics can help solve problems in cosmology (e.g. a determination of the mass of the neutrino has a bearing on whether the Universe will eventually collapse or not).

Figure 8.1 Bohr and Einstein argued about the correct interpretation of quantum theory. Recent experiments have confirmed that Bohr's interpretation was right. His philosophy of complementarity underpins the traditional view of the theory. He included the motto 'opposites are complementary' in his family coat of arms.

THE BIG BANG AND COSMIC EXPANSION

A brief history of the Universe

In the beginning there was... well, we can't quite say yet, but physics does give an excellent account of the evolution of the Universe from about 10^{-20} s onwards. This is the standard view:

- Between ten and twenty billion (10^9) years ago the Universe was created in an incredible explosion called the **Big Bang**.

- This was no ordinary explosion. An ordinary explosion has matter flying out into *pre-existing* empty space. The Big Bang was the explosion of space, time and matter. It is wrong to think there was an empty Universe before the Big Bang and then, at some point and at some time our Universe burst into being. There was *nothing* before the Big Bang (probably not even a 'before', because time too is *part* of the Universe and comes into being with it).
- Immediately after the Big Bang matter and energy were confined in a tiny volume and all kinds of exotic high-energy events occurred continually.
- The energy of the explosion caused space to expand rapidly, and as it did so the matter it contained moved apart. This is the theory of the **expanding Universe**. It is better to think of this as the stretching of space rather than the movement of matter through fixed space (the whole idea of 'fixed space' doesn't work).
- The expanding Universe cooled, allowing matter as we know it to condense out and form atoms and molecules.
- Gravity shaped the large scale structure of the Universe by making clumps of above average density matter coalesce to form stars and galaxies and clusters of galaxies.
- We live on a planet orbiting a star in an arm of one galaxy among billions and as we look out into space we see other galaxies moving away from us as the Universe continues to expand and cool. We don't yet know enough about the matter in the Universe to say whether its mutual gravitation will be sufficient to make it re-collapse into a **Big Crunch** or whether it might continue expanding and cooling forever.

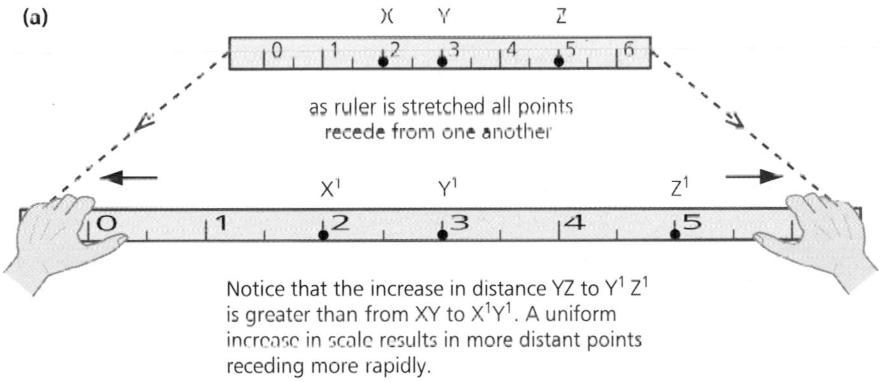
(a)
X Y Z
0 1 2 3 4 5 6
as ruler is stretched all points recede from one another
X¹ Y¹ Z¹
0 1 2 3 4 5
Notice that the increase in distance YZ to Y¹ Z¹ is greater than from XY to X¹Y¹. A uniform increase in scale results in more distant points receding more rapidly.

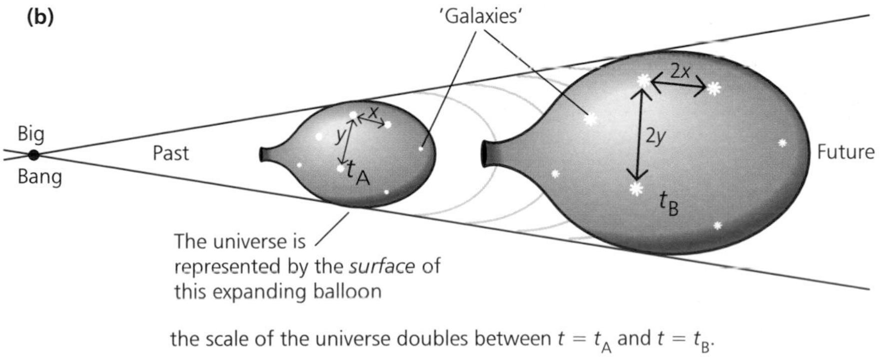
(b)
'Galaxies'
Big Bang
Past
x
y
tA
2x
2y
tB
Future
The universe is represented by the surface of this expanding balloon
the scale of the universe doubles between t = tA and t = tB.

Figure 8.2(a) As the Universe expands its scale increases and the distances between galaxies get larger. A very simple way to visualise this is to think of a stretchy ruler. The farther apart two points were to start with, the faster they recede from one another. This is just like the observed motions of galaxies in our Universe, they are moving apart and those farthest from us seem to be moving away most rapidly.
(b) The Universe is not expanding into empty space. Space itself is expanding and the galaxies move apart as the space between them stretches. Einstein's theory tells us that matter distorts the geometry of space and may even close space on itself like the closed surface of a sphere (but in more dimensions). If this is the case the Universe may be finite in size and yet have no edge or boundary. Its expansion can then be likened to the expansion of a balloon as it is inflated. The galaxies ride on the surface of the balloon.

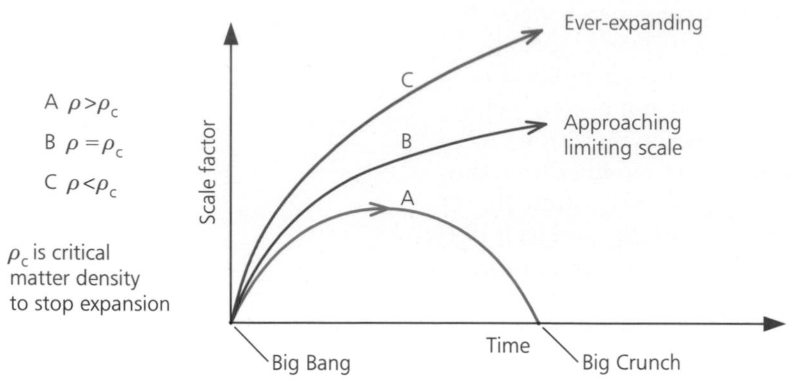

Figure 8.3 The expansion of the Universe is being slowed by the mutual gravitational attraction of all the things in it. Whether or not it will ever stop and re-collapse depends on the density of matter in the Universe . The matter observed in galaxies and so on, is not sufficient to halt the expansion but there is evidence that there is some form of '**dark matter**' which we have not yet detected. This may consist of new types of particle or exotic combinations of known types.

Evidence for the Big Bang

Although the expansion of the Universe follows quite naturally from Einstein's general theory of relativity it was discovered experimentally by Hubble and Slipher in the 1920s. Slipher was measuring the spectra of light emitted from different galaxies and noticed that the vast majority were red-shifted. Hubble was measuring the distances to galaxies and realised that greater red shifts correspond to greater distances. The conclusion was that galaxies are moving away from us at a rate that increases with distance.

Seen from the Earth it is as if we are at the centre of a great explosion. In fact it would look the same from *any* point, the Earth is not special in this respect. Think of the 'galaxies' painted on the expanding balloon in the diagram above. Whichever one of those galaxies you choose to look out from, the view is always the same, all the others are moving away, and the farther away they are the faster they recede from you.

Red shifts

The '*eeeeeeeeeaaawwwwwwhhh*' sound of a fast car passing is an example of the **Doppler effect**. Waves emitted by a source that moves toward us get compressed between the source and us, and the frequency we receive rises above the frequency of the source. If the source moves away the waves are stretched and the received frequency drops. This affects all types of wave, including electromagnetic waves. (The electromagnetic Doppler shift is often used to measure the velocity of a moving source or moving reflector – this is used by the police to catch speeding motorists and by astrophysicists to measure the rotation rate of the Sun or a planet.)

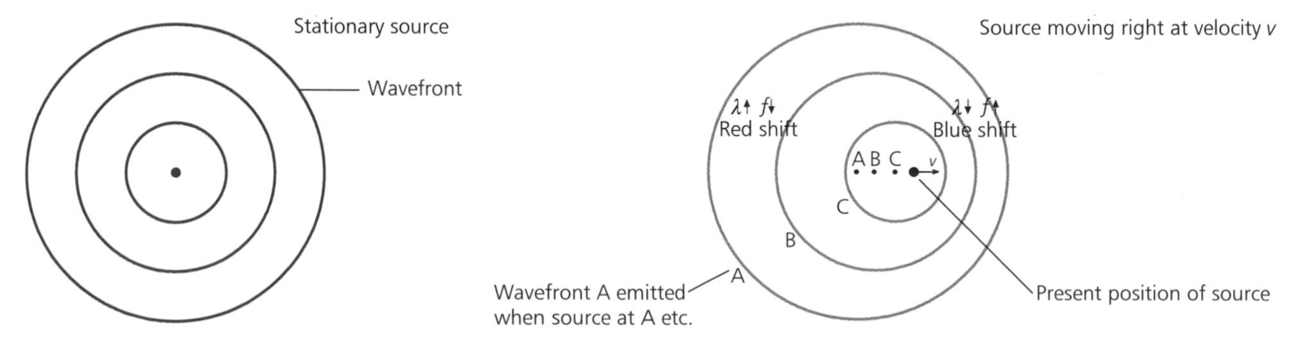

Figure 8.4 Successive wavefronts from a moving source are emitted from different positions. This affects their apparent frequency for a stationary observer.

The Doppler shift is also used to measure the recession velocities of distant galaxies. Electromagnetic waves that reach us from space carry the 'fingerprints' of the atoms that radiated them. They have a characteristic spectrum corresponding to the energy jumps in the radiating atoms. Prominent spectral lines in these spectra can be compared with spectra from similar atoms on Earth and identified. Slipher noticed that the spectral lines from galactic sources were almost all displaced toward longer wavelengths (hence the name 'red shift' because red is the longest wavelength in the visible spectrum). They had been stretched – this could be explained if the galaxies are all moving *away* from us.

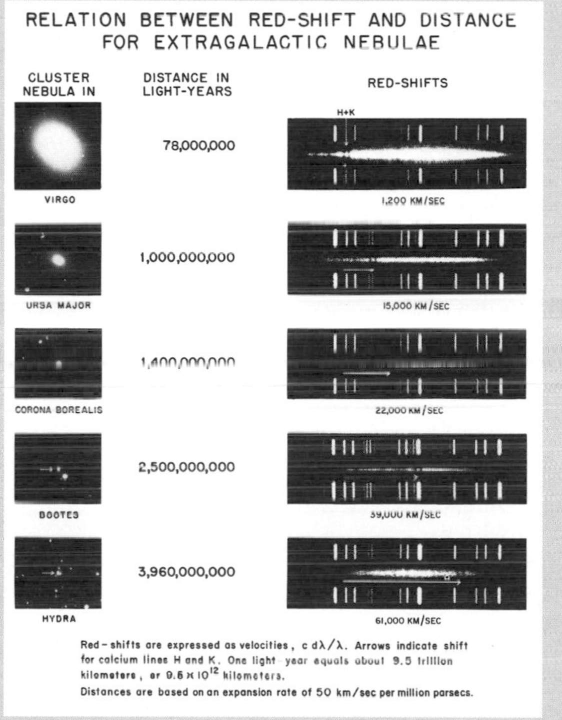

Figure 8.5 The distinct wavelengths emitted by a particular atom form a 'line spectrum'. The images show the galaxies as they are seen through a telescope and their spectra (these are the horizontal 'smears' between standard spectral markers). Within each spectrum the H and K lines (emitted by calcium ions) are easily identified. The more distant the galaxy, the further to the right (longer wavelengths, redder) these lines appear. The 'red shift' (indicated by the right facing arrows) are used to calculate the recession velocity v of the galaxy using the equation $\delta\lambda/\lambda = v/c$.

The recession velocity can be calculated from the red shift. Hubble showed that the recession velocities increase in direct proportion to the distance of the galaxy that emits them. This leads to the **Hubble law**:

$$v = H_0 d$$

v is recession velocity
H_0 is the Hubble constant
d is the distance of the galaxy

In principle this should allow us to calculate the age of the Universe. If the galaxies are moving apart now we can extrapolate back to a time when they were very close together, and ultimately to the moment of creation. Unfortunately the measurement of distances is fraught with difficulty and there are considerable uncertainties about the value of the Hubble constant. Most estimates place the Big Bang between ten and twenty billion years ago.

Although the red shifts can be explained in terms of the relative motion of galaxies this is misleading. The space between the galaxies is expanding and this stretches the waves that pass through it. The effect is the same but the interpretation different. Galactic red shifts are caused by the increase in *scale* of the Universe during the time the radiation takes to travel to us. In a sense the red shift is a measure of the age of the galaxy that transmitted the radiation, the greater the red shift the older the galaxy. The largest observed red shifts are from quasars, intense enigmatic energy sources that seem to have been much more common in the early Universe than now. Quasar PC1158+4635 has such a large red shift that the light we are now receiving must have left the quasar when the Universe was only about 25% of its present size. The farther out into space we look the farther back in time we see.

In 1964 Arno Penzias and Robert Wilson discovered a persistent microwave signal that seemed to be coming from all directions in space. The existence of this **background radiation** had been predicted by George Gamow and Ralph Alpher in 1948. It is the 'echo' of the Big Bang – thermal radiation that filled the early Universe and has been 'stretched' to longer and longer wavelengths as the Universe expanded. It has a spectrum characteristic of a hot body (black-body radiation) at a temperature of about 2.7 K.

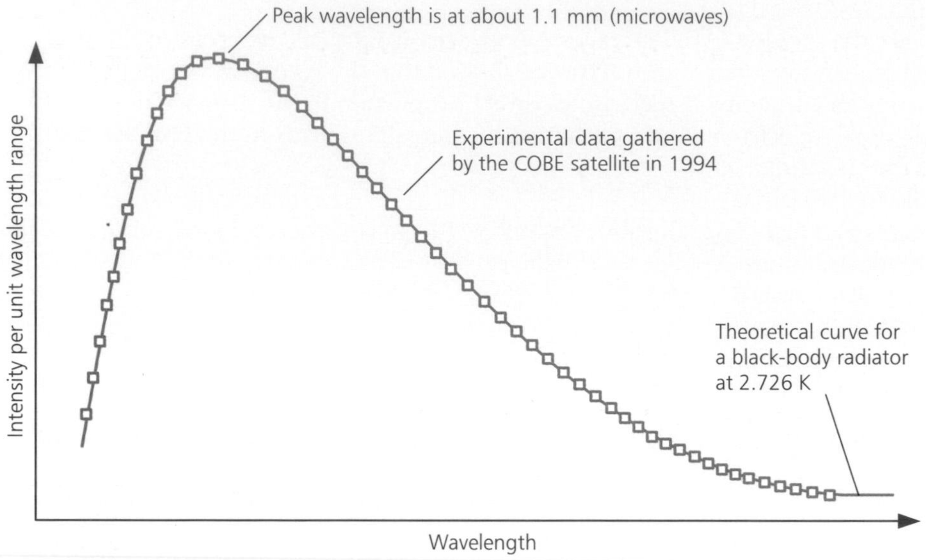

Figure 8.6 All warm bodies radiate. The higher their temperature the more high frequency radiation they emit. The background radiation spectrum closely fits the theoretical spectrum of an ideal black-body radiator.

Recent surveys of the background radiation have been made by the **COBE** (cosmic background explorer) satellite and these show that it is not quite equally intense in all directions. This is good news for the Big Bang theory because the distribution of radiation now tells us about the distribution of matter in the early Universe. If it was too uniform the galaxies would not have formed as we observe them, as small regions of higher or lower than average density are needed to act as 'gravitational centres' to begin the condensation of stars and galaxies.

Particles in the expanding Universe

The Big Bang was the ultimate particle physics 'experiment'. All the matter and energy of the entire Universe was compressed into a singularity which exploded with devastating power. As it expanded it cooled and different particles dominated different epochs.

Table 8.1

Time after Big Bang	Typical energy	Comments
$<10^{-20}$ s	$>10^5$ GeV	QUANTUM GRAVITY theory required to deal with very early Universe. Matter and antimatter annihilate but matter predominates (why?) This is called the 'baryon asymmetry'. At high energy the strong, weak and EM forces may be comparable in strength and unified.
10^{-20} s to 10^{-5} s	10^5 GeV to 10 GeV	QUARK–LEPTON ERA. Density of Universe far in excess of density of nuclei, so no 'ordinary matter' exists. High-energy collisions between quarks, leptons and gauge bosons continually convert particle/antiparticle pairs. W and Z particles involved in many interactions. e.g. $e^+ + e^- \rightarrow q + q^-$ Modern accelerators are able to test matter at the lower end of this energy range.
10^{-5} s to 10^{-2} s	10 GeV to 100 MeV	HADRON ERA Colour forces cause quarks to form hadrons: mesons and baryons form. Protons, neutrons and pions predominate. Collisions between these occur continually, and a balance between protons, neutrons and leptons is maintained e.g. $\pi^- + p^+ \rightarrow n + \rho^o$ (via strong interaction) $p^+ + e^- \rightarrow n + \nu_e$ (via weak interaction)

10^{-2} s to 10^2 s	100 MeV to 100 keV	HELIUM SYNTHESIS As the temperature drops protons and neutrons fuse to form deuterium and helium. The weak interactions which maintained the balance between protons and neutrons can no longer occur below about 200 keV so neutrinos 'decouple' from hadrons and the ratio of protons to neutrons is fixed at about 5 to 1. The present ratio of hydrogen to helium depends on this ratio.
10^2 s to 10^5 y	100 keV to 1 eV	PLASMA ERA A plasma is a gas of ionised particles. Until the Universe cooled to about 5000 K atoms could not form. Electrons, protons, deuterons and helium nuclei would bounce around and any atoms that did appear would be re-ionised by the sea of photons (about a billion for every proton) filling the Universe).
10^5 y to now (10^{10} y)	1 eV to 10^{-3} eV	THE OBSERVABLE UNIVERSE Atoms form. Atoms bind into molecules. Photons decouple from matter – this is the origin of the background radiation. It is thermal radiation from this era that has expanded and cooled with the Universe . Gravity forms stars and galaxies. Life evolves.

QUESTIONS OF SYMMETRY

Grand unification and broken symmetry

The mathematical models that describe the forces of Nature are based on a branch of mathematics called **group theory** and form a simple hierarchical structure.

- Electromagnetism acts on a *single* (N = 1) type of electric charge.
- The weak interaction changes the flavour of quarks and converts electrons to neutrinos. It acts on a quantity called 'weak isospin' which plays the same role as charge in electromagnetism but comes in *doublets* (N = 2). (The doublets in the quark–lepton symmetry are distinguished by different values of weak isospin).
- The strong force acts on colour charges which form *triplets* (N = 3).

The mathematical groups are called U(1), SU(2) and SU(3) respectively. In general a group with symmetry SU(N) will contain N different particles which can convert into one another by the exchange of gauge bosons (in the SU(N) symmetries there are $N^2 - 1$ gauge bosons). This is the link to the general theory of symmetry – conversion of one particle into another is like a rotation of a symmetric body that leaves it apparently unchanged.

Table 8.2

Symmetry	N	Acts on	$N^2 - 1$	Gauge bosons
U(1)	1	charge singlet	n/a	γ
SU(2)	2	weak isospin doublet	4 – 1 = 3	W^+ W^- Z^0
SU(3)	3	colour charge triplets	9 – 1 = 8	8 gluons

We have already noted that the colour force gets *weaker* at very high energies and short distances. This is also true of the weak force, though at a slower rate. Electromagnetism, on the other hand, gets *stronger* at very high energy. This means that the strengths of these forces may be similar at very high energy. The average particle energy we are talking about is 10^{15} GeV, the kind of energy that existed in the Universe about one billionth of a second after the Big Bang.

Group theory

Group theory is a very general branch of mathematics that describes symmetry operations. A very simple example involves an object with bilateral symmetry, e.g. a hand. A reflection of the hand is different from the original. However, a reflection of the reflection is the same as the original, so if the operation of reflection is repeated it is equivalent to doing nothing. We can describe this state of affairs by introducing two 'operators':

I is the 'do nothing' operator (identity)
R is the reflection operator.

A reflection of a reflection can be written: R.R and is equal to I.

All possible operations are summarised by:

I.I = I   I.R = R   R.I = R   R.R = I

These form a **closed set** since repeated operations continue to produce members of the original group.

Group theory is important in particle physics because the patterns of relationships between particles correspond to the properties of certain simple symmetry groups. This means that general predictions can be made about particle interactions simply from the symmetry of the corresponding groups.

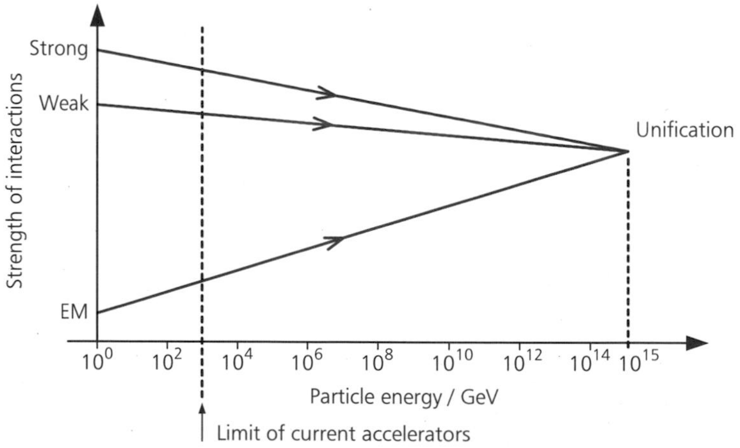

Figure 8.7 What we know about the forces of nature at present accelerator energies suggests that they may all have comparable strength at particle energies of about 10^{15} GeV. If this is the case the separate forces we observe may result from a broken symmetry in some 'super-force'. (Extrapolating from present energies the lines do not actually meet at a point; however, if the effects of supersymmetric particles are added, they do.)

This raises the intriguing possibility that the forces of nature were completely symmetric in the very early Universe and the distinctions in strength and action we now see came about when this symmetry was broken by the expansion and cooling of the Universe. This idea of **spontaneous symmetry breaking** is familiar from other branches of physics. The atomic magnets in a piece of hot iron are randomly oriented, but when the iron cools they align to form domains with well-defined local symmetries. The molecular orientations in a liquid are random but when the liquid cools crystals form. By analogy we can regard the spontaneous symmetry breaking in the early Universe as a kind of *phase change*.

Taking the argument further we can try to construct mathematical models by combining the symmetries of the individual interactions into a higher order symmetry or grand unified theory. The unification of the electromagnetic and weak interactions into a single electroweak theory is a perfect example of this – its mathematics belongs to a symmetry group formed by combining the groups that separately describe electromagnetism and the weak interaction: SU(2) × U(1).

Inevitably these higher order theories predict the existence of more force-carrying particles (SU(5) for example is a combination of U(1), SU(2) and SU(3) and predicts the existence of $5^2 - 1 = 24$ force-carrying particles). The new particles must *do* something, so new phenomena are predicted. In particular some particles will be able to convert quarks to leptons and vice versa. This means that the proton should decay to a meson and a lepton as one quark converts to a positron by the exchange of a new particle.

$$\mathbf{p^+ \rightarrow e^+ + \pi^o}$$

$$Q \quad 1 = \quad 1 + 0$$

$$L \quad 0 \neq -1 + 0$$

$$B \quad 1 \neq \quad 0 + 0$$

This is an example of an interaction that *does not* conserve baryon number or lepton number. However, if the conjectures about unification are correct this should happen at very high energy and would have been common in the early Universe .

The extremely high energy at which this symmetry applies means the force carrying gauge bosons are very massive and so have extremely short range (about 10^{-29} m). This in turn makes the probability of this kind of decay very small and the lifetime of the proton very long indeed (we know it is at least 10^{32} years).

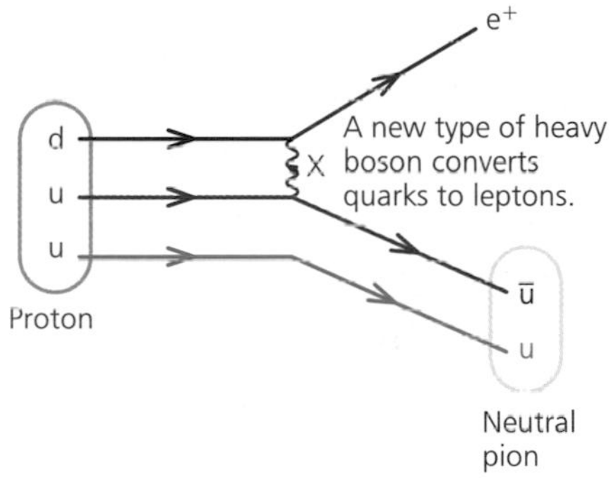

Figure 8.8 Unlike neutron decay, in which a quark changes its flavour, proton decay requires the conversion of a quark to a lepton – no known interaction allows this.

What happened to all the antimatter?

There is another asymmetry that seems to have established itself very early on in the evolving Universe. There is a shortage of antimatter. If the laws of physics are symmetric with respect to matter and antimatter we should have expected equal amounts of each to be produced in the Big Bang. These would then have annihilated to leave the Universe dominated by the photons created in the annihilation. However, this is not what we see in the Universe today. We are certainly surrounded by photons – there are over a billion photons per baryon as far as we can tell, but all the baryons seem to be *matter* rather than antimatter.

The evidence from space is that the Big Bang produced a slight surplus of matter over antimatter. When the original matter and antimatter annihilated, perhaps 10^{-33} s after the Big Bang, this surplus was left over. The background radiation we detect today is mainly the red shifted remnant of the gamma rays emitted in the annihilation of the rest of the matter and antimatter.

The origin of the original asymmetry is still uncertain. It is thought to originate in the asymmetric decay of exotic high-energy particles present in the early Universe. Exactly why this asymmetry occurs is unclear but it is probably related to the peculiar behaviour of the uncharged kaons and their antikaons. These too show a slight asymmetry between the behaviour of matter and antimatter (see box).

K^0 is not just strange it's peculiar!

The neutral kaon and its antiparticle can decay in corresponding ways:

$$\mathbf{K^0 \rightarrow e^+ + \pi^- + \nu_e}$$
$$\mathbf{\overline{K^0} \rightarrow e^- + \pi^+ + \bar{\nu}_e}$$

The K^0-bar decay is the direct antimatter equivalent of the K^0 decay so if there is complete symmetry between matter and antimatter these decays should occur at the same rate. However, the observed rates are slightly different, the matter decay being about 0.7% more frequent. The remaining kaons decay to pi-plus/pi-minus pairs.

This remarkable result could be a clue to the way the Big Bang might create equal numbers of particles and antiparticles which then decay to give a small preponderance of matter over antimatter.The idea is illustrated using a simplified example involving a hypothetical 'N-particle' which can decay either to a quark or an antilepton:

Matter decays:	$\mathbf{N \rightarrow q}$	**or**	$\mathbf{N \rightarrow \bar{l}}$
Antimatter decays:	$\mathbf{\bar{N} \rightarrow \bar{q}}$	**or**	$\mathbf{\bar{N} \rightarrow l}$

Think of 100 N and $\bar{N}$ particles created from high-energy photons in the Big Bang. If both matter and antimatter decay by each mechanism at equal rates this will produce 50 quark/antiquark pairs and 50 lepton/antilepton pairs. These will annihilate completely to photons. However, if the N decays more frequently to quarks than to leptons (say in a ratio 60:40) and yet the $\bar{N}$ decays equally to either then a preponderance of matter over antimatter results:

60 quarks and 40 antileptons from N decays.
50 antiquarks and 50 leptons from $\bar{N}$ decays.
After annihilation to photons 10 quarks and 10 leptons remain.

Note that two things are necessary for this to be possible – an interaction that does not conserve baryon or lepton numbers (involving our hypothetical N particles), and an asymmetry between matter and antimatter.

The technical name for the symmetry which is violated by the anomalous kaon decays is **CP-violation** (charge-parity violation). CP symmetry requires the laws of physics to give the same results if all charges are reversed and all particle coordinates change sign. This seems to hold for everything except the neutral kaon decays (sometimes) and the Universe as a whole. Is there a connection? (If time reversal is added to a CP transformation the resulting CPT symmetry does hold. So far no observed particle events have ever violated CPT symmetry.)

STARS

Nucleosynthesis

Where did the variety of elements around us come from? This is a serious question, because the Big Bang doesn't provide much more than hydrogen and helium. One second after the Big Bang the Universe had cooled sufficiently for protons and deuterons to form. By three minutes pretty well all the neutrons available would have been packed into helium nuclei by fusion reactions. Predictions based on particle interactions in the early Universe give a ratio of about nine protons to every one helium nucleus. This agrees pretty well with the ratio calculated from observation.

Deuteron formation:

$$\mathbf{{}^{1}_{0}n + {}^{1}_{1}p^{+} \rightarrow {}^{2}_{1}H + {}^{0}_{0}}\gamma$$

Helium formation:

$$\text{(i)} \quad \mathbf{{}^{2}_{1}H + {}^{2}_{1}H \rightarrow {}^{3}_{2}He + {}^{1}_{0}n}$$

$$\text{(ii)} \quad \mathbf{{}^{3}_{2}He + {}^{2}_{1}H \rightarrow {}^{4}_{2}He + {}^{1}_{0}n}$$

The unusually high binding energy per nucleon of helium (relative to adjacent nuclei) and the absence of stable nuclei with $A = 5$ or $A = 8$ meant that little else was produced. The Universe then continued to cool until the charged nuclei could hold onto electrons to form hydrogen and helium atoms.

The heavier elements were also produced by nuclear fusion, but later, in stars. The temperature and pressure at the centre of a star is sufficient to fuse protons and eventually form helium. The big problem with fusion is getting protons or nuclei close enough so that the strong force can overcome electrical repulsion. The centres of stars are hot but they are not that hot. The fact that fusion reactions happen there relies on a peculiar quantum property that allows particles that are almost close enough to fuse to '**tunnel**' through a potential barrier and fuse anyway (see page 122). Hydrogen is converted to helium by two different cycles, the proton cycle (which dominates in lower main sequence stars like our Sun) and the carbon cycle (which occurs in upper main sequence stars). In both cycles the net effect is the conversion of four protons to a helium nucleus.

The proton cycle:

$$\mathbf{{}^{1}_{1}p^{+} + {}^{1}_{1}p^{+} \rightarrow {}^{2}_{1}H + {}^{1}_{0}e^{+} + {}^{0}_{0}}\nu$$

$$\mathbf{{}^{1}_{1}p^{+} + {}^{2}_{1}H \rightarrow {}^{3}_{2}He + {}^{0}_{0}}\gamma$$

$$\mathbf{{}^{3}_{2}He + {}^{3}_{2}He \rightarrow {}^{4}_{2}He + {}^{1}_{1}p^{+} + {}^{1}_{1}p^{+}}$$

The carbon cycle:

$$\mathbf{{}^{1}_{1}p^{+} + {}^{12}_{6}C \rightarrow {}^{13}_{7}N}$$

$$\mathbf{{}^{13}_{7}N \rightarrow {}^{13}_{6}C + {}^{0}_{1}e^{+}\ {}^{0}_{0}}\nu \mathbf{\ + {}^{0}_{0}}\gamma$$

$$\mathbf{{}^{1}_{1}p^{+} + {}^{13}_{6}C \rightarrow {}^{14}_{7}N + {}^{0}_{0}}\gamma$$

$$\mathbf{{}^{1}_{1}p^{+} + {}^{14}_{7}N \rightarrow {}^{15}_{8}O}$$

$$\mathbf{{}^{15}_{8}O \rightarrow {}^{15}_{7}N + {}^{0}_{1}e^{+} + {}^{0}_{0}}\nu$$

$$\mathbf{{}^{1}_{1}p^{+} + {}^{15}_{7}N \rightarrow {}^{12}_{6}C + {}^{4}_{2}He + {}^{0}_{0}}\gamma$$

The proton and carbon cycles were originally proposed by Hans Bethe in the1930s. The proton cycle releases about 25 MeV of thermal energy for every four protons fused to helium and our Sun consumes about 600 tonnes of hydrogen per second in its core. It also releases neutrinos (two for each helium nucleus) and these can be detected (with difficulty) here on Earth. This opens up a new field of neutrino astronomy and gives us a way of monitoring and measuring solar nuclear reactions. Bethe worked out the details of the proton cycle to relieve the boredom of a long train journey.

The quantum tunnel effect

A fast moving roller coaster can climb to the top of a steep hill and descend the other side without any additional power input (figure 8.9(a)). It does this by converting some of its kinetic energy to gravitational potential energy on the way up and converting it back again on the far side of the hill. If it approaches the hill too slowly (figure 8.9(b)) its kinetic energy will be insufficient to get it over the hill, it will rise part way up the slope, slow to a stop and roll back again. We can illustrate this on a graph showing how the car's potential energy varies with position over the hill.

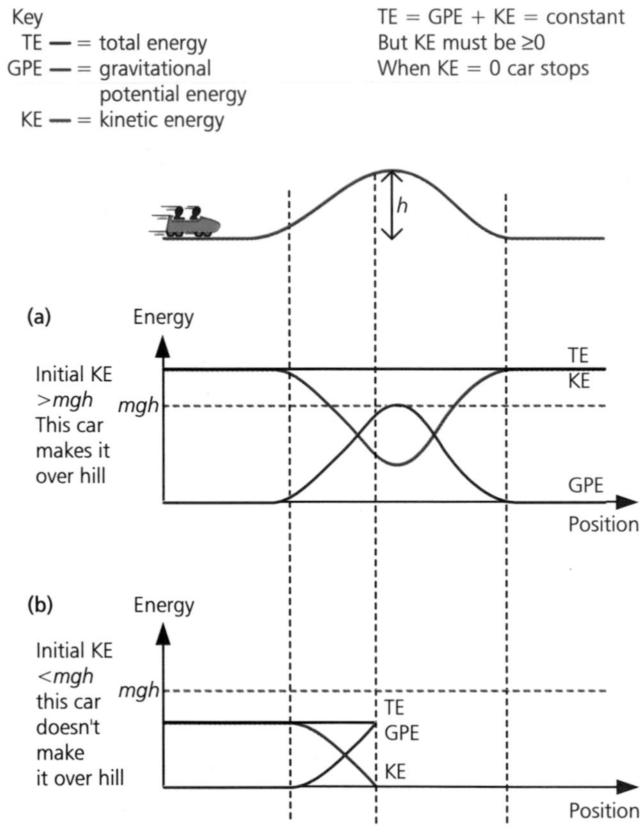

Figure 8.9

From the graph the condition that the car passes this potential energy hill is:

$$\text{KE} > mgh$$

where h is the height of the hill.

In a similar way the condition for two nuclei to fuse involves an **activation energy** that gets the nuclei past their own electrical potential energy hill. As the nuclei approach *they do work* against the repulsive forces from their positive charges – this stores electrical potential energy in the field between them and reduces their own kinetic energies. However, as they get closer together the strong force begins to attract them and this does work *on* them increasing their total potential energy. If they have enough initial kinetic energy they can pass over the potential energy hill created by electrostatic repulsion and fuse by the strong force.

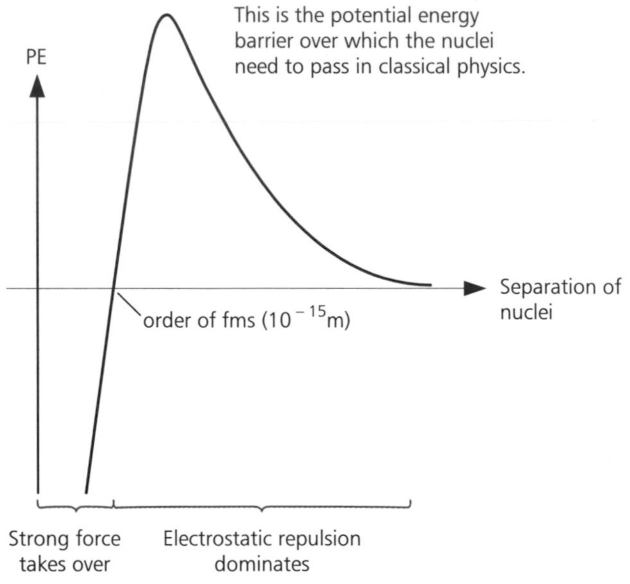

Figure 8.10

The size of the potential energy hill can be calculated. This tells us how hot a plasma of nuclei should be for fusion to occur. If we do the calculation for proton–proton fusion we get an answer much hotter than the core of the Sun (where this sort of fusion takes place quite readily). What has gone wrong?

The problem is that we have treated protons like billiard balls when we should have treated them as quantum mechanical entities. The quantum theory of a proton describes it as a **wavefunction** whose intensity is related to the probability of finding the proton at any particular place. Since the wavefunction is spread out in space there is a chance that the proton is found anywhere within the wave (which could in principle mean anywhere in the Universe, but which in practice usually gives significant probabilities only over a small region of space). When two protons collide with a little less than the energy needed to scale the potential barrier their wavefunctions decay into the barrier so that there is a small but finite chance of finding the proton on the far side of the barrier even though they do not have enough energy to pass over it. Classically this could not happen because they 'pass through' a region where their kinetic energy would be negative! This is why the process is called the **tunnel effect**.

The tunnel effect allows nuclear fusion to occur at a lower temperature. The centre of the Sun is thought to be at less than 15 million kelvin whereas conventional collisions would require a temperature of several billion kelvin to sustain nuclear fusion. Even so, only about 1 in 10^{26} proton–proton collisions result in fusion to deuterium! The tunnel effect is also responsible for alpha decay – alpha particles formed inside a large unstable nucleus tunnel out and escape – and it is used in many electronic devices (e.g. the tunnel diode).

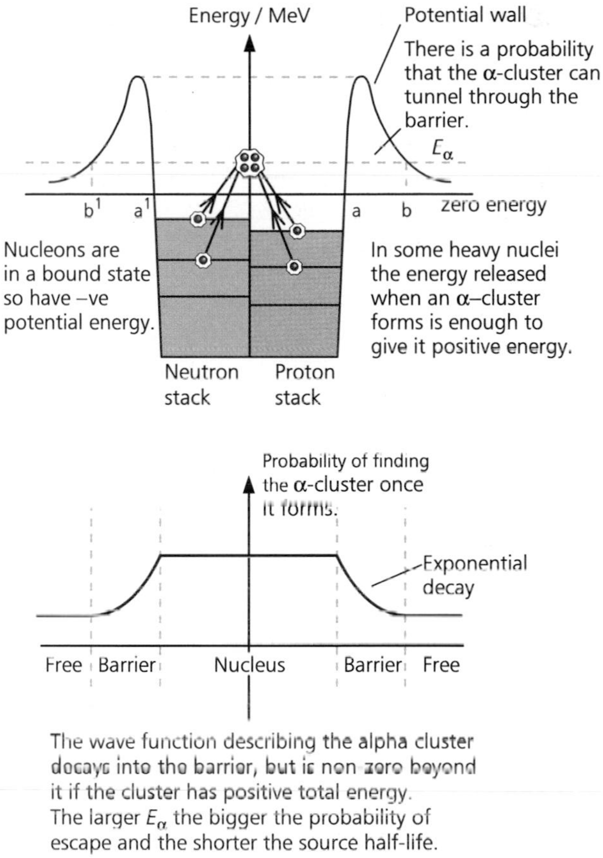

Figure 8.11 Alpha decay was a problem for physicists in the early part of the twentieth century. The energy of emitted alpha particles is far less than the peak energy of the nuclear potential barrier. For uranium the barrier height is about 30 MeV but the emitted alpha particles have about 4 MeV. This is like having a wall around a garden that appears 30 m high from the outside but can be scaled using a 4 m ladder from the inside. George Gamow solved the problem – alpha particles tunnel out!

The Sun converts hydrogen to helium, but these were both produced in the Big Bang anyway, so this still fails to explain where the other elements come from. Once stars have consumed most of their hydrogen fuel they begin to collapse under the force of their own gravity. What happens next will depend on the star's mass, but in all cases the temperature and pressure in the stellar core increase as the star collapses. It may become intense enough to re-ignite nuclear fusion and fuse helium to create carbon and oxygen. The star then bursts back into life.

This collapse as fuel is used up, and the initiation of more complex fusion reactions, may be repeated several times producing all the heavier nuclei up to iron. Then it stops. Iron has the greatest binding energy per nucleon in the Periodic Table so no more energy will be released by fusing iron nuclei. A star that reaches this point is about to explode as a **supernova**. Its collapse becomes catastrophic and the energy that is suddenly available from gravitational potential energy pays for the endothermic production of heavier nuclei. A great pressure of radiation and neutrinos from nuclear reactions builds up and the star explodes, briefly glowing brighter than an entire galaxy and blasting its outer layers (and a periodic tableful of elements) out into space.

The core, meanwhile, continues to collapse. The pressure becomes so great that the remaining heavier nuclei are broken up until all that remains are protons, neutrons and electrons. The electrons are forced into the protons to form more neutrons and a **neutron star** is formed. If it is very massive it continues to collapse; even the neutrons are crushed by gravity and eventually a **black hole** is formed.

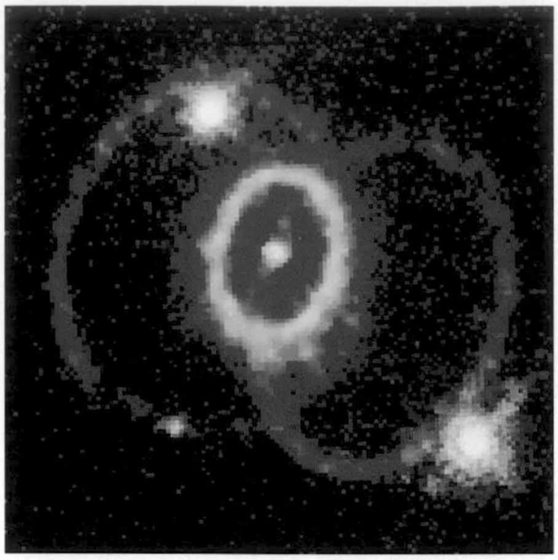

Figure 8.12 Supernova 1987A announced its arrival by a blast of neutrinos followed by an enormous increase in visible intensity (exactly as predicted by theory). The supernova is 169 000 light years away, and lies in the dwarf galaxy called the Large Magellanic Cloud, which can be seen from the southern hemisphere.

The solar neutrino problem

The nuclear reactions taking place in the Sun release large numbers of neutrinos (one for each proton that converts to a neutron). By monitoring the neutrino flux here on Earth we can study the electroweak interaction under the conditions at the centre of a star. This gives us a way to test our models of stellar physics. Although the proton cycle generates most of the solar neutrinos, higher energy neutrinos are produced in some of the rarer reactions that produce heavier nuclei (these occur alongside the dominant helium producing reactions). The first experiments to detect solar neutrinos relied on the neutrinos emitted when beryllium-7, an unstable isotope, captures a proton to become boron-8. This is a very rare event since the proton and nucleus must overcome a high energy barrier to fuse and it is estimated to occur only once for every 5000 helium nuclei produced in the proton cycle.

$$^{3}_{2}\mathrm{He} + ^{4}_{2}\mathrm{He} \rightarrow ^{7}_{4}\mathrm{Be} + ^{0}_{0}\gamma$$

$$^{7}_{4}\mathrm{Be} + ^{1}_{1}\mathrm{p}^{+} \rightarrow ^{8}_{5}\mathrm{B} + ^{0}_{0}\gamma$$

$$^{8}_{5}\mathrm{B} \rightarrow ^{8}_{4}\mathrm{Be} + ^{0}_{1}\mathrm{e}^{+} + ^{0}_{0}\nu_{e}$$

The experiments carried out to date all have one thing in common – they all detect too few neutrinos. Proportions vary from one experiment to another but only about one third of the expected neutrino flux is detected. Originally this polarised opinions in physics and astronomy. Physicists asked whether our model of solar reactions is accurate while astronomers wondered whether our knowledge of neutrino physics is good enough. Nowadays we have great confidence in our model of solar fusion reactions and the answer to the riddle of the missing solar neutrinos is expected to come from particle physics.

One suggestion is that the neutrinos oscillate between electron-, muon- and tau-neutrinos so that the flux of electron-neutrinos at the Earth (our detectors only register the electron-neutrinos) is only a third of the total flux. If this is correct it has important implications. In the Standard Model this kind of oscillation can only occur with *massive* particles. If the neutrinos do have a rest mass then this has a bearing on cosmology: they could contribute significantly to the 'missing mass' and may even tip the balance between an ever-expanding Universe and one that eventually collapses.

Detecting solar neutrinos

Neutrinos interact weakly with matter, so huge detectors containing hundreds or thousands of tonnes of material are needed to detect them. The detectors must also be shielded from cosmic rays so that the neutrino interactions stand out from the background. The first solar neutrino experiment was set up in 1962 by the chemist Raymond Davis using an underground tank filled with 600 tonnes of a dry cleaning fluid called perchloroethylene in a gold mine in South Dakota. The reason for this strange choice of material is that about a quarter of the chlorine atoms in perchloroethylene are the isotope chlorine-37, which captures neutrinos to become argon-37. The captured neutrino converts a neutron to a proton in the chlorine-37 nucleus.

$$^{0}_{0}\nu_{e} + ^{37}_{17}\mathrm{Cl} \rightarrow ^{37}_{18}\mathrm{Ar} + ^{0}_{-1}\mathrm{e}^{-}$$

This is not the only way to look for neutrinos. A Japanese experiment (Kamiokande II) detects the Čerenkov radiation from electrons scattered by high-energy neutrinos in 680 tonnes of ultra-pure water. Experiments in Russia (SAGE, Soviet American Gallium Experiment) and Italy (Gallex) detect low-energy proton-cycle neutrinos when they collide with large gallium detectors in underground chambers. The fact that these experiments also show a lack of solar neutrinos emphasises the importance of this problem.

The Sudbury Neutrino Observatory (SNO) in Canada is using yet another approach. It captures neutrinos in a thousand tonnes of heavy water (D_2O) when they scatter a proton and neutron from deuterium. This is a 'neutral current' interaction (the proton and neutron are not changed in the process) and allows the experimenters to measure the energies of individual neutrinos. This is a crucial extra piece of information because the shape of the energy spectrum (according to the Standard Model) should be independent of the actual flux. If the SNO results give a different energy spectrum it will suggest problems with neutrino physics in the Standard Model.

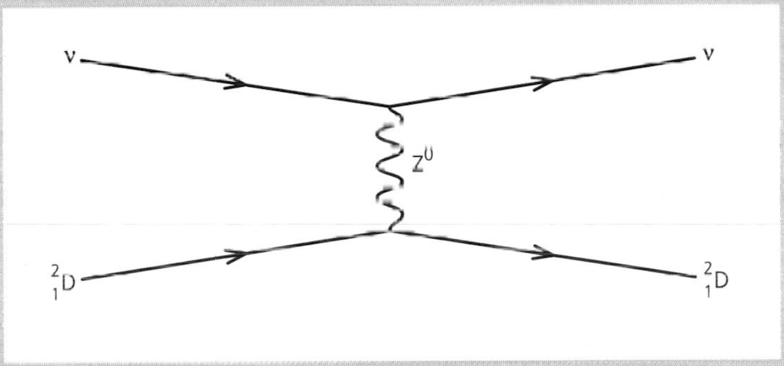

Figure 8.13 Neutral current events involve the exchange of a Z^0 and leave the nature of the interacting particles unchanged.

Looking for neutrino oscillations – the CHORUS experiment

At CERN muon-neutrino beams are produced by bombarding a beryllium target with high-energy protons from the Super Proton Synchroton (SPS). Many other particles are also created but these can easily be blocked by solid material that has virtually no effect on the muon-neutrinos. The 'beam' diverges as it leaves the collision site and is the order of a metre across when it passes through the CHORUS experiment. (One interesting point is that other experiments are set up in series along the beam since the vast majority of muon-neutrinos will pass through all of them!) The purpose of CHORUS is to look for evidence of tau-particles produced from the decay of energetic tau-neutrinos. The key part of the detector is a photographic emulsion which can resolve particle tracks with a resolution of 1 μm (the tau particles would leave a track of about 100 μm before decaying to a muon and associated neutrinos). The emulsion is exposed to the muon-neutrino beam for two years before being developed. If tau-particles are present the tau-neutrinos that produced them can only have come from the muon-neutrinos – this would be strong evidence for neutrino oscillations. A positive result would imply that neutrinos do have mass and that the missing solar neutrinos have changed to other 'flavours' after leaving the Sun.

Dark matter problems

It is not just neutrinos that are missing – astronomers can only detect about one tenth of the matter predicted by their favoured Big Bang models. On top of this, models for the structure and formation of galaxies require a halo of matter about ten times as massive as the galaxies themselves. A third problem is that the large scale structure of the Universe cannot be adequately explained by the observed amount of ordinary baryonic matter (i.e. protons and neutrons). These three puzzles may all be solved by the discovery of one type of **dark matter** ('dark' in the sense that we do not see it) or they may each require a different solution.

The Big Bang theory predicts the observed proportions of hydrogen and helium very accurately. It also predicts the total amount of baryonic matter that should be present. This prediction is about *ten times* the observed amount and suggests that the massive halos around galaxies might be almost entirely hydrogen and helium, but in what form? The clue is that the matter is dark, it does not radiate significantly. The leading candidates for **baryonic cold dark matter** must be small gravitationally bound objects like brown dwarf stars and planets. These are not massive enough to ignite hydrogen fusion at their cores and so will be virtually invisible. The Hubble Space Telescope is the ideal observatory for testing this theory and is being used by several research groups to count the numbers of faint stars in galaxies. Recent surveys (1996) have discovered brown dwarfs in our galaxy, but it is not clear whether there are enough to account for the mystery of the missing baryonic mass.

On a larger scale a lot of baryonic matter could be locked up in dark dwarf galaxies whose low intensity in the night sky makes them rather hard to detect. Recent surveys have found these in large numbers, but not nearly sufficient to account for the missing mass.

One further possibility is that the mass is spread very thinly in near invisible gas clouds that are kept ionised by photons from star-forming galaxies and quasars. This gas would have to be at a temperature of about 10^4 to 10^5 K so it is too hot to radiate with the characteristic 21 cm hydrogen line and yet not hot enough to emit X-rays. On the cosmic scale there are further problems. The observed motions of galaxies imply the existence of more mass than the upper limit of baryonic matter predicted by the Big Bang. This may be due to massive neutrinos or other as yet unsuspected forms of matter.

Conjectures and refutations?

The next generation of accelerators was supposed to begin with the construction of the Superconducting Super Collider (SSC) in a 53 mile long tunnel at a site south of Dallas USA. Construction did start, but then Congress withdrew funding and the project has been abandoned. It seems unlikely that anyone will now build such an enormous machine, at least in the near future (CERN's LHC will run in the existing 27 km LEP tunnel). This means that particle physics faces a very difficult and frustrating time. Present accelerators will be tweaked and tuned to get the last giga-electronvolt of particle energy, and exciting new results *will* continue to emerge. But it is likely to be a time of diminishing returns. There are tantalising clues to the way our present theories may be unified and there are exciting unanswered questions about the fundamental nature of matter and its bearing on the past and future history of the Universe, but we may not be able to carry out the experiments that will answer them.

The philosopher Karl Popper said that science progresses by bold conjectures that are tested by experiments that could (in principle) refute them. We may be entering a period when our conjectures are so bold that they cannot be tested simply because the experimental techniques are beyond our power or budget. If incorrect theories cannot be refuted by experiment we may have to fall back on Dirac's criterion and let the beauty of the mathematics persuade us what theory to adopt or reject – or maybe some new Rutherford will come along and show us how to keep probing into the very heart of the matter.

SUMMARY

- The current scientific view of the creation of the Universe has everything (space, time and matter) coming into being in an explosion called the **Big Bang**. Since the explosion space has continued to expand, carrying matter with it and increasing the scale of the Universe.
- The Doppler shift causes light from a receding source to be 'shifted' to the red end of the spectrum. These **red shifts** can be used to measure the rate at which distant galaxies are moving away from the Earth, and provided important early evidence for the Big Bang theory.
- Further evidence for the Big Bang theory comes from the microwave **background radiation** – thermal radiation that filled the early Universe and which has 'stretched' to longer wavelengths as the Universe has expanded.
- At the high energies existing immediately after the birth of the Universe, the four interactions may have been completely symmetric. If this is the case it leads to the important prediction that protons may decay to pions and positrons. It also predicts that the proton lifetime is extremely large. This is consistent with our existing knowledge of the proton.
- The predominance of matter over antimatter in our Universe is thought to come from the asymmetric decay of particles in the early Universe, leading to the production of more matter than antimatter.
- Interactions in the early Universe produced matter predominantly in the form of hydrogen and helium. Heavier elements have been produced by the process of **nuclear fusion in stars**.
- Under certain conditions, subatomic particles may tunnel through a potential energy barrier rather than having to pass over it. The probability of this occurring is only significant over very small regions of space – when two particles collide, for example. Tunnelling explains why protons can fuse in the centre of the Sun, even though its temperature is lower than required for this to happen in theory.
- The neutrino flux from the nuclear reactions in the Sun is less than that predicted by models. One possible explanation for this is that neutrinos oscillate between electron-, muon- and tau-neutrinos. If this is so, neutrinos have a rest mass, and may then contribute to some of the missing mass of the Universe.

QUESTIONS

1 **a** How can observational astronomy help to test theories in particle physics?
b How can experiments in accelerators help to settle questions of cosmology?

2 Galaxy A has a red shift of 0.2 whilst galaxy B has a redshift of 0.6.
a What do you conclude about the magnitude and direction of the velocities of these two galaxies relative to the Earth?
b Which galaxy is farther from the Earth? (Explain what assumption lies behind your answer).
c What is the Hubble law and why does it suggest that the Universe came into being in a hot Big Bang?
d Accelerators on Earth can reach energies of about 1 TeV (10^{12} eV). At this energy many interesting and exotic reactions take place. How long after the Big Bang would these reactions have stopped happening?

3 **a** The Sun emits a great flux of neutrinos into space. What are the reactions that create these neutrinos?
b What is the 'solar neutrino problem'?
c What are the physical principles behind the detection of neutrinos?

4 **a** What is meant by red shift?
b What information can we get from the red shift of a distant galaxy?
c Give two ways in which the red shift of a galaxy might arise. Which of these is thought to be responsible for most of the red shifts we observe?
d A few galaxies have blue shifts, how do these arise?

5 **a** What is the microwave background radiation?
b It is an almost black body spectrum – what does this tell you about the state of the Universe when radiation decoupled from matter?
c Why did astronomers expect to detect fluctuations in the intensity of the background radiation from different parts of the sky?
d Detectors designed to pick up the background radiation must be cooled to very low temperatures, why?

6 Why were there no atoms in the very early Universe?

7 What conservation laws would be violated if a proton decayed to positron and a neutral pion?

8 Explain why elements up to iron are created by nuclear fusion reactions inside stars whereas heavier elements are only created in violent supernova explosions.

9 The net effect of fusion reactions in the Sun is to fuse four protons to form one helium nucleus and two positrons, releasing a great deal of energy in the process.
a What other particles must also be emitted?
b What will happen to the positrons?
c Explain why it is highly unlikely that the reaction described above would happen in one go.
d How *are* protons fused to form helium in the Sun?
e Why will these fusion reactions eventually stop?
f What do you think will happen to the Sun when they do stop?

9 Nuclear power

A NEW SOURCE OF ENERGY?

When Einstein published the mass–energy equation, $E = mc^2$, in 1905 he ended by saying that the theory might explain the origin of the energy emitted by radioactive materials. He was thinking in particular of radium. Radium-226 emits alpha particles of energy 4.78 MeV and has a half-life of 1622 years. A quick calculation shows that the energy released by the decay of all the atoms in 1 kg of radium is enormous:

$$\textbf{Number of atoms in 1 kg of Ra-226} = \frac{1000\text{ g}}{226\text{ g}} \times 6.0 \times 10^{23} = 2.7 \times 10^{24}$$

$$\textbf{Energy release} = 2.7 \times 10^{24} \times 4.78 \times 10^{6} \times 1.6 \times 10^{-19}\text{ J} = 2.1 \times 10^{12}\text{ J}$$

This is roughly equivalent to the energy released when 70 000 kg of coal is burnt! Why the big difference?

Radioactive decay is a nuclear reaction whereas combustion is a chemical reaction. Nuclear reactions involve the rearrangement of nucleons which are very tightly bound particles (by the strong nuclear force over a range of about 10^{-15} m) whereas chemical reactions involve the rearrangement of outer electrons which are relatively weakly bound (by electromagnetic forces at a distance of about 10^{-10} m). For comparison, the average binding energy per nucleon for radium-226 is 7.5 MeV whereas the first ionisation energy for carbon (as in coal) is a mere 11 eV.

In *both* cases the energy released (as kinetic energy of the emitted alpha particles or excited molecules) is at the expense of a reduction in rest mass of the remaining particles and can be calculated from Einstein's equation. However, the mass change in a chemical reaction is always absolutely tiny (and so neglected) whereas the mass change in a nuclear reaction (though small) is measurable (by comparing the masses of the reactant and products).

At first sight it looks as if radioactive sources could be a wonderful new energy resource, but there is a problem. The half-life of the source is independent of external conditions so we cannot control the rate at which this nuclear energy is released. A quick calculation shows that the power generated by 1 kg of radium-226 is rather unremarkable.

$$\textbf{Decay equation:} \quad N = N_o e^{-\lambda t}$$

$$\textbf{Rate of decay} = \textbf{Activity} = -\frac{dN}{dt} = \lambda N_o e^{-\lambda t}$$

$$\textbf{Initial activity} = \lambda N_o = \frac{N_o \ln 2}{t_{\frac{1}{2}}} = \frac{2.7 \times 10^{24} \ln 2}{1622 \times 3.16 \times 10^{7}\text{s}} = 3.7 \times 10^{13}\text{ s}^{-1} \text{ (Bq)}$$

$$\textbf{Power of source} = 3.7 \times 10^{13}\text{ s}^{-1} \times 4.78 \times 10^{6} \times 1.6 \times 10^{-19}\text{ J} = 28.3\text{ W}$$

On the other hand the combustion rate of coal can be controlled. If a furnace burns coal at a rate of 1 kg s^{-1} its output power is about 30 MW!

'Moonshine' and a chain reaction

In 1919 Rutherford was first to split the atom, but in 1933 he said that, '*The energy produced by the breaking down of the atom is a very poor kind of thing. Anyone who expects a source of power from the transformation of these atoms is talking moonshine*.' Although individual nuclei can be split in violent collisions, the process does not continue spontaneously (unlike chemical combustion, where the energy release from bond formation enables more bond-forming collisions to occur) so only a tiny amount of the available energy can be released in any reasonably short time. But Rutherford was wrong – there *is* a way to 'burn' nuclear fuel, but it was not discovered during his lifetime.

Rutherford died in 1937, two years before Hahn, Strassmann and Meitner discovered that uranium nuclei can be split when they are bombarded by neutrons. This process is called **nuclear fission** and as well as creating two new daughter nuclei it *emits neutrons*. In 1939 Otto Frisch (Meitner's nephew) was the first to recognise the significance of this. If these neutrons could induce fission in other uranium nuclei a **chain reaction** might be possible in which a significant proportion of the nuclei undergo fission in a short period of time. A **nuclear chain reaction** transfers a great deal of nuclear energy to kinetic energy in the fission fragments – about 200 MeV per fission. Released uncontrollably it is a weapon of mass destruction (the 'atom bomb'); released in a controlled way it is the energy source in the core of all thermal nuclear reactors (generating about 25% of the electricity in England and Wales and about 50% in Scotland).

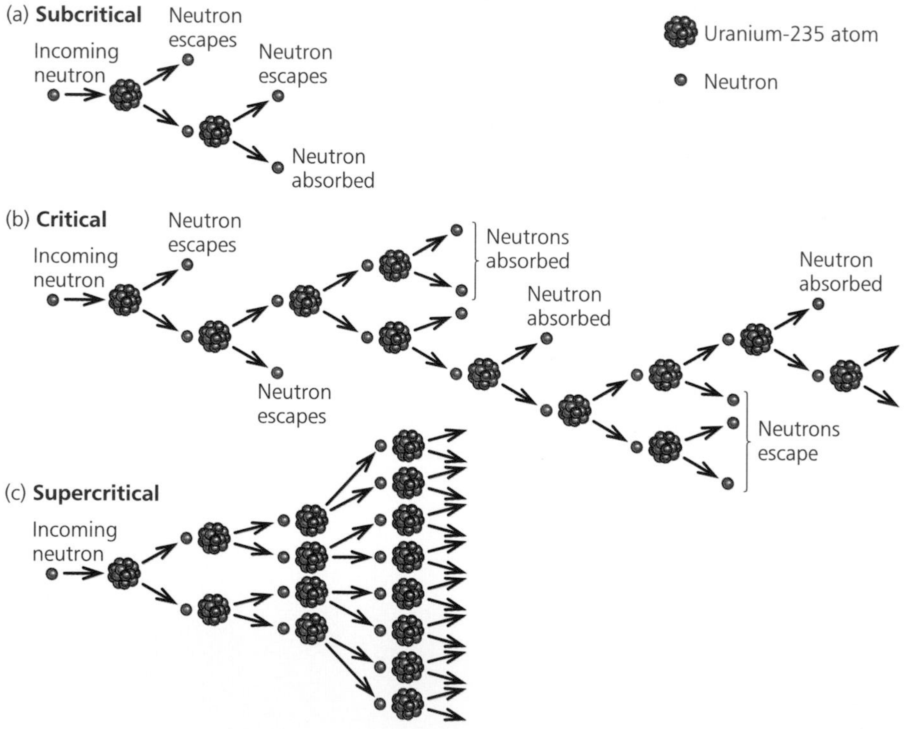

Figure 9.1 Fast neutrons have velocities close to the speed of light and the distance between atoms is a few times 10^{-10} m, so the time between 'generations' of fission reactions in the chain reaction is tiny (even in a reactor where the neutrons must undergo several collisions with a moderator before inducing another fission).

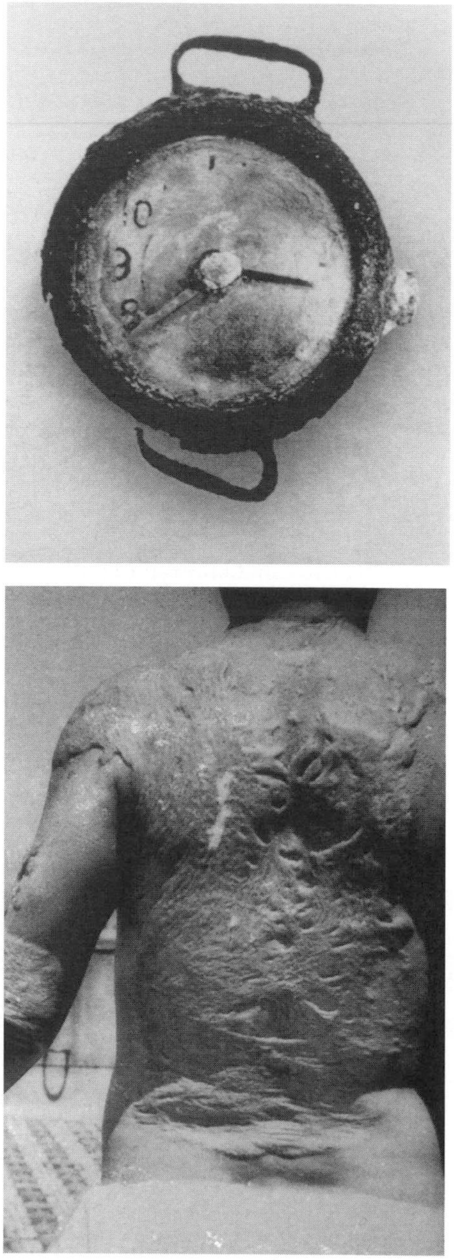

Figure 9.2 The first atom bomb used in conflict was dropped from the US bomber the Enola Gay on 6 August 1945. It released as much energy as the explosion of about 20 000 tonnes of TNT. This Hiroshima clock stopped at 8.15 am, the moment of the explosion. The bomb killed 140 000 people by the end of 1945 and a further 60 000 from wounds or radiation sickness by 1950.

Nuclear binding energy

Nucleons are bound together by the strong nuclear force. To break a nucleus into separate nucleons we would have to pull against this force to separate them. This transfers energy to the nucleons. The conclusion is that the nucleus itself has less rest mass and less rest energy than the sum of rest masses or energies of its constituent nucleons when they are free particles. This explains why the nucleons are bound in the nucleus – they do not have enough energy to escape. The difference between the mass of the nucleons in a particular nucleus (as free particles) and the nucleus itself is called the **mass defect**, and the energy equivalent to this mass is the **binding energy** of the nucleus. Oxygen-16 is used as an example below.

Figure 9.3 The Sellafield: the domed building is the prototype gas-cooled reactor (now inoperative).

$^{16}_{8}O$ nucleus contains 8 protons and 8 neutrons
mass of 8 protons = $8 \times 1.007276\,u = 8.058208\,u$
mass of 8 neutrons = $8 \times 1.008665\,u = 8.069320\,u$
total mass of free nucleons = $16.127528\,u$

mass of $^{16}_{8}O$ nucleus = $15.994915\,u$

mass defect = $\Delta m = 0.132613\,u$
binding energy BE = $\Delta m \times 931.5\,MeV = 123.5\,MeV$

It is very important to realise that binding energy is not an energy that the nucleus has, it is the energy that would need to be supplied to it to split it into completely separate nucleons.

To compare nuclei it is better to look at the **binding energy per nucleon** rather than the total binding energy (which increases roughly in proportion to nucleon number, *A*). For oxygen-16 this is about 5.6 MeV per nucleon. The graph below shows the variation of binding energy per nucleon for the elements. These are recorded as negative values to emphasise that the nucleons are in a lower energy state inside the nucleus than as free particles (where their energy is zero by definition).

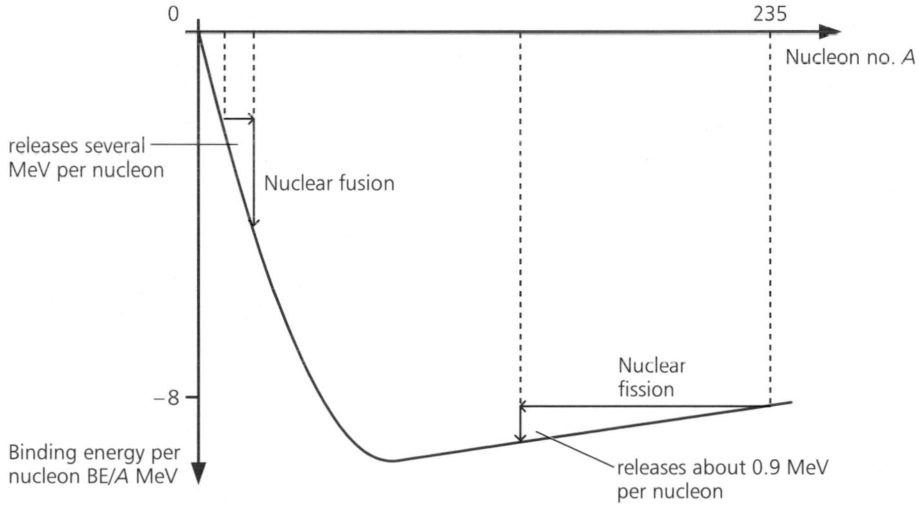

Figure 9.4 A graph of binding energy per nucleon versus nucleon number.

The most important thing to notice here is that as *A* increases the magnitude of binding energy per nucleon increases until we reach iron-56 and then it reduces. This means that if there is some way to convert a heavy nucleus into two smaller nuclei the nucleons will all go into lower potential energy states and the difference in energy will be released (as kinetic energy of the new nuclei and any other ejected particles). Nuclear fission does just this.

On the other hand, energy can also be released if light nuclei can be fused to form heavy nuclei, this is nuclear fusion. Fusion reactions in the centres of stars generate all their energy and are responsible for the creation of nuclei of elements heavier than hydrogen. They are also used in the 'hydrogen bomb'.

Nuclear fission

Nuclei of fissile elements may undergo spontaneous fission, but this is rare and reactors and bombs both depend on the induced fissions that occur when nuclei are struck by neutrons. One such reaction for U-235 is shown below:

$$^{1}_{0}\mathrm{n} + ^{235}_{92}\mathrm{U} \rightarrow ^{148}_{57}\mathrm{La} + ^{85}_{35}\mathrm{Br} + 3^{1}_{0}\mathrm{n}$$

The total rest mass of the reactants is 236.1 u.
The rest mass of the products is 235.9 u.
The mass defect for the reaction is 0.2 u.
This means that the kinetic energy to be shared between the two daughter nuclei and three neutrons is the energy equivalent of 0.2 u.
Energy released in this fission reaction = $0.2 \times 931.5\,\mathrm{MeV} \approx 200\,\mathrm{MeV}$.

The charged liquid drop model of the nucleus (see pages 71–2) is helpful in understanding the mechanism of nuclear fission and the origin of the energy released. When a nucleus of U-235 absorbs a neutron it goes into a metastable (temporary) state of U-236. This nucleus 'wobbles' about, rather like a drop hanging on the end of a dripping tap before it breaks off and falls. As it wobbles it will contort into various shapes, some of which will be like two smaller nuclei separated by a narrow 'neck' of nucleons. The binding energy per nucleon curve shows that these smaller nuclei are more strongly bound than the original nucleus so it is likely that the U-236 nucleus will break apart when it reaches this point and form two new daughter nuclei. It may also eject some neutrons. It is unlikely to eject protons because the ratio of neutrons to protons for stable heavy elements is greater than for stable light elements, so the daughter nuclei are likely to be neutron rich anyway.

When the U-236 is spherical the nucleons will be bound to one another by the strong force and this will be stronger than the repulsion of proton pairs. However, as the nucleus stretches into its 'hourglass' shape just prior to fission the two 'bulbs' that will become the daughter nuclei have moved away from one another so that the strong attraction between them is less significant. The strong force drops off much more rapidly than electrostatic forces, so there is a point at which the electrostatic repulsion between the two 'bulbs' will continue to drive them apart, giving them the kinetic energy that we want

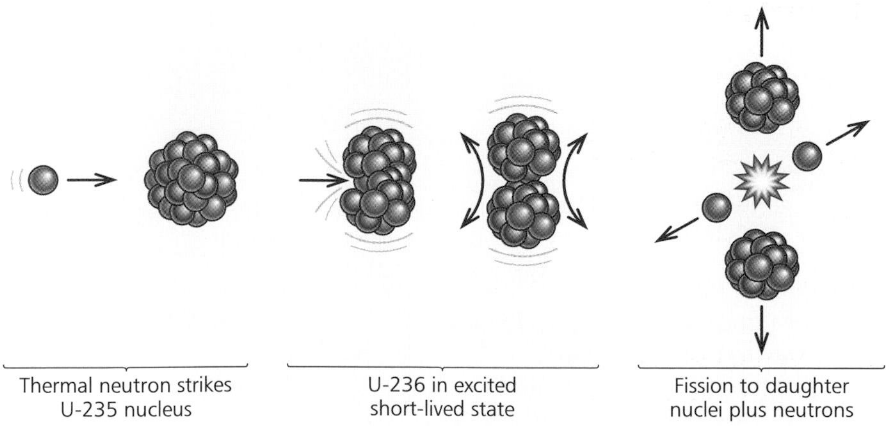
Thermal neutron strikes U-235 nucleus
U-236 in excited short-lived state
Fission to daughter nuclei plus neutrons

Figure 9.5 Nuclear fission can be modelled as the break up of a charged liquid drop. As the 'drop' oscillates it reaches a point at which the electrostatic repulsion of the two daughter nuclei is sufficient to drive them apart.

from the fission reaction. To see if this model is reasonable we can carry out a simple calculation to work out the kinetic energy gained by two nuclei of roughly half the size of U-236 if they start off in contact and spring apart under the sole influence of the electrostatic repulsion between their positive charges.

A nucleus of $A = 236/2 = 118$ and $Z = 92/2 = 46$ would have a radius of roughly $r = r_0 A^{\frac{1}{3}} = 10^{-15}\,\text{m} \times 118^{\frac{1}{3}} \approx 4.9 \times 10^{-15}\,\text{m}$

The separation of two such nuclei in contact is about 10^{-14} m.

Their total electrostatic potential energy is given by

$$\text{EPE} = \frac{q_1 q_2}{4\pi\varepsilon_0 d} = \frac{(4.6 \times 1.6 \times 10^{-19}\,\text{C})^2}{4\pi \times 8.9 \times 10^{-12}\,\text{F m}^{-1} \times 10^{-14}\,\text{m}^2} = 4.8 \times 10^{-11}\,\text{J} \approx 300\,\text{MeV}$$

This is a bit larger than the actual energy release per fission (about 200 MeV) but is certainly of the right order of magnitude. The discrepancy may be because it is incorrect to completely discount the work done against the strong force from this point on.

Fuel consumption

If we take an average value of 200 MeV per fission we can estimate the rate of consumption of nuclear fuel in a 500 MW nuclear power station. The first thing to realise is that if the electrical output power is 500 MW then the rate of production of thermal energy in the core must be much greater than this (because the process is necessarily inefficient). A reasonable estimate of the efficiency of the reactor is 33%, so the fuel must be generating thermal energy at a rate of 1500 MW

Power generated by fission = 1500 MW

Energy release per fission = 200 MeV = 3.2×10^{-11} J

$$\text{Number of fissions per second} = \frac{1.5 \times 10^9\,\text{W}}{3.2 \times 10^{-11}\,\text{J}} = 4.7 \times 10^{19}\,\text{s}^{-1}$$

Mass of U-235 consumed per second

$$= \frac{0.235\,\text{kg}}{6.0 \times 10^{23}} \times 4.7 \times 10^{19}\,\text{s}^{-1} = 1.8 \times 10^{-5}\,\text{kg s}^{-1}$$

Assume that the U-235 content in the fuel is enriched to 3%. The total rate of consumption of uranium will then be:

$$\frac{100}{3} \times 1.8 \times 10^{-5}\,\text{kg s}^{-1} = 6.1 \times 10^{-4}\,\text{kg s}^{-1}$$

In one year this will amount to about 20 tonnes of uranium.

For comparison, coal releases about $2.5 \times 10^7\,\text{J kg}^{-1}$, so to generate 1500 MW would require the consumption of coal at a rate of about:

$$\frac{1.5 \times 10^9\,\text{W}}{2.5 \times 10^7\,\text{J}} = 60\,\text{kg s}^{-1}$$

In one year this will amount to about 2 million tonnes of coal – about 10^5 times greater!

The quantities of waste products from the two processes will be in a similar ratio and this must be taken into account when considering potential environmental impact.

Building the bomb

At the end of the 1930s Germany was the most advanced nation in nuclear physics research and the allies feared that Hitler's secret weapon might be a nuclear weapon (it turned out to be a rocket, but there are still doubts about the role of prominent German scientists such as Heisenberg in helping or obstructing research into nuclear weapons). Einstein himself was persuaded to write to President Roosevelt in 1939 and 1940 to urge him to take this threat seriously and to start a secret research project to develop a nuclear capability. This led to the Manhattan Project based at Los Alamos in the New Mexico Desert which was led by the physicist Robert Oppenheimer and the US Army General Leslie Groves. It was the biggest single research project in history and resulted in the bombs that flattened the Japanese cities of Hiroshima and Nagasaki killing more than 150 000 people at the time, and many more since (as a result of immediate exposure and later contamination by radioactive fallout).

The Hiroshima bomb contained two sub-critical masses of U-235 that were fired together by a chemical explosive detonator to make a super-critical mass in which the chain reaction grew exponentially, releasing an energy equivalent to the explosion of about 20 kilotonnes of TNT. The Nagasaki device was different in two important respects. It used plutonium instead of U-235 and detonated it by compressing a sphere of plutonium using shaped chemical explosives placed around it. (This squeezes the plutonium into a smaller volume and reduces its surface area, making it super-critical.) This was also equivalent to about 20 kilotonnes of TNT.

A critical assembly

There is a very simple condition that must be satisfied if a chain reaction is to grow: each nucleus that fissions in one generation must lead to more than one fission in the next. This will happen if, on average, more than one neutron emitted per fission goes on to induce fission in another nucleus. When a large nucleus like uranium splits it can do so in many ways, to produce a wide variety of daughter nuclei (this is one of the reasons spent nuclear fuel is difficult to deal with – it contains a cocktail of radioactive elements). Each possible fission results in two new daughter nuclei and may release one or more fast neutrons. The average number of neutrons released per uranium nucleus is about 2.5 and at least one of these must induce fission otherwise the reaction will die away. The problem faced in producing a self-sustaining nuclear chain reaction is to select fuel and arrange it in such a way that this can occur. An arrangement in which exactly one neutron per fission goes on to induce another fission is called a critical assembly.

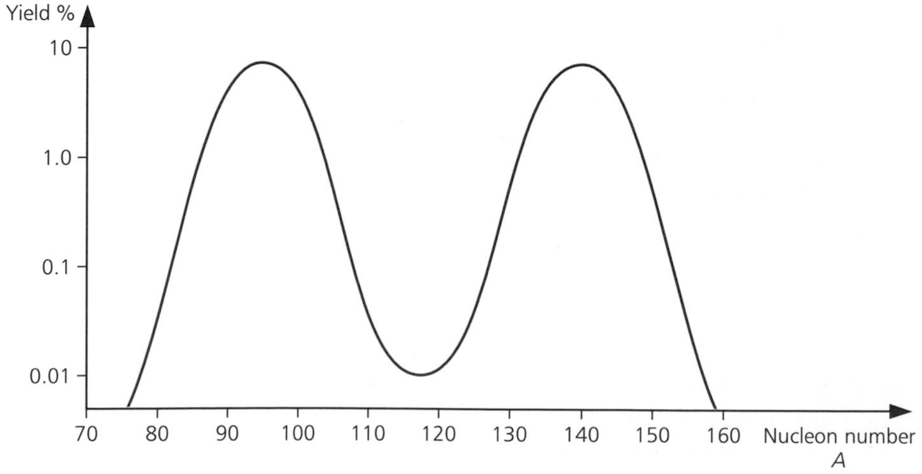

Figure 9.6 Distribution of nuclei produced by thermal neutron fission of U-235.

To understand what makes a critical assembly we must look at what might happen to the neutrons emitted in fission:

- they may induce fission in another nucleus
- they may be absorbed by another nucleus without causing fission
- they may be lost from the surface of the material.

We need to enhance the probability of fission and reduce the probability of absorption and loss, so it is worth looking at each of these in more detail.

Natural uranium consists almost entirely of two isotopes, uranium-238 (99.3%) and uranium-235 (0.7%). If a fast neutron hits U-238 there is a small probability that it fissions and a larger probability that it absorbs the neutron and (after two beta decays) transforms to plutonium.

$${}^{1}_{0}\mathrm{n} + {}^{238}_{92}\mathrm{U} \rightarrow {}^{239}_{92}\mathrm{U}$$

$${}^{239}_{92}\mathrm{U} \rightarrow {}^{239}_{93}\mathrm{Np} + {}^{0}_{-1}\beta^{-}$$

$${}^{239}_{93}\mathrm{Np} \rightarrow {}^{239}_{94}\mathrm{Pu} + {}^{0}_{-1}\beta^{-}$$

(The reprocessing of nuclear fuel is primarily to remove the plutonium which is itself fissionable and is used in nuclear weapons and reactors.) Other elements are also neutron absorbers, so their use must be minimised in the reactor core (unless they are used to control the reaction rate).

U-235 is more readily fissionable, but the probability of fission increases significantly if the neutrons are slow rather than fast. If the neutrons are slowed down so that their kinetic energy is comparable with the mean kinetic energy of particles at the surrounding temperature they are called **thermal neutrons**.

These considerations suggest three strategies to increase the chance of fission and reduce the chance of absorption:

- enrich the nuclear fuel by increasing the proportion of U-235
- slow down the fast neutrons emitted in fission reactions and use thermal neutrons
- avoid the use of neutron absorbing elements in fuel rods and reactor structure.

None of these affects the loss of neutrons from the surface of the reactor core or explosive. However, the rate of neutrons produced depends on the volume of fuel whereas the rate of loss depends on its surface area. The surface area depends on the square of length whereas the volume depends on its cube, so increasing the linear dimensions will reduce the proportion of neutrons lost from the surface. Any particular geometry will therefore have a critical mass at which a chain reaction will grow. The geometry with the smallest surface area to volume ratio is a sphere, so the critical mass is smallest for this arrangement. With U-235 the critical mass is a few kilograms and the sphere is about the size of a grapefruit. Its explosive power is equivalent to about 20 000 tonnes of TNT (a powerful chemical explosive). One further way to reduce the effect of neutron losses is to surround the assembly with a neutron reflector so that the neutrons leaving the surface will be sent back into the fuel and be given a second chance to induce fission. So we have two more rules of thumb:

- reduce the surface area to volume ratio of the reacting core
- surround the core with neutron-reflecting material.

NUCLEAR REACTORS

A thermal nuclear reactor

The only major respect in which the generation of electricity from a nuclear power station differs from the generation in a fossil-fuelled power station is in the way the thermal energy is generated. The thermal energy is then used to raise steam to drive turbines and generators. This is why they are called thermal reactors – they transfer nuclear energy to thermal energy in the reactor core and it also means that their overall efficiency is limited by the laws of thermodynamics in the same way as a fossil-fuelled power station. The most important aspect of this is that the maximum theoretical efficiency of any heat engine (which is basically what a power station is – a device that extracts work from heat) is limited by the range of temperatures between which it operates. Efficiency is increased if the core temperature is higher and the exhaust temperature lower. So in addition to building a critical assembly it would be nice to make it a *hot* critical assembly!

A fission bomb depends on an uncontrolled chain reaction that grows exponentially. A reactor for electricity must achieve a chain reaction that is balanced so that every fission results in exactly one more fission so that the reaction rate is constant. It must also be controllable, so that it can be switched off rapidly if something goes wrong, and there must be a means of extracting the thermal energy from the core so that it can be used to raise steam to drive the turbogenerators. The core will also need to be shielded to protect personnel and the environment from the intense radiation. There are a number of different designs for thermal nuclear reactors, but they all do basically the same thing, although they may achieve this using different materials. Figure 9.7 shows a Pressurised Water Reactor, the most common reactor type in the world.

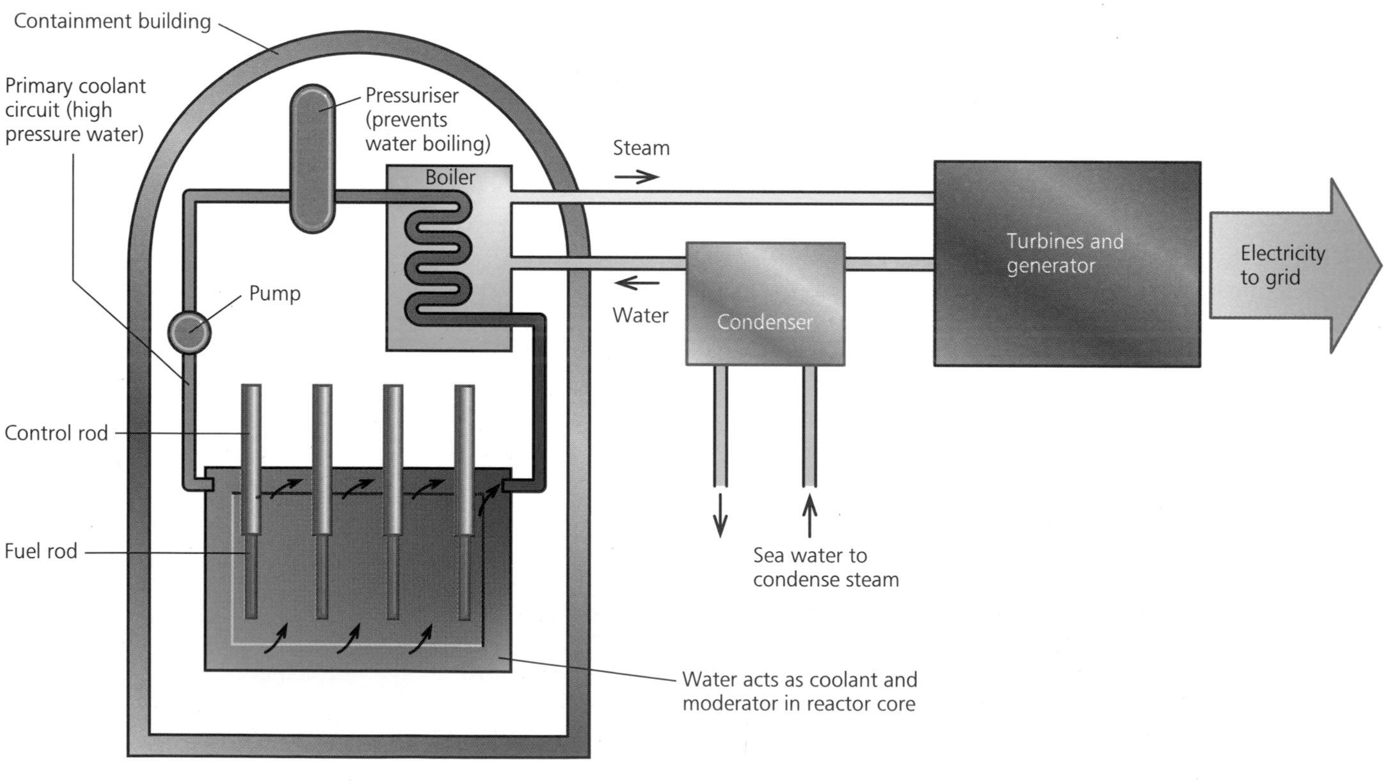

Figure 9.7 A Pressurised Water Reactor (PWR).

There are five essential components of any thermal nuclear reactor.

Fuel

The fissionable nuclei are usually U-235, but Pu-239 is used in experimental 'fast reactors' and to enrich the fuel in some thermal reactors. The early British 'Magnox' reactors used natural uranium, but most other designs use enriched uranium oxide because it has a higher melting point and so the reactor core temperature can be higher leading to greater overall efficiency (the nuclear properties of U-235 are not affected by the fact that the uranium atoms are in a chemical compound). 'Enriched fuel' means that it has an artificially increased amount of the isotope U-235 (or Pu-239), the enrichment usually being between 2% and 4%. The fuel is assembled in pellets which are arranged into fuel rods that can be inserted through tubes in the reactor core, and can be removed and replaced when they become depleted in U-235.

Figure 9.8 Loading a nuclear fuel rod with pellets of uranium oxide. One AGR/PWR fuel pellet is roughly equivalent to one and a quarter tonnes of coal.

Moderator

The core of the reactor is filled with a material whose job is to slow down the fast neutrons and make them into thermal neutrons. It is essential that this material is not a strong neutron absorber, and it is desirable that it has a small atomic mass number. This ensures that more of an incident neutron's momentum is transferred to a nucleus of the moderator as the neutron bounces off it (think of what happens when a table tennis ball bounces off a large ball-bearing compared to when it bounces off another table tennis ball). Various materials have been used: carbon (graphite in Magnox reactors), carbon dioxide (in Advanced Gas Cooled Reactors, AGRs), heavy water (in Canadian CANDU reactors) and light (normal) water in PWRs. Fast neutrons from fission in one of the fuel rods will undergo several collisions with nuclei in the moderator before passing through another fuel rod and inducing fission.

Control rods

A chain reaction can be 'switched off' if the neutron flux in the core is reduced so that less than one neutron per fission goes on to induce further fission reactions. To achieve this, neutron-absorbing control rods are inserted into tubes that pass through the reactor core. Suitable materials are boron or cadmium, both of which have nuclei with a large capture cross-section for neutrons (i.e. if a neutron goes near a nucleus it is likely to be absorbed). Raising the control rods increases the reaction rate and lowering them reduces it. If there is a problem in the core (e.g. a loss of coolant leading to a rapidly increasing core temperature) they are automatically lowered to shut down the reactor.

Coolant

A fluid is pumped through the reactor core to extract thermal energy from it. When the reactor is running at a steady rate the power extracted by the coolant equals the power generated by the fuel so the core temperature remains constant. Water is usually used as a coolant (although AGRs use carbon dioxide and some fast reactors use liquid sodium). Backup systems are also in place in case the primary coolant fails. This is important because a loss of coolant leads to a rapidly increasing core temperature that could cause the fuel rods and core to go into meltdown.

Containment and biological shielding

The arrangement of a thermal nuclear reactor is different from a bomb and even a meltdown (when loss of coolant allows the core to overheat and melt) will not create the intense conditions needed for a nuclear explosion. However, if something does go wrong the temperature will rise and chemical explosions are likely. The biggest danger is that a chemical explosion will breach the reactor walls and eject large quantities of highly radioactive waste into the atmosphere (as happened at Chernobyl in 1986). To prevent this there are many fail-safe systems employed to shut down the reactor quickly if anything unusual happens, but the last line of defence is a steel pressure vessel that surrounds the core and a thick layer of concrete to absorb neutrons and gamma rays from within.

Cross-sections

If 100 small coins are dropped at random onto a large chess board about half will fall into a black square. This is because exactly half the cross-sectional area of the board is black – the probability of landing on a black square is directly related to the *area* of blackness. A similar idea is used to measure the probability of events occurring when subatomic particles collide.

If a neutron strikes a nucleus it may be absorbed by the nucleus or it may pass through it. If 50% of incident neutrons passing close to a particular nucleus are absorbed we say that its **neutron capture cross-section** is half its geometric cross-section. Since the nuclear diameter is about 10^{-14} m, capture cross-sections are usually of the order of 10^{-28} m^2 (this is called a 'barn' as in barn door!) Capture cross-sections vary from a small fraction of a barn (if the nucleus is 'transparent' to neutrons) up to many barns (if the nucleus captures neutrons that would actually miss it). A particular nucleus will have different cross-sections for different processes – absorption, fission, inelastic scattering etc. and these will depend on the incident neutron energy. For example, the fission cross-section for U-235 increases about 1000 times if the energy of the incident neutrons is reduced from about 2 MeV (fast neutrons from nuclear fission) to about 0.1 eV (thermal neutrons). The neutron capture cross-section for U-238 also increases when the neutrons are slowed down, but by a much smaller amount, so using a moderator to slow the neutrons tips the balance in favour of fission.

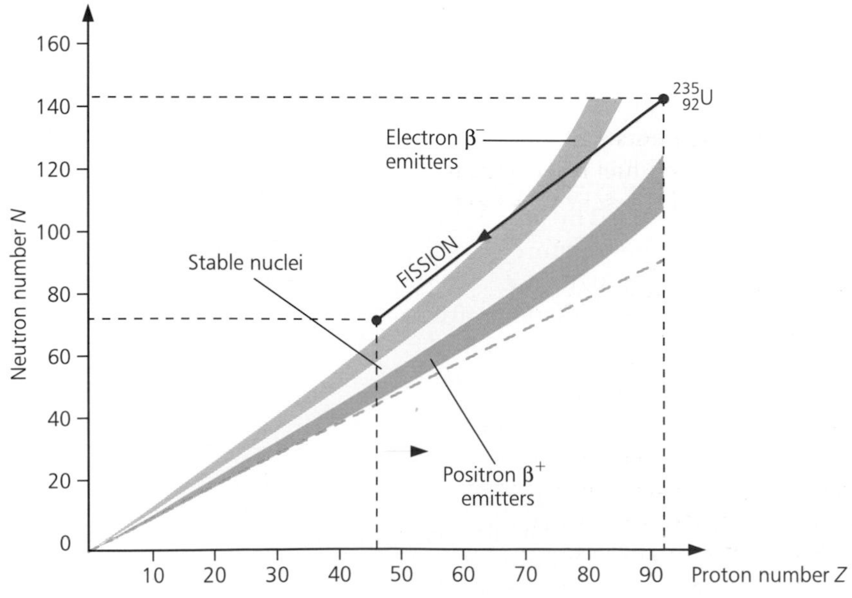

Figure 9.9 Light nuclei have equal numbers of protons and neutrons but heavy nuclei have an excess of neutrons.

Reprocessing spent fuel and disposing of high-level waste

If the number of neutrons ($N = A - Z$) is plotted against the number of protons (Z) in stable nuclei an interesting pattern emerges. Light nuclei have roughly equal numbers of protons and neutrons, but heavy nuclei have an excess of neutrons (the reasons for this are discussed in detail in chapter 5). If a heavy nucleus splits in half the ratio of neutrons and protons would be the same in each half as in the original nucleus – but this ratio would be bigger than required for stability of the lighter nucleus. This has two consequences:

- neutrons are ejected in most fissions – this makes a chain reaction possible
- the daughter nuclei are neutron-rich so tend to decay by beta emission (which converts a neutron to a proton in the nucleus) and they tend to have very short half-lives (since they are far from a stable form).

During the lifetime of a fuel rod the fissionable nuclei (usually U 235) are gradually converted to lighter nuclei. Since most of these are neutron-rich they have short half-lives and decay by beta emission, often accompanied by gamma rays. In addition to this there is an extremely high neutron flux in the core which will produce artificial radioisotopes when the neutrons are absorbed by U-238 (to produce plutonium), by nuclei in the surrounding materials (e.g. the fuel cladding) and in the decay products of the daughter nuclei. This means that the uranium becomes depleted in U-235, and the power available per unit volume of fuel falls. Eventually the fuel rods have to be removed and replaced with new ones. But that is not the end of the story – spent fuel is highly radioactive, highly toxic, hot and contains some potentially valuable resources (plutonium and depleted uranium). Its immediate fate is to be dumped under water in large cooling ponds at the reactor site. The water acts as a radiation shield and as a coolant (the great activity increases the thermal energy and temperature of the waste). The spent fuel is left under water until most of the short-lived isotopes formed by fission have decayed to products with longer half-lives. The activity is then lower and it can be transported in sealed flasks to be reprocessed.

Nuclear fuel reprocessing is designed to separate the components of irradiated fuel into three parts.

- Depleted uranium (about 96% of the spent fuel). This has both nuclear and non-nuclear uses. It can be used in fast reactors to 'breed' plutonium when it is irradiated with neutrons from the reactor core. It can also be used as a dense metal for armour plating on military vehicles and, ironically, for armour-piercing shells.
- Plutonium-239 (about 1%). This is fissile and can be used as a fuel in fast reactors or as an explosive in nuclear weapons.
- Liquid fission waste (about 3%) – various radioactive elements and compounds plus the irradiated materials from the stripped fuel rods. This is categorised as 'high level' waste and is stored for disposal. Present plans are to convert the liquid waste into a glassy solid by a process of 'vitrification'. These solid pellets will be stored for about 50 years (to allow them to cool and become less active) and then be placed in sealed containers and buried in deep mines inside stable geological formations.

Plans for reprocessing at factories such as THORP (thermal oxide reprocessing plant) at Sellafield in Cumbria were rather undermined by the end of the Cold War, which made the price of plutonium drop dramatically!

High-level nuclear waste will remain hazardous for tens of thousands of years, so any approach to the problem of disposal must ensure that it cannot seep back into the environment over this time scale. On the other hand the volume of high-level waste from nuclear reactors is tiny compared to the volume of waste from fossil-fuelled power stations. This is a direct consequence of the fact that fission releases millions of times more energy per atom than chemical reactions. The annual volume of vitrified high-level waste from electricity production in the UK is about 30 m^3 compared with 7 000 000 m^3 per annum of fly ash from coal-fired power stations.

Figure 9.10 Glass disc showing how much vitrified waste would be produced in one person's lifetime if all their electricity was produced by nuclear power.

Intermediate and low-level waste

As well as high-level waste UK nuclear reactors generate about 2000 m^3 of intermediate and 44 000 m^3 of low-level waste per year:

- low-level waste – mainly rubbish such as discarded protective clothing, used wrapping materials and worn-out or damaged plant and equipment
- intermediate-level waste: this is about 1000 times more radioactive than the low-level waste. It includes the metal fuel 'cans' in which the nuclear fuel was held; metalwork from within the reactor and various other materials that have been irradiated by the reactor core or fuel handling processes.

Low-level waste can be handled safely using rubber gloves, overalls and common sense. In the UK most of it is buried at a special dump at Drigg in Cumbria. Intermediate-level waste must be handled remotely and shielded to protect people from its radiation. It is stored on site in special containers and eventually will be 'fixed' in concrete and packaged in steel or concrete containers for transport to an underground disposal centre.

The ultimate fate of high and intermediate level nuclear waste will be a deep underground repository, but where? Many things have to be considered in searching for a suitable site. The main worry is that groundwater may become contaminated by radioactive materials and bring them back into the biological environment, so any chosen site should be in a stable geological formation with very little groundwater movement.

Plutonium, weapons and fast reactors

Plutonium forms when U-238 absorbs a neutron and undergoes two successive beta decays. It is fissionable and so contributes to the energy output of a reactor as the original U-235 is used up. Many of the early reactors were designed to optimise the production of plutonium which can then be extracted by reprocessing and used as the fissile material in nuclear weapons. This is why the development of nuclear power often goes hand in hand with the development of nuclear weapons and adds an extra political dimension to international attempts to limit the proliferation of nuclear weapons. To optimise plutonium production it is important to remove the fuel rods early before the Pu-239 absorbs neutrons and converts to Pu-240, Pu-241 and Pu-242. Pu-240 is a problem for weapons manufacturers because it undergoes spontaneous fission fairly readily, but does not fission when hit by a neutron. This makes weapons with too much Pu-240 rather unpredictable! Furthermore, it is almost impossible to separate Pu-239 from Pu-240 because they have identical chemistry (same electronic configuration) and differ only by 1 part in 240 in mass.

Only 0.7% of natural uranium is the fissile isotope U-235. However, since U-238 converts to fissile plutonium when it absorbs a neutron it is possible to increase the amount of nuclear fuel by *'breeding'* plutonium from uranium. This is done in a *'fast reactor'*, so-called because it has no moderator and uses the fast neutrons from fission to create a chain reaction in a small, hot, energy dense core. If the core is surrounded by a 'blanket' of depleted uranium, escaping neutrons will 'breed' plutonium in the blanket. It is possible to extract more fissile material from a fast reactor than was used to fuel it, so it really does *breed* fuel. This fuel can then be used to enrich the fuel for other thermal or fast reactors. An alternative use for a fast reactor is to 'burn' plutonium without breeding any more fuel – this could be used to reduce the world's stockpile of military plutonium.

At the time of writing there are just a few prototype fast reactors worldwide and it is not certain that this part of the nuclear fuel cycle will ever be fully developed.

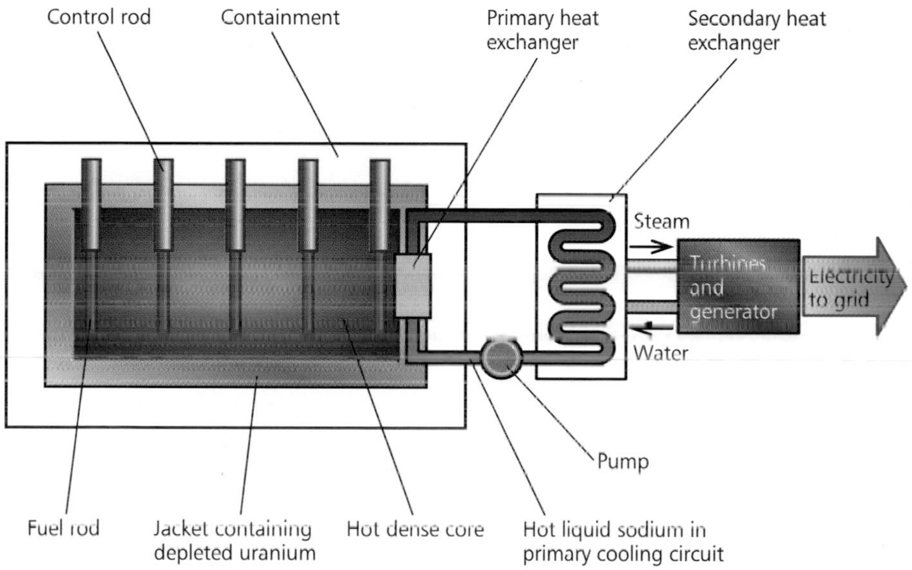

Figure 9.11 The essential components of a fast reactor.

Radiation exposure

We are continually exposed to low levels of natural radiation from radioisotopes present in rocks in the Earth and in our own bodies and by cosmic rays from space. In addition we may increase our personal exposure by having medical or dental X-rays, certain kinds of treatment using tracers or deliberate irradiation (e.g. in radium therapy for cancer) or by carrying out experiments with radioactive sources in a school laboratory. The major source for most people in the UK is the build up of radioactive thoron and radon in houses. An alien carrying out an autopsy on our bodies would be able to estimate the number of atomic bomb tests that have taken place on Earth from the overabundance of certain isotopes they would find inside us.

We do not know enough about the effects of radiation on our bodies and on the environment to be able to state any absolute rules for safe levels that must not be exceeded, so a sensible approach is to compare the extra irradiation caused by using nuclear technologies with the background levels in which we live. There is no doubt that very high levels of radiation over short times can harm or kill us, but it is not clear whether exposure to low levels for a long time is also harmful, or what actually constitutes a 'low enough' level. The effects of radiation on humans is divided into two classes.

Early effects

These follow shortly after exposure to radiation and are usually caused by large doses received over a short time. A large dose will kill more cells than can be readily repaired or replaced naturally and the person is likely to suffer nausea, vomiting, diarrhoea, and burns if the skin is exposed. Rapidly dividing cells in the immune system are particularly vulnerable to large radiation doses so the immune system is depressed after exposure and victims may then die from a secondary infection such as pneumonia. Following the Chernobyl accident in 1986, 28 people died from radiation exposure, a further 300 workers and fire-fighters suffered radiation sickness of whom 10 died in the next 8 years.

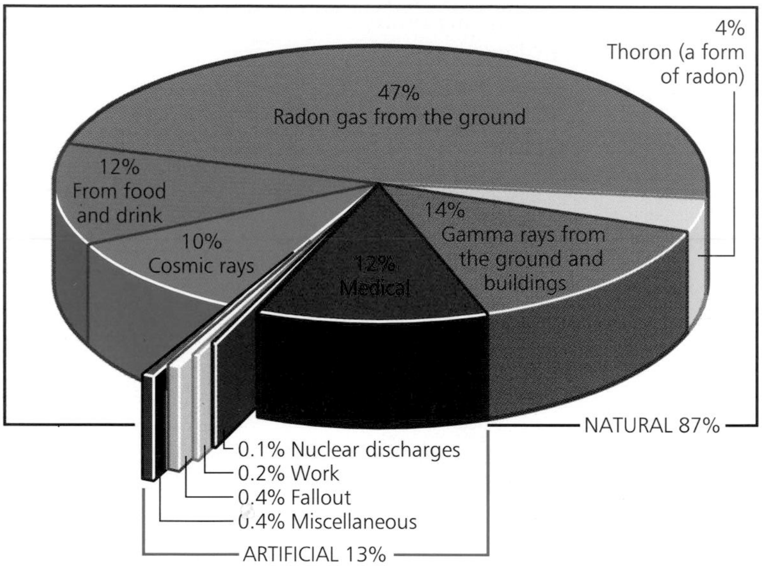

Figure 9.12 Average breakdown of radiation exposure for the UK population.

Measuring radiation exposure

The activity of a source is measured in disintegrations per second or becquerels, Bq:

$$1\ \text{Bq} = 1 \text{ disintegration per second.}$$

- The average activity of radon gas is 20 Bq per cubic metre of air inside houses in the UK.

An older unit is the curie, Ci:

$$1\ \text{Ci} = 3.7\times10^{10}\ \text{Bq}$$

- School sources are usually limited to 5 μCi, which means 1.85×10^5 atoms of the source disintegrate per second.

The absorbed dose is measured in energy absorbed per unit mass or **gray**, Gy:

$$1\ \text{Gy} = 1\ \text{J kg}^{-1}$$

However, for human irradiation the effect depends not just on the absorbed dose but also on the tissue exposed, so a dose-equivalent is calculated by multiplying the dose in gray by a weighting factor that is greater for the more vulnerable tissues. The result is a value in sievert, Sv, which are also J kg^{-1}, since weighting factors have no units.

- The average annual dose to the UK population is 2.5 millisieverts (mSv), but there are large geographic and occupational variations.
- Workers in the UK nuclear industry receive an annual dose of 4.5 mSv.
- 1 mSv is the annual dose limit (from unnatural sources) for members of the public.
- 20 μSv is the average dose from a single chest X-ray.

Delayed effects

Radiation damages cells and can affect the genetic material passed on to the next generation of cells. These altered cells are called **mutants** and may behave abnormally. Over the years these changes may result in cancer in the person exposed or (if sex cells are affected) hereditary defects in future generations.

The information in figure 9.12 is interesting, but not the whole story. It is not just the total exposure that matters but the way in which that exposure occurs. For example, a particular isotope may only represent a tiny fraction of the total radiation dose, but if it is concentrated in certain sugars in the food chain and then concentrated in certain organs when that food is consumed, it may cause significant irradiation of certain tissues resulting in an increased incidence of cancer. It is important to know what is present and where as well as how much. One particularly worrying isotope is iodine-133 which has a short half-life and accumulates in the human thyroid. Following an accident at Windscale (now part of the Sellafield complex) in 1957, 20 000 curies of iodine-133 were released into the atmosphere and the Ministry of Agriculture, Fisheries and Food decided to dispose of all milk (which may have been contaminated by iodine-133) from cattle grazing in an area of 500 km^2 around the reactor. Local farmers were compensated by the government.

Fusion

The rapid increase in the magnitude of binding energy per nucleon with nucleon number for the light elements suggests that a great deal of energy per nucleon could be released in nuclear fusion (more than in fission because of the steeper line) if light nuclei could be made to stick together to produce heavy nuclei. This is the process that gives stars their energy source and it has also been harnessed destructively, though not yet in conflict, on Earth in the 'H-bomb'. The main problem in persuading light nuclei to fuse is in making them approach one another closely enough so that the strong nuclear force can overcome their electrostatic repulsion and bind them together. The enormous mass of a star is sufficient to raise the temperature and pressure at its core to such a level that self-sustaining fusion reactions take place. In the 'H-bomb' these conditions are created by detonating a small fission weapon to get the fusion reactions going. The great challenge is to create controlled self sustaining fusion reactions on Earth. Progress has been made in this direction, particularly using the 'Tokamak' design of Andrei Sakharov, but even optimistic proponents of fusion as a solution to the world's energy problem do not expect commercial reactors to be available before the middle of the twenty-first century.

There are many possible fusion reactions, and most of them take place inside stars, but the most promising reaction for a terrestrial fusion reactor is to fuse two isotopes of hydrogen, deuterium and tritium:

$$^{2}_{1}\mathrm{D} + ^{3}_{1}\mathrm{T} \rightarrow ^{4}_{2}\mathrm{He} + ^{1}_{0}\mathrm{n}$$

The main obstacle to doing this commercially is that the deuterium–tritium fuel mixture has to be heated to over 100 million kelvin (at which temperature it is a plasma of nuclei and electrons) and contained within the reactor at this temperature for a couple of seconds before self-heating from the fusion reactions takes over. The problem of containment is a serious one – no material can withstand such temperatures (several times hotter than the centre of the Sun) – so the approach taken in the Tokamak is to suspend the plasma away from the walls of the reactor vessel using magnetic fields.

If this can be done and the reaction becomes self-sustaining the next problem is to extract the thermal energy to raise steam and drive a turbogenerator. This will be done by pumping water through a blanket of lithium surrounding the plasma.

Why lithium? Lithium is plentiful on Earth and is converted to tritium (fuel) and helium when it absorbs a neutron. Known supplies of lithium could supply enough fuel for fusion reactors to last for 1000 years.

$$^{6}_{3}\mathrm{Li} + ^{1}_{0}\mathrm{n} \rightarrow ^{3}_{1}\mathrm{T} + ^{4}_{2}\mathrm{He}$$

Deuterium is easily extracted from water (and there is enough of it available on Earth to provide for all our energy needs for 10 million years if this all came from fusion).

The consumables in a fusion reactor would be deuterium and lithium, both readily available, and there would be no radioactive heavy elements as waste products that would need long term storage and disposal. There would be some waste, however, since reactor materials would be irradiated by neutrons, but this would not require very long term storage management (100 years rather than many thousands). One other advantage is that the fuel is fed into the reactor continuously so the amount in the reactor at any time is only sufficient for a few tens of seconds operation. This makes the Tokamak an inherently safe design.

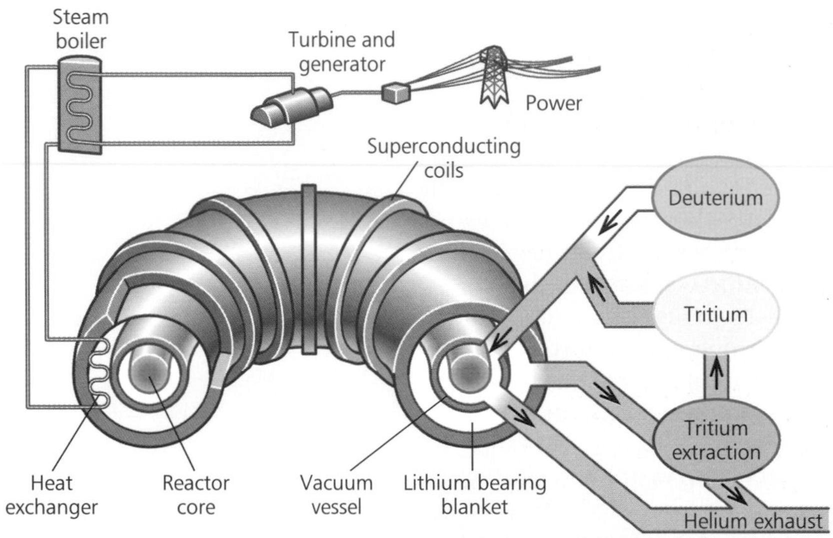

Figure 9.13 The essential components of a fusion reactor.

Figure 9.14 Maintenance work at the Joint European Torus (JET) at Culham in Oxfordshire. This is the world's largest fusion experiment and is run by the European Atomic Energy Community (Euratom). Its work will be continued by the Next European Torus (NET) and the International Thermonuclear Experimental Reactor (ITER) in the twenty-first century.

The Tokamak is not the only approach to nuclear fusion. Recently advances have been made using a technique of **inertial confinement**, in which powerful lasers are focused onto a pellet of fusion fuel causing it to implode and reach conditions for fusion reactions to take place, but this is a long way from the continuous generation of power in a reactor.

Decommissioning

Like fossil-fuelled power stations, nuclear reactors will eventually reach the end of their safe working life. They will then be decommissioned. This has three distinct stages:

- removal of all spent fuel, drainage of coolant, and closure of the plant
- removal of all reactor structure except the reactor itself
- removal of the reactor to leave a 'green field site' available for any future use.

So far this has never been carried out for any commercial reactor and estimates of the cost involved vary enormously (although everyone agrees it will be very expensive and technologically challenging). In the UK all electricity bills carry a levy to contribute toward the future cost of decommissioning nuclear reactors.

SUMMARY

- **Nuclear fission** is the process in which a heavy nucleus splits into two new, smaller nuclei, producing energy as it does so.
- Neutrons are produced in nuclear fission. These neutrons may cause further heavy atoms to fission. If each fission produces more than one neutron on average, and if each of these neutrons causes another heavy atom to fission, a **chain reaction** results, in which large numbers of heavy nuclei fission in a very short period of time. This is what happens in 'atom bombs'.
- **Nuclear fusion** is the joining together of two lighter nuclei to form a heavier nucleus, releasing energy.
- The energy released in fission and fusion can be understood by looking at the **binding energy per nucleon** of the nuclei involved. Because iron-56 is the most stable element (it has the greatest binding energy per nucleon), splitting atoms heavier than iron-56 to produce lighter ones releases energy, as does joining nuclei lighter than iron-56 to make heavier ones.
- A **nuclear fission reactor** controls the fission process. A **moderator** slows down neutrons to ensure that they are likely to cause fission, and **control rods** absorb the neutrons, allowing the fission reaction to be slowed down and stopped.
- A **nuclear fusion reactor** would fuse deuterium and tritium to produce helium. The **plasma** in which this reaction would take place would need to be at a temperature of around 10^8 K, and would be confined in a magnetic field.
- The generation of electricity from nuclear reactions, whether fission or fusion, relies on extracting energy from the reactor by means of a **coolant**, and using this to run steam turbines.
- The waste from nuclear fission reactors requires a careful management. The waste is of three types: **high level**, which is small in volume but which will remain highly radioactive for tens of thousands of years; **intermediate**, which must be handled remotely and shielded to protect

people; and **low-level waste**, which can safely be handled using simple protective equipment.

- All people are exposed to ionising radiation, from radioactive atoms in our environment, and from sources such as X-rays. Scientists are unsure whether there is any 'safe' dose of radiation, or whether exposure to radiation at all levels is potentially harmful.

QUESTIONS

1 a Calculate the mass defect for (i) helium-4 and (ii) helium-3.

Particle	Mass/u
electron	0.00055
neutron	1.00867
proton	1.00727
helium-4 (atom)	4.00260
helium-3 (atom)	3.01603

b What is meant by nuclear binding energy?
c Calculate the total nuclear binding energy, and binding energy per nucleon for helium-4 and helium-3 nuclei.
d Which is more stable? Explain.
e After the Big Bang about 25% of the hydrogen present was fused to helium, virtually all of which was helium-4. Why?

2 Use the curve of binding energy per nucleon to explain why:
a nuclear fission of heavy nuclei can result in a release of energy
b nuclear fusion of light nuclei can result in a release of energy
c nuclear fusion in stars does not create any nuclei beyond iron-56 (except when the star explodes)
d fusion reactors would yield more energy per kilogram of fuel than fission reactors.

3 The equation below is for an induced fission reaction.

$$^{235}_{92}\mathbf{U} + ^{1}_{0}\mathbf{n} \rightarrow ^{144}_{56}\mathbf{Ba} + ^{90}_{36}\mathbf{Kr} + 2^{1}_{0}\mathbf{n}$$

a Why is this called 'induced' fission? What other kind of fission is there?
b What is the likely kinetic energy of the incident neutron, 10 eV, 10 keV or 10 MeV? Explain.
c What is the significance of the two neutrons emitted in the reaction?
d What is meant by the 'mass defect' of this reaction?
e How is it possible for a reaction to have a mass defect and yet obey the law of mass conservation?
f Is energy conserved in this reaction?

4 a Use the values given below to calculate the total energy released by the induced nuclear fission described in question 3.

Particle	Mass / u
U-235 (atom)	235.044
Ba-144 (atom)	143.923
Kr-90 (atom)	89.920
neutron	1.009

b What form does this energy take?

5 A lump of natural uranium will never become critical, no matter what size or shape it has, and yet the British Magnox reactors used natural uranium as fuel.
a What is meant by 'going critical'?
b What prevents natural uranium from going critical?
c How is it still possible to build a fission reactor which uses natural uranium as fuel?

6 Natural uranium consists mainly of the isotopes U-238 (99.3%) and U-235 (0.7%). The half-lives of these two isotopes are 4.51×10^9 years and 7.13×10^8 years respectively.
a What is meant by the term 'isotope'?
b Why is it difficult to separate these two isotopes experimentally?
c How (roughly) has the ratio of U-238 to U-235 changed over time since the formation of the Earth (about 4.5 billion years ago)?
d Geologists have discovered that a vast fission reactor formed naturally in uranium-rich strata in west Africa two billion years ago. It remained critical for millions of years.
(i) How was this possible then but almost impossible now?
(ii) What evidence would reveal that the fission reactions took place?

7 Explain why the daughter nuclei created in nuclear fission reactions are usually beta emitters.

QUESTIONS

8 Assume that a typical fission reaction releases 200 MeV per U-235 nucleus.

- **a** What is 200 MeV in joules?
- **b** How many U-235 nuclei in 1 kg of U-235?
- **c** How much energy is released when all nuclei in 1 kg of U-235 undergo fission?
- **d** At what rate (kg s^{-1}) is U-235 consumed in a nuclear reactor that is 30% efficient and generates 1000 MW of electrical energy?
- **e** What mass of uranium fuel would be needed per year for such a reactor if the fuel pellets are enriched to 2% U-235?
- **f** What is the advantage of enrichment?

9 How does the chain reaction in the core of a thermal nuclear reactor differ from that in an exploding atom bomb?

10
- **a** Why is it necessary to slow down the neutrons emitted by fission reactions in a nuclear reactor?
- **b** How is this achieved?
- **c** What material properties are required in a moderator?
- **d** What is meant by the terms 'fast neutrons' and 'thermal neutrons'?
- **e** Estimate the energy in eV of a thermal neutron inside the core of a reactor.
- **f** If a neutron collides with a stationary carbon-12 nucleus it can lose up to 25% of its incident kinetic energy. What is the minimum number of collisions required to reduce its energy from 1 MeV to 10 eV?

11 Give one advantage of using uranium oxide in fuel pellets rather than uranium.

12
- **a** Explain in general terms the essential steps involved in converting the energy released in nuclear fission reactions to electricity.
- **b** What are the essential properties of the material used as a coolant inside a reactor?
- **c** What is a heat exchanger and why are they used?
- **d** What might happen if the coolant drains out of the core while it is critical?
- **e** What safety procedures should be initiated as soon as a loss of coolant is detected?

13
- **a** Explain why a lump of U-235 the size of a golf ball would be 'sub-critical' whereas one the size of a soccer ball would be 'super-critical'.
- **b** Why does a spherical assembly have a lower critical mass than one of any other shape?
- **c** How can compressing a spherical lump of just sub-critical plutonium make it go critical?

14
- **a** How does the charged liquid drop model explain induced nuclear fission?
- **b** Estimate the electrostatic contribution to the energy released in fission by calculating the change in electrical potential energy for two daughter nuclei as they move from a position of contact to a very large separation. (Use the fission equation in question 3 and estimate the nuclear radii using $r = 1.3 \times 10^{-15} A^{1/3}$ m.)

15 The table below lists some scattering and absorption (capture) cross-sections σ for various nuclides.

Nuclide	H	D	B	C	O	Cd	U
$\sigma_{scatt}/10^{-28}\,m^2$	20	3.4	3.6	4.8	3.8	5.6	8.9
$\sigma_{abs}/10^{-28}\,m^2$	0.33	0.00053	760	0.0034	0.00027	2500	7.6

- **a** One nuclide is much more likely to absorb an incident neutron than scatter it. Which one? What might this material be used for in a reactor?
- **b** Describe how uranium nuclei are likely to interact with incident neutrons.
- **c** Which of these materials would be particularly good moderators? Which would be no good at all for moderation?

16 It is extremely difficult to separate the isotopes U-235 and U-238.

- **a** Why?
- **b** How might this be done?

17
- **a** Plutonium does not occur naturally in any significant quantities. Explain where most of the plutonium on Earth came from.
- **b** What are the main uses of plutonium?
- **c** How can it be used in a fast reactor programme?

18
- **a** The net effect of most fusion reactions in the Sun is to convert four protons to one nucleus of helium-4. This reaction continues via several intermediate steps but can be summarised in a single reaction equation. Write down the equation. Comment on the particles that are created and calculate the energy released per helium nucleus created.

Particle	Mass / u
proton	1.0073
helium-4 (atom)	4.0026

- **b** Why is it not necessary to know the mass of the positron to do this calculation?

19
- **a** What is the difference between a 'hydrogen bomb' and an 'atom bomb'?
- **b** Which is the most destructive?

QUESTIONS

20 The most promising reaction for terrestrial fusion reactors seems to be:

$${}^{2}_{1}\mathrm{D} + {}^{3}_{1}\mathrm{T} \rightarrow {}^{4}_{2}\mathrm{He} + {}^{1}_{0}\mathrm{n}$$

Particle	Mass / u
deuterium (atom)	2.014102
tritium (atom)	3.016050
helium (atom)	4.002603
neutron	1.008665

a Why is this more promising than the fusion of hydrogen to helium as in the Sun? (see question 18)
b Calculate the energy yield (in MeV) per helium nucleus created.
c How does the energy yield per kilogram for this fusion reaction compare with the fission of U-235? (about 200 MeV per fission)
d Where would we find the fuel for a fusion reactor and what are its main waste products?

21 **a** If there is an energy advantage in fusing light nuclei (which there is) why don't they fuse spontaneously (in other words why is an element like hydrogen stable)?
b Why are such high temperatures required for fusion to take place?
c What is a plasma?
d There are advantages to the fact that fusion reactions take place in a plasma – what are they?

22 **a** Use the equation

$$\tfrac{1}{2}m\overline{v^2} = \tfrac{3}{2}kT$$

to estimate the temperature at which fusion could occur between tritium and deuterium nuclei.
b In practice fusion occurs at a significantly lower temperature. Can you suggest why this is?

23 When a nuclear reactor reaches the end of its life it will have to be decommissioned. Spent fuel rods are removed and disposed of separately but the remaining structure has also become radioactive and must be dismantled and disposed of safely. For a graphite cored reactor there are three main structural materials involved – concrete, graphite and steel.

a Explain why contamination by daughter nuclei is a minimal contribution to the radiation in these materials.
b What is the main cause of their radioactivity?
c Why would you expect the initial activity to be dominated by short half-life isotopes and the long term activity to be dominated by long half-life isotopes?
d Ten years after the reactor is shut down the activity in the steel of iron-55 is 2.4×10^{15} Bq whereas that of nickel-63 is 2.4×10^{14} Bq, a ratio of 10 to 1. The half-lives of these two isotopes are 2.7 years and 92 years respectively. What will the ratio of their activities be (i) 60 years (ii) 110 years after shutdown?
e Chlorine-36 has an activity of 1.3×10^{12} Bq in the graphite 10 years after shutdown. It has a half-life of 3.1×10^{5} years. Comment on its activity in the graphite after a further 10, 100 and 1000 years.
f The total activities in the three main materials 10 years after shutdown are:

graphite	8.9×10^{7} Bq kg^{-1}
steel	9.7×10^{8} Bq kg^{-1}
concrete	2.9×10^{5} Bq kg^{-1}

Suggest reasons for the range of values.

24 The neutron flux inside a thermal reactor is around $10^{16}\,\mathrm{m^{-2}\,s^{-1}}$ whereas a safe level outside is about $10^{4}\,\mathrm{m^{-2}\,s^{-1}}$.
a Why are neutrons dangerous?
b The half-thickness of concrete for neutrons is about 14 cm. What is the minimum thickness of concrete shielding required to protect the environment and people?
c Sketch how you would expect the neutron flux to fall with distance into the concrete shield from its inner surface to its outer surface.

25 Can you suggest a biological reason why a small rate of exposure to radiation for a long time might be less harmful than a large rate of exposure for a short time? (Assume the total doses absorbed are the same.)

Exam questions

DATA FOR EXAM QUESTIONS

Atomic masses

$^{2}_{1}H$	2.014102 u
$^{3}_{1}H$	3.016030 u
$^{4}_{2}He$	4.002603 u
$^{60}_{29}Cu$	64.92889 u
$^{65}_{30}Zn$	64.92923 u
$^{220}_{86}Rn$	220.01139 u
$^{224}_{88}Ra$	224.02020u
$^{235}_{92}U$	235.04394 u

Masses

electron	0.000549 u
proton	1.007276 u
neutron	1.008665 u

$1\,u = 931.5\,MeV/c^2 = 1.661 \times 10^{-27}\,kg$

Constants

$c = 2.998 \times 10^8\,m\,s^{-1}$

$\varepsilon_0 = 8.854 \times 10^{-12}\,F\,m^{-1}$

$k = 1.381 \times 10^{-23}\,J\,K^{-1}$

$e = 1.602 \times 10^{-19}\,C$

1 **a** The diagram represents a cross section through part of a linear accelerator which is used to accelerate particles to high energies in an evacuated tube. A high frequency alternating p.d. is applied between adjacent electrodes.

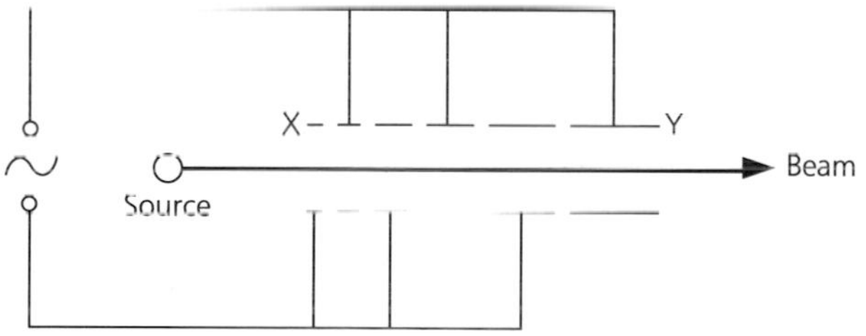

i Using basic physical principles, explain how charged particles directed into the accelerator from the source end X emerge at end Y with very high energies.

ii Why do the electrodes increase in length from X to Y? **(5 marks)**

b An antiproton from a linear accelerator operating at 6 GeV is annihilated when it collides with a stationary proton.

i Show that the total energy released in this process is approximately 8 GeV.

ii Explain qualitatively why not all of this energy is available to create further particles and antiparticles. **(5 marks)**

c State **two** advantages of using a linear accelerator compared to a synchrotron for accelerating protons. **(2 marks)**

(Total 12 marks)

(NEAB 1997)

2 The diagram below represents an outline of a cyclotron used to accelerate protons to 10 MeV. The protons enter the cyclotron at the centre and spiral outwards.

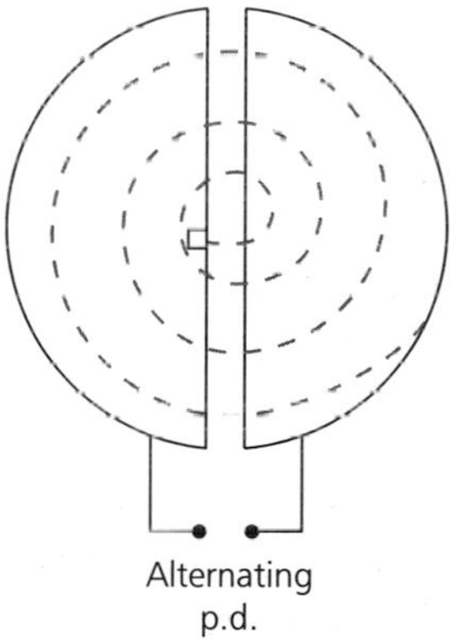

a Explain why the speed of a proton increases each time it moves from one half of the cyclotron into the other half. **(2 marks)**

b The maximum radius of curvature of the path of the protons inside the cyclotron is equal to the radius, R, of the cyclotron. Show that the maximum speed of a proton is equal to

$\frac{BQR}{m}$ where B is the magnetic flux density of the magnetic field, Q is the charge of the proton and m is its mass. Neglect relativistic effects. **(3 marks)**

c Calculate the maximum speed of protons in a 1.20 m diameter cyclotron when the magnetic flux density is equal to 0.50 T. Hence determine the frequency of the alternating p.d. which must be applied to achieve this speed. **(4 marks)**

(Total 9 marks)

(NEAB 1996)

3 In a synchrotron, charged particles are confined by magnets to a ring while being accelerated to high energies. The particles radiate electromagnetic waves, referred to as synchrotron radiation, as they move round the ring. The maximum kinetic energy of a particle is limited by synchrotron radiation. For particles of the same energy, the synchrotron radiation is greater for lighter particles and for rings of smaller diameter.

a **i** Explain why, after a particle has reached maximum energy, it is necessary to continue to boost its energy each time it passes round the ring.

ii Suggest why it is more difficult, using a synchrotron, to accelerate electrons to the same high energy as protons. **(3 marks)**

b Why does a collision between a particle of kinetic energy E and an antiparticle of kinetic energy E, moving in opposite directions, release more energy than a collision between an antiparticle of kinetic energy $2E$ and a stationary particle? **(2 marks)**

(Total 5 marks)

(NEAB 1995)

4 **a** State **one** difference and **one** similarity in the principle of operation of a cloud chamber and a bubble chamber. **(2 marks)**

b The diagram represents a photograph of two events, labelled X and Y, from a bubble chamber in which pair production has occurred as a result of a gamma photon creating an electron and a positron. In event X an electron has also been ejected from an atom. The track created by this electron is labelled 'atomic electron'. The tracks created by pair production are labelled A, B, C and D.

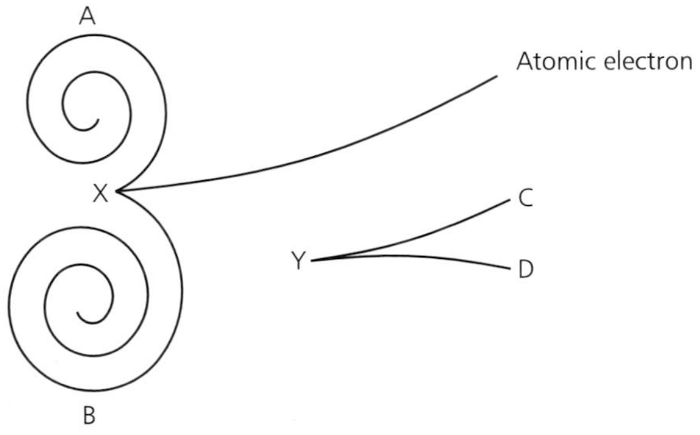

i Which **two** of the tracks A, B, C and D were produced by positrons?

ii Explain why gamma photons do not leave visible tracks.

iii Explain why the tracks created by pair production in event X are much more curved than those produced in event Y. **(6 marks)**

(Total 8 marks)

(NEAB 1996)

5 **a** **i** $^{65}_{30}$Zn is a radioactive isotope of zinc that emits positrons to form an isotope of copper. Write an equation to represent this change.

ii Show that the energy released in this process is 0.32 MeV. **(4 marks)**

b When a positron is emitted by a nucleus, a proton inside the nucleus changes into a neutron.

i Describe how the quark composition alters when the proton changes to a neutron.

ii Sketch a Feynman diagram to represent this process. **(5 marks)**

c **i** Copy the axes below and sketch a graph to show the energy spectrum of beta radiation from a beta-emitting radioactive isotope.

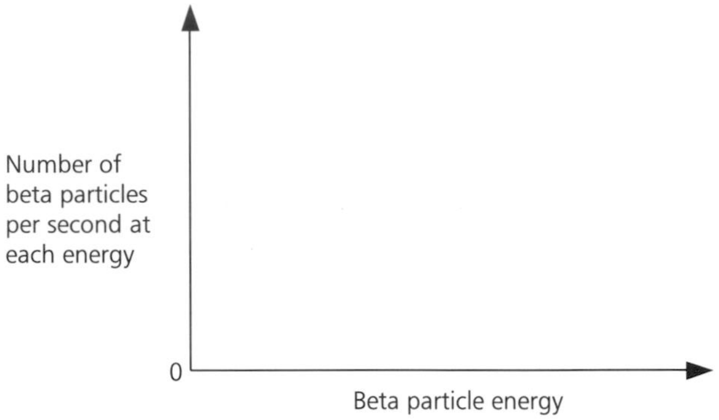

ii Explain why the kinetic energy of the beta particle emitted by a given radioactive isotope can vary up to a maximum value. **(6 marks)**

(Total 15 marks)

(NEAB 1996)

6 K^+ mesons are sub-atomic particles of half-life 8.6 ns when at rest. In an accelerator experiment, a beam of K^+ mesons travelling at a speed of 0.95 c is created, where c is the speed of light.

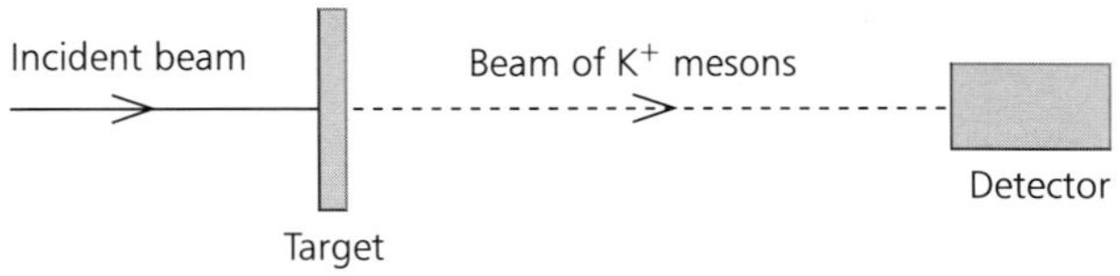

a Calculate the half-life of the K^+ mesons in the beam measured in the laboratory frame of reference.

b What is the greatest distance that a detector could be sited from the point of production of the K^+ mesons to detect at least 25% of the K^+ mesons produced? **(Total 5 marks)**

(NEAB 1995)

7 The figure shows tracks produced in a bubble chamber when an electron and a positron are created simultaneously in a uniform magnetic field directed into the diagram.

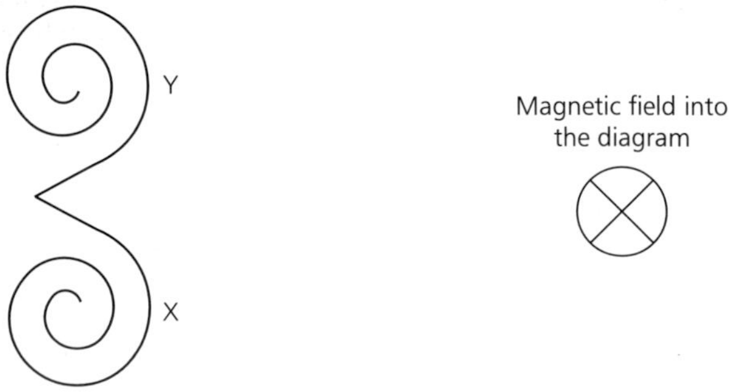

a Explain why the tracks curve in opposite directions.

b Explain why each track spirals inwards.

c Which track, X or Y, is created by the positron? **(Total 5 marks)**

(NEAB 1995)

8 A narrow beam of monoenergetic electrons of high energy is directed normally at a thin metal sample, as shown in the diagram. A detector is used to measure the intensity of the scattered electrons at different angles, producing results which are shown on the graph below.

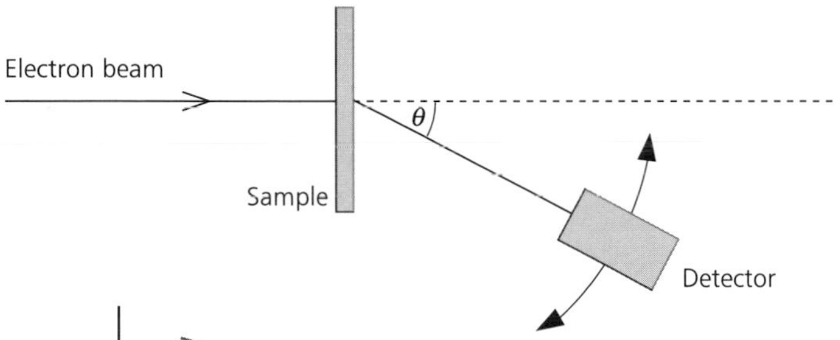

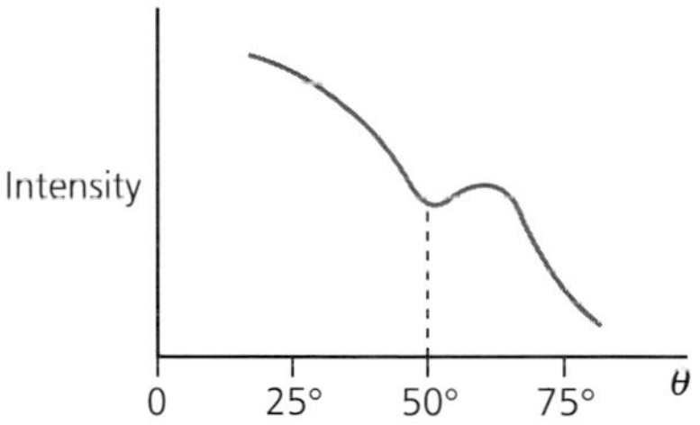

a **i** State how the wavelength of the electrons would differ if the momentum of each electron was doubled.

ii The first minimum of the above graph occurs at angle θ' from the direct beam and where

$$\sin \theta' = 0.61\ \lambda/R.$$

λ is the electron wavelength and R is the radius of the nuclei in the target. Sketch a graph similar to the one above to show the results you would expect if the momentum of the electrons had been doubled.

iii Explain why, in such scattering experiments, it is important that all the electrons in the beam have the same momentum.

(4 marks)

b The results of electron scattering experiments using different target elements show that

$$R = r_0 A^{\frac{1}{3}},$$

where A is the nucleon number of the target nuclei and r_0 is a constant.

i Use this equation to show that the density of a nucleus is independent of its mass.

ii State **two** properties of the strong nuclear force that have been deduced from the result that the density of the nucleus is constant. **(5 marks)**

(Total 9 marks)

(NEAB 1995)

9 **a** The nuclide $^{224}_{88}$Ra is unstable and decays by emitting an alpha particle.

i Write down an equation to represent this process.

ii Calculate the energy released in MeV in this process. **(4 marks)**

b **i** In the process described in (a) above, the kinetic energy of the alpha particle is a fixed proportion of the energy released. Explain why the alpha particle does not take away all the energy released.

ii Calculate the kinetic energy of an alpha particle emitted by a $^{224}_{88}$Ra nucleus. **(6 marks)**

(Total 10 marks)

(NEAB 1996)

10 A beam of 5.0 MeV alpha particles is directed at a thin gold foil, as illustrated in the diagram.

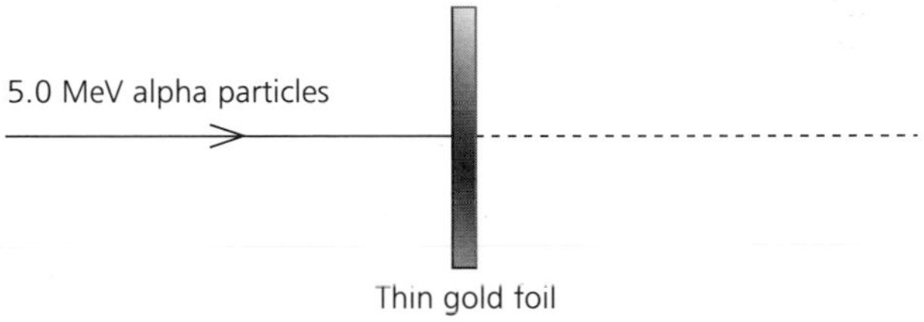

a Explain why a small proportion of the alpha particles incident on the foil are deflected through large angles.

b Show that the closest distance of approach of a 5.0 MeV alpha particle to a stationary gold nucleus is approximately 5.0×10^{-14} m. Assume the permittivity of free space, $\varepsilon_0 = 8.9 \times 10^{-12}\,\text{F m}^{-1}$. The proton number of gold is 79.

(4 marks)

(Total 7 marks)

(NEAB 1996)

11 **a** **i** Explain what is meant by the term *binding energy* for a nucleus.

ii Copy the axes below and sketch a graph of the average binding energy per nucleon against nucleon number A, giving approximate values of the scale on each axis.

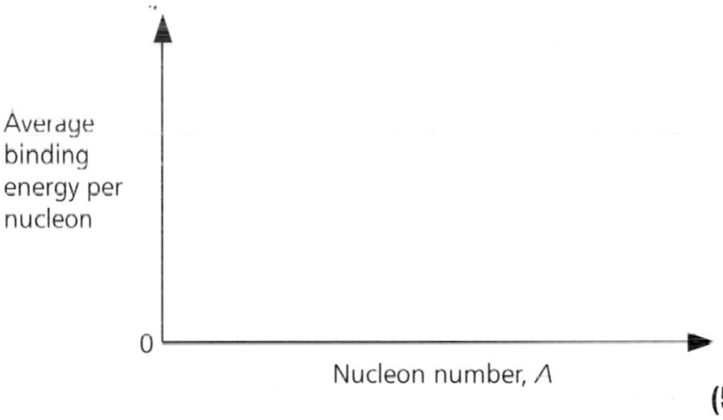

(5 marks)

b Use your graph to explain why energy is released when a $^{235}_{92}$U nucleus is fissioned by a neutron colliding with it. **(3 marks)**

(Total 8 marks)

(NEAB 1996)

12 **a** **i** The formula, $R = r_0 A^{\frac{1}{3}}$, relates the radius of a nucleus to its nucleon number. How does the density of nuclear matter depend on the nucleon number? Justify your answer.

ii Alpha particles are aimed at $^{238}_{92}$U nuclei with an energy of 14 MeV using a Van de Graaff accelerator.
Show that the closest distance of approach for a head-on collision is 18.9 fm, assuming that the $^{238}_{92}$U nucleus remains stationary.
mass of an α particle $= 6.7 \times 10^{-27}$ kg **(5 marks)**

b If the α particles have an energy higher than 17 MeV, the scattering characteristics change from those expected with simple electrostatic repulsion. The α particle scattering at 17 MeV gives a measurement of 15.6 fm for the radius of a $^{238}_{92}$U nucleus. This radius may be used to calculate the radii of other nuclei.

i Calculate a value for the radius of a $^{59}_{27}$Co nucleus.
ii Using electron diffraction the radius of a $^{59}_{27}$Co nucleus is found to be 4.82 fm, rather than the value calculated in (b)(i). Explain why electron diffraction is used in preference to α particle scattering in determining nuclear radii. **(5 marks)**

c What data would be necessary in order to determine the radius by electron diffraction in part (b)(ii)? **(2 marks)**

(Total 12 marks)

(NEAB 1997)

13 a i State the quark composition of the proton.
ii State the charge, baryon number and strangeness of the proton.
iii The π^+ meson has a charge of 1 and strangeness of 0. State its composition in terms of quarks and antiquarks. **(3 marks)**

b In β^+ decay, a proton changes into a neutron because one type of quark in the proton changes into a different type of quark. The Feynman diagram for this process is shown below.

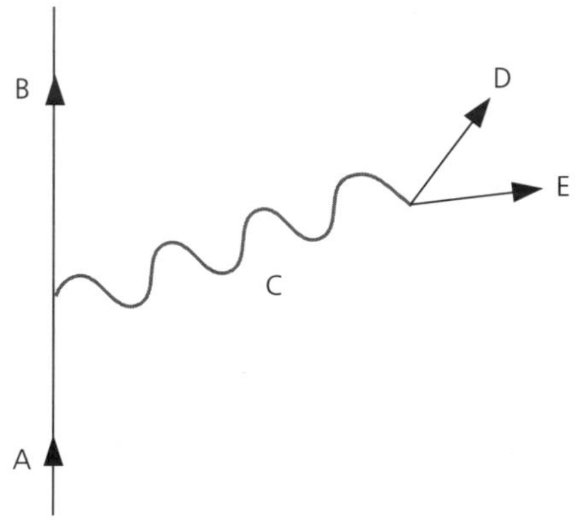

i What type of quark is represented at A?
ii What type of quark is represented at B?
iii What particles are represented at C, D and E respectively?
iv Which of the particles A, B, C, D and E are leptons? **(6 marks)**

(Total 9 marks)

(NEAB 1995)

14 a i State the difference between a hadron and a lepton in terms of the type of force experienced by each particle.
ii Give **one** example of a hadron and **one** example of a lepton.
iii Hadrons are classified as either baryons or mesons. In terms of quark composition, explain the difference between a baryon and a meson. **(6 marks)**

b i State the quark composition of a neutron.
ii Describe, in terms of quarks, the process of β^- decay when a neutron changes into a proton. Sketch a Feynman diagram to represent this process. **(4 marks)**

(Total 10 marks)

(NEAB 1996)

15 a State the quark composition of
i a proton,
ii a K$^+$ meson (i.e. a positive kaon). **(2 marks)**

b A meson consists of a quark and an antiquark.
i State the charge, strangeness number and identity of the meson composed of an up antiquark, $\overline{u}$, and a down quark, d.
ii In a collision with a proton, the up antiquark of the meson in (i) annihilates an up quark of the proton to release a high-energy gamma photon. The remaining quarks form a baryon b, as shown in the equation.

$$(\overline{u} + d) + \mathrm{p} \rightarrow \gamma + \mathrm{b}$$

Identify the baryon formed and state its quark composition.
(5 marks)

(Total 7 marks)

(NEAB 1997)

16 a State **three** advantages nuclear fusion would offer compared to nuclear fission as a potential source of power. **(3 marks)**

b One of the most productive fusion reactions occurs when a deuterium nucleus fuses with a tritium nucleus to form an alpha particle and a neutron.
i Write down the equation which represents this reaction.
ii Calculate the Q-value (energy released) in MeV for this reaction. Your calculation should make it clear how you have allowed for the electron masses. **(4 marks)**

c i Calculate the radius of a deuterium nucleus and the radius of a tritium nucleus, using $R = r_0A^{\frac{1}{3}}$ and taking r_0 to be 1.3 fm.
ii By considering these two nuclei as charged spheres in contact, calculate the minimum energy in MeV which must be supplied to them if they are to overcome their Coulomb barrier and fuse together. **(5 marks)**

d i Use the equation

$$\tfrac{1}{2}m\overline{v^2} = \tfrac{3}{2}kT$$

to estimate the temperature at which deuterium and tritium nuclei would have enough kinetic energy to undergo fusion.
ii How would you expect deuterium and tritium atoms to be changed by such a high temperature? **(4 marks)**

(Total 16 marks)

(NEAB 1995)

17 a Calculate the average binding energy per nucleon of $^{235}_{92}$U.
(4 marks)

b By reference to the liquid drop model of the nucleus, outline the stages by which a spherical nucleus divides into two principal fragments after being bombarded by a thermal neutron. Discuss the energy changes which occur to a charged liquid drop as it divides, and show how the liquid drop model explains the origin of the energy released by the fission of a nucleus. **(6 marks)**

c

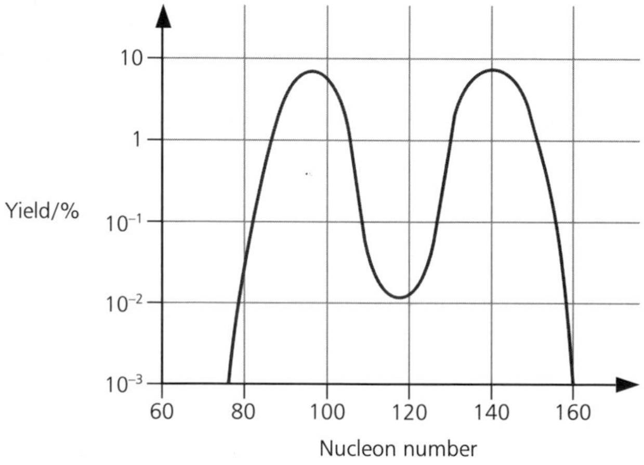

The figure shows the distribution of the fission fragments from the thermal fission of $^{235}_{92}U$.

i Sketch a neutron–proton diagram for all the naturally occurring nuclides up to $^{235}_{92}U$.

ii Add to your sketch a line close to which all fission fragments from $^{235}_{92}U$ must lie. Label this line L.

iii Discuss the principal features of the fission yield represented by the figure given above. By reference to your neutron–proton diagram suggest reasons for these features. **(6 marks)**

(Total 16 marks)

(NEAB 1994)

18 a Explain what is meant by a *chain reaction* in induced nuclear fission.

b Explain why, for a particular shape of fissile material, there is a minimum mass which must be exceeded for the reaction to continue. **(5 marks)**

(Total 5 marks)

(NEAB 1995)

19 a A copper sample is placed in a nuclear reactor and then removed. Explain why it has become radioactive.

b Explain what type of radiation you would expect such a sample to emit. **(6 marks)**

(Total 6 marks)

(NEAB 1996)

20 a i What is meant by a chain reaction of induced fission?

ii Outline how induced fission in a thermal reactor is maintained at a constant rate. **(7 marks)**

b i Explain the purpose of a moderator in a thermal reactor.

ii Water is used as both the moderator and the coolant fluid in the Pressurised Water Reactor (PWR). Describe, with a reason in each case, **two** effects which would occur if a PWR suddenly lost this water. **(6 marks)**

(Total 13 marks)

(NEAB 1996)

21 a The fuel rods of a thermal nuclear reactor contain mostly uranium-238 and a small proportion of uranium-235.

i Describe what happens to uranium-238 and to uranium-235 when they are being bombarded by neutrons inside a working nuclear reactor.

ii Describe the **controlled** chain reaction by which energy is released from the fuel in a thermal nuclear reactor. **(8 marks)**

b i Describe the function of the moderator in a thermal nuclear reactor.

ii State a material suitable for use as a moderator in a thermal nuclear reactor, giving a reason for your choice. **(4 marks)**

(Total 12 marks)

(NEAB 1997)

22 a

Type of quark	Charge	Baryon number	Strangeness
u	$+\frac{2}{3}$	$\frac{1}{3}$	0
d	$-\frac{1}{3}$	$\frac{1}{3}$	0
s	$-\frac{1}{3}$	$\frac{1}{3}$	–1

There are nine possible ways of combining u, d and s quarks and their associated antiquarks to make nine different mesons. List all the possible combinations. From your list select any strange mesons and state the charge and strangeness of each of these. Three of the mesons in the list have zero charge and zero strangeness. What will distinguish these mesons from each other? **(6 marks)**

b The diagram shows the track of a charged particle in a magnetic field. The field is at right angles to the plane of the paper, and its direction is out of the plane of the paper. AB is a thin sheet of lead through which the particle passes.

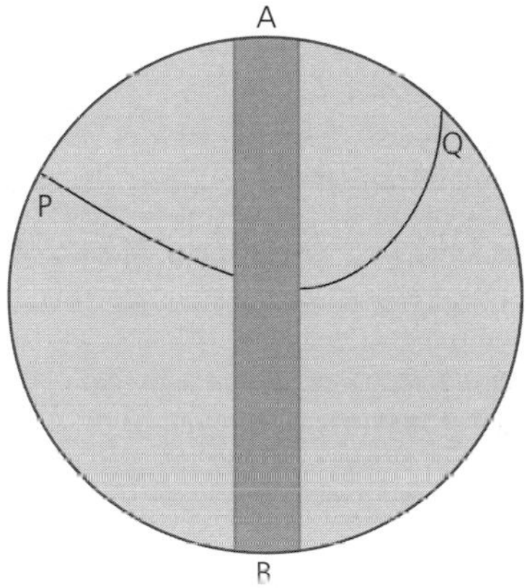

Deduce the direction of movement of the particle and the sign of the charge on the particle. Explain clearly how you made your deductions. **(4 marks)**

c In a colliding beam experiment a greater proportion of the colliding particles' total kinetic energy is available for producing new particles than in a fixed target experiment. Explain why this is so. When might a fixed target experiment be preferable? **(5 marks)**

A moving proton of kinetic energy 2.12 GeV collides with a stationary antiproton. These particles annihilate and a new particle of rest mass 2.74 GeV/c^2 and momentum 2.91 GeV/c is produced. Show that no other new particles have been produced as a result of this collision.

(Rest mass of proton = 0.938 GeV/c^2.) **(3 marks)**

(Total 18 marks)

(London 1994)

23 a What do you understand by the term *antiparticle*? What is the quark composition of an antineutron? (The up quark carries a charge of $+\frac{2}{3}$, the down quark $-\frac{1}{3}$.)

High-energy particle physics experiments often result in the production of electron–positron pairs. Sketch the tracks that such a pair of particles might produce in a bubble chamber, assuming that the particles are moving at right angles to a uniform magnetic field. Show clearly on your diagram the direction of motion of the particles, the direction of the magnetic field and identify which particle is the electron and which is the positron. What change is observed in the shape of the tracks as the particles slow down? Calculate the minimum energy in joules required to produce an electron–positron pair. Convert your answer to GeV and hence state the rest mass of the electron in units of GeV/c^2. **(11 marks)**

b Explain the importance of the Doppler effect in providing evidence for the Big Bang model of the Universe. State Hubble's law and from it deduce the units of the Hubble constant, H.
Current estimates of H vary by as much as a factor of 2.
What is the problem in obtaining a reliable value for H?
The approximate age of the Universe, t_0, can be obtained from the formula $t_0 = 1/H$. What assumption has been made in obtaining this formula? **(7 marks)**

(Total 18 marks)

(London 1995)

24 a State why it is possible to achieve much higher energies using circular accelerators than using linear ones of a similar size.
Explain why the particles in an accelerator must be contained within a vacuum tube.
What other two factors in the design of a circular accelerator limit the maximum energy available?
A charged particle moving in a plane perpendicular to a uniform magnetic field follows a circular path. Show that, if the speed of the particle is increased, the radius of the circular path increases but the period remains constant **(10 marks)**

b In 1962 the existence of a particle with strangeness –3 was predicted. The particle Ω^- was identified in 1964 in an experiment involving a strong interaction between a K^- meson of strangeness –1 and a proton in a hydrogen bubble chamber. The interaction involved was

$$K^- + p \rightarrow \Omega^- + K^+ + K^0$$

Is the Ω^- particle a baryon or a meson? Give two reasons for your answer.
Using the information given in the table below, deduce the quark composition of all the particles involved.

Type of quark	Charge	Strangeness
u	$+\frac{2}{3}$	0
d	$-\frac{1}{3}$	0
s	$-\frac{1}{3}$	–1

The Ω^- (lifetime 8.2×10^{-11} s) subsequently decayed in a three stage process to a proton and a number of pi-mesons. Pi-mesons have zero strangeness. What fundamental interaction must be involved at some stage in this process? Give two reasons for your answer.
What exchange particle(s) could be mediating this process? **(10 marks)**

(Total 20 marks)

(London 1996)

25 a In a head-on collision between two protons of equal kinetic energy the following interaction was observed:

$$p + p \rightarrow p + 7\pi^- + 7\pi^- + K^+ + \Lambda$$

Data: mass of p $= 938\,\text{MeV}/c^2$
mass of π^+ or π^- $= 140\,\text{MeV}/c^2$
mass of K^+ $= 494\,\text{MeV}/c^2$
mass of Λ $= 1115\,\text{MeV}/c^2$

Calculate the minimum kinetic energy in MeV of each proton for this interaction to occur.
Explain why this is the minimum possible value.
Why would this interaction not be observed if one of the protons were stationary and the other had twice your calculated minimum kinetic energy? **(6 marks)**

b Sketch a graph showing the energy spectrum of β^- particles emitted during β^- decay.
Explain in detail why the shape of this graph led to the prediction of the existence of the neutrino. **(7 marks)**

c An electron and a positron can annihilate by either of the following mechanisms.

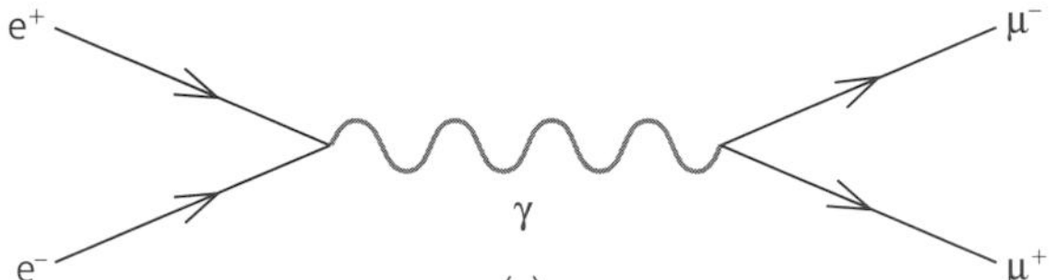

(a)

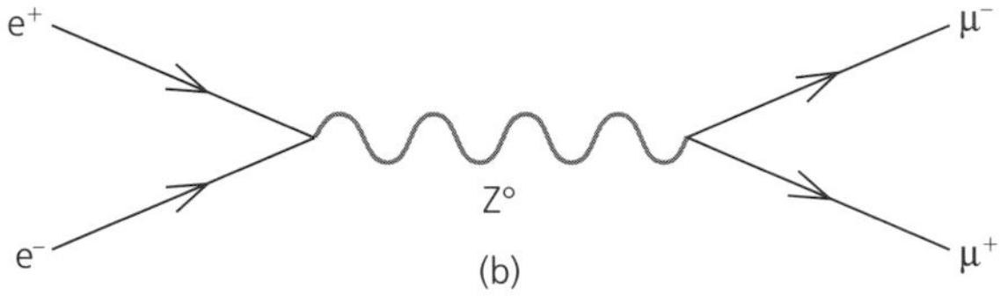

(b)

Which of the fundamental interactions is represented by each figure?
Which figure illustrates the most frequent mechanism for electron–positron annihilation?
Why is the interaction shown in (b) short range compared to that shown in (a)?
Draw another diagram to illustrate the exchange of a π^+ between a neutron and a proton. **(7 marks)**

(Total 20 marks)

(London 1996)

26 a Calculate the force of repulsion between two protons separated by a distance of 1.0×10^{-14} m in an atomic nucleus. **(2 marks)**
The Rutherford scattering experiment was used to investigate the structure of the atom. Deep inelastic scattering provided evidence about the structure of protons and neutrons. Outline the similarities and differences between these two experiments.
What conclusion was drawn from the deep inelastic scattering experiment? **(7 marks)**
The quarks in a nucleon are held together by the strong interaction. What exchange particle mediates this interaction?
What evidence is there that the range of this exchange particle is less than 10^{-14} m? **(4 marks)**

b State one piece of evidence that supports the Big Bang Theory and explain how it does so.
The very early Universe was made up of a collection of quarks, leptons and exchange particles. Through what stages has it passed in order to reach its present state?
Explain why atoms were unstable when the Universe was at a temperature greater than about 4000 K. **(7 marks)**

(Total 20 marks)

(London 1997)

Answers

Note that only numerical answers are given.

ANSWERS TO END-OF-CHAPTER QUESTIONS

Chapter 1

1 a Solar.
b 7.6×10^{-13} J
c 3.6×10^{10} Bq (s^{-1})
d 0.91 kg
2 a (i) 2000 eV (ii) 2 keV (iii) 0.002 MeV (iv) 3.2×10^{-16} J
b (i) same as for electron (ii) double that of the electron.
c 2.7×10^{7} m s^{-1}
d just ok, $\gamma = 1.005$.
3 a (i) 2560 V (iii) 4.7 MV
4 b $v = 6.9 \times 10^{5}$ ms^{-1} i.e. $v > c$
c 3.53 **d** $0.96c$ **e** $\gamma = 1.001$, no
5 a $m_e = 5.49 \times 10^{-4}$ u $m_p = 1.007$ u
b (i) 8.19×10^{-14} J, 1.50×10^{-10} J
(ii) 0.511 MeV, 938 MeV
(iii) 0.51 Mev, 940 MeV (iv) 5.1×10^{-4} GeV, 0.94 GeV
c 5.11×10^{-14} GeV/c^2, 0.938 Gev/c^2
6 a 50.94 GeV/c^2 **b** 50.94 GeV
c $0.9998c$ **d** 50.93 GeV/c
7 a 4.0×10^{26} W **b** 4.4×10^{9} kg s^{-1} **c** 1.4×10^{13} y
8 a $1 : \sqrt{2}$ **b** 1.0
10 a 0.00458 u
b 4.28 MeV
e $E_\alpha = 234E_{Th}/238$
11 a As v approaches c, m approaches infinity.
c Photons have zero rest mass.
13 a 30 GeV **b** 11 GeV
14 a $r = p/Bq$
b $T = 2\pi m/Bq$
d 7.6 MHz
f At 25 MeV $\gamma = 1.04$ so a 4% increase in mass. Therefore only a few orbits will put particles out of phase with accelerating AC.
17 a 6.7 MVm^{-1}
b Drops a mere 4.9×10^{-10} m (comparable to the diameter of an atom) – no.

Chapter 2

2 a 2.26×10^{8} m s^{-1}
b 0.266 MeV

Chapter 3

4 a 2.4×10^{-8} m
b $\gamma = 10$ so laboratory lifetime is 8×10^{-16} s
c 2.4×10^{-7} m
7 a 1.8 km
b 1.8 km
c 60 km
d Lengths contract in the direction of motion. (This is the Lorentz contraction, $l' = \gamma l$)

Chapter 4

4 a (i) $r = p/Bq$ so larger radius implies greater momentum and kinetic energy. Particle is moving from 140 mm radius towards 51 mm radius.
b 63 MeV (140 mm) 23 MeV (51 mm)

Chapter 5

1 b $r < 2.8 \times 10^{-14}$ m (combined nucleus and alpha radii)
4 c 4.6×10^{-15} m
5 b (i) 3.9×10^{-11} m (ii) 1.2×10^{-12} m
(iii) 1.2×10^{-15} m
7 a $10^{12} : 1$

Chapter 6

2 b $E_\mu = 109.8$ MeV $E_\gamma = 29.8$ MeV
6 b $\lambda = h/p$, shorter wavelengths give higher resolving power, therefore need larger linear momentum and so larger kinetic energy.

Chapter 7

3 f (i) Violates conservation of baryon number.
(ii) Violates conservation of lepton number.
4 d Strangeness is not conserved in (c).
5 a 10^{-23} s
7 a Λ^o is the lightest strange baryon, so its decay cannot conserve strangeness.
b

	Λ^o	$\rightarrow$	p^+	+	e^-	+	$\bar{\nu}_e$
Q	0	=	1	–	1	+	0
L	0	=	0	+	1	–	1
B	1	=	1	–	0	+	0

c 176 MeV
d proton: uud, lambda-zero: sud. Strange quark changes flavour to become an up quark in decay.
10 b Violates conservation of lepton number.
c Violates conservation of muon-lepton number.
g Violates conservation of lepton number.

11 Conservation of number of quarks.

12 a photons **b** $W^{\pm}$, Z^0
c pions **d** gravitons (hypothetical)
e gluons **f** Strong force derives from colour force.

15 $\Delta E \Delta t \approx h$ **for EM** $\Delta E = hf \geq 0$.

Range $R = c\Delta t \approx \dfrac{ch}{\Delta E} = \dfrac{ch}{hf} = \dfrac{c}{f} = \lambda$

There is no upper limit to photon wavelength so EM interaction has infinite range.
For strong force,

$$\Delta E \geq m_o c^2 \text{ so } \Delta t \leq \frac{h}{m_o c^2} \text{ and } R \leq c\Delta t = \frac{h}{m_o c}$$

(speed of exchange particle close to speed of light).
So strong force has limited range because the minimum energy that must be 'borrowed' equals the rest mass of the pion.

16 a Violates conservation of baryon and lepton numbers.
b (i) very short range (ii) very low (iii) very long.

17 c Ω^- is sss, Pauli exclusion principle does not allow three identical fermions in the same quantum state. Spin can distinguish two but a new property (colour) is needed to distinguish three.

Chapter 8

2 a $v_B = 3v_A$
b B (neglecting superimposed local motions)
c $v = Hd$
d $t \leq 10^{-10}$ s

Chapter 9

1 a (i) 0.0304 u (ii) 0.0083 u
c helium-4 BE = 28 MeV BE/A = 7.1 MeV
helium-3 BE = 7.7 MeV BE/A = 1.9 MeV

4 a 180 MeV

8 a 3.2×10^{-11} J
b 2.6×10^{24}
c 8.2×10^{13} J
d 4.1×10^{-5} kg s^{-1}
e 65 tonnes per year

10 f 40

14 b about 230 MeV

18 a 0.027 u, 25 MeV

20 b 17.6 MeV
c fusion: about 3.4×10^{14} J kg^{-1} fission: about 8.2×10^{13} J kg^{-1}

22 a Assume their centres need to approach within about 5 fm, then $T > 10^{13}$ K.

23 d (i) $t = 60$ y nickel is 25 000 times more active.
(ii) $t = 110$ y nickel is 6.6×10^9 times more active.
e Virtually unchanged since $t \ll t_{\frac{1}{2}}$

24 b 40 half-thicknesses, about 5.6 m.

ANSWERS TO EXAM QUESTIONS

The author takes responsibility for these answers, which have not been provided by the Examination Boards.

2 c 5.7×10^7 m s^{-1}, 15 MHz

5 a $^{65}_{30}\text{Zn} \rightarrow {}^{65}_{29}\text{Cu} + {}^{0}_{1}\text{e}^+ + {}^{0}_{0}\nu_e$

6 a 28 ns **b** 16 m

9 a i $^{224}_{88}\text{Ra} \rightarrow {}^{220}_{86}\text{Rn} + {}^{4}_{2}\alpha$
ii 5.8 MeV
b ii 5.7 MeV

12 b i 9.8 fm

13 a i uud
ii Q = +1, B = +1, S = 0
iii u$\bar{\text{d}}$
b i u **ii** d **iii** C: W^-, D: e^-, E: $\bar{\nu}$ **iv** D and E

14 b udd

15 a i uud **ii** u$\bar{\text{s}}$
b i Q = −1, S = 0, π^-
ii udd, neutron

16 b i $^{2}_{1}\text{H} + {}^{3}_{1}\text{H} \rightarrow {}^{4}_{2}\text{He} + {}^{1}_{0}\text{n}$
ii 17.6 MeV (electron masses cancel)
c i deuteron radius 1.6 fm, triton radius 1.9 fm
ii 0.41 MeV
d i 3.2×10^9 K

17 a 7.39 MeV/nucleon

22 a u$\bar{\text{u}}$, d$\bar{\text{d}}$, s$\bar{\text{s}}$ have zero charge and zero strangeness. They have different masses.
b Direction P to Q. Charge negative (from FLHR).
c Total incident energy is 4.00 MeV.
Total energy of new particle is also 4.00MeV, so nothing else is created. (Use $E^2 = E_0^2 + p^2c^2$)

23 antineutron $\bar{\text{u}}\bar{\text{d}}\bar{\text{d}}$, $E_{min} = 1.6 \times 10^{-13}$ J = 1.0 MeV = 0.0010 GeV
electron rest mass = 0.00051 GeV/c^2

24 K^- s$\bar{\text{u}}$; p uud; Ω^- sss; K^+ u$\bar{\text{s}}$; K^0 d$\bar{\text{s}}$

25 a 1.316 GeV per proton.
c LHS: electromagnetic; RHS: weak.
Electromagnetic is most frequent.
Z^0 has a large rest mass, photon has zero mass.

26 a 2.3 N

Glossary

ACTIVITY Number of decays per second in a radioactive source, measured in becquerels, ($1\ Bq = 1\ s^{-1}$) or curies ($1\ Ci = 3.7 \times 10^{10}\ Bq$).

ANTIMATTER All particles either have antimatter counterparts or are their own antiparticles. Antiparticles have the same rest mass as the corresponding particle but opposite values of Q, B, L, S, etc. When a matter/antimatter pair meet they may annihilate to produce other particles or just gamma rays.

BARYON A hadron containing a colourless combination of three quarks.

BIG BANG The beginning of spacetime and matter, some ten to twenty billion years ago.

BLACK-BODY RADIATION Characteristic spectrum of thermal radiation from an ideal hot body.

BOSON Particle with integer spin – not subject to the Pauli Exclusion Principle.

BOTTOM Third generation quark flavour (paired with top).

ČERENKOV RADIATION Electromagnetic radiation emitted from a charged particle exceeding the speed of light inside a particular medium.

CHARM A second generation quark flavour (paired with strangeness).

CHARGED CURRENT A weak interaction mediated by a $W^{\pm}$.

COLLIDER Accelerator like LEP at CERN which collides beams of particles travelling in opposite directions.

COLOUR Property that distinguishes quarks. Quarks may be red, blue or yellow (sometimes green). Colour plays the role of 'charge' in QCD and all hadrons are formed from 'colourless' combinations of quarks (rgb triplets form the baryons and colour/anticolour pairs form the mesons).

COSMIC RAYS High-energy particles (mainly protons) arriving from deep space. Cosmic rays contain particles of far greater energy than any produced in accelerators on Earth.

CYCLOTRON Early circular accelerator using a fixed a.c. frequency voltage to accelerate particles during each of their orbits.

DE BROGLIE RELATION $\lambda = h/p$ relates the wave-like property of all particles (wavelength) to their particle-like property (momentum).

DEEP INELASTIC SCATTERING Scattering in which the types or numbers of particles change as a result of the interaction.

DEUTERON (heavy hydrogen) Nucleus consisting of one proton and one neutron.

DOPPLER EFFECT Shift of wavelength and frequency of radiation because of relative movement between source and observer.

DOWN QUARK First generation quark.

EIGHTFOLD WAY Geometrical scheme to classify the hadrons.

ELASTIC SCATTERING A process that conserves total kinetic energy.

ELECTROWEAK FORCE Unified theory of electromagnetism and the weak interaction.

FERMION Particle with half-integer spin. Fermions obey the Pauli Exclusion Principle.

FEYNMAN DIAGRAM Diagram representing particle interactions and transformations.

FISSION Splitting of heavy nucleus to form two lighter nuclei.

FIXED TARGET EXPERIMENT Collision experiment where a beam is incident on a fixed target.

FLAVOUR Properties that distinguish different quarks, e.g. up, down, strangeness, charm, bottom and top. Can also be applied to leptons to distinguish electron from muon from tau.

FUSION Nuclear reaction in which light nuclei coalesce to form heavier nuclei.

GAMMA RAY Photon emitted from an excited nucleus.

GENERAL RELATIVITY Einstein's theory of gravitation involving spacetime curvature.

GENERATION Quark and lepton patterns repeat three times at progressively greater rest mass. The up and down quarks and electron and electron-neutrino form the first of three generations of fundamental particles.

GLUON Vector boson carrier of the colour force between quarks.

HADRON Particle that interacts by the strong force. Hadrons are made of quarks and divide into mesons and baryons.

HIGGS BOSON Hypothetical particle that endows other particles with mass.

HUBBLE'S LAW Galactic redshifts are proportional to distance. This implies universal expansion.

INTERMEDIATE VECTOR BOSON Force carrier in the weak interaction, $W^{\pm}$ and Z^0.

LEPTON Particles that do not feel the strong force but can interact by gravitation, electromagnetism (if charged) and the weak interaction.

LINAC Linear Accelerator.

MAGIC NUMBERS Nuclei with magic numbers of nucleons are especially stable.

MAGNETIC MOMENT Strength of a particle's interaction with an applied magnetic field.

MESON Hadron made of two quarks. Integer spin (boson).

NEUTRAL CURRENT Weak interaction mediated by the Z^0. The natures of the particles affected are unchanged by the interaction.

NUCLEON Proton or neutron in the nucleus.

PARITY Many interactions make sense (i.e. still represent real physical processes) when all spatial co-ordinates are inverted. These conserve parity. Some weak interactions do not.

QCD Quantum Chromodynamics, theory of the colour force between quarks.

QED The most accurate physical theory so far discovered – a quantum field theory of the interaction of light and matter.

QUARK Fundamental (?) particle present as part of all hadrons.

REDSHIFT Fractional increase in wavelength of radiation reaching us from distant galaxies. This shift is caused by the expansion of the space between us and the galaxy.

RESONANCE Short-lived hadron that decays by the strong force with a characteristic lifetime of around 10^{-23} s.

REST MASS Mass of a particle measured in its own rest frame. Its rest energy is the energy equivalent of this mass.

SPECIAL RELATIVITY Einstein's theory of space and time. Time dilation, mass increase with velocity, and mass–energy equivalence are three important consequences.

SPIN The intrinsic angular momentum of a particle. All particles have either integer spin (bosons) or half-integer spin (fermions). Fermions obey the Pauli Exclusion Principle.

STRANGENESS A quark flavour. Strangeness is conserved in strong and electromagnetic interactions but not in some weak interactions.

STRONG INTERACTION This interaction is felt by all hadrons but not by leptons. It is responsible for binding neutrons and protons together in the nucleus.

SYNCHROTRON Particle accelerator which accelerates particles repeatedly as they move around a fixed orbit. The magnetic field used to bend the beam into a near circular path is only applied at the circumference of the orbit.

SYNCHROTRON RADIATION Charged particles radiate when accelerated. The centripetal acceleration in a synchrotron results in significant power losses to synchrotron radiation, especially for electrons.

TOP Quark flavour. The top quark was the last one to be positively identified.

UNCERTAINTY PRINCIPLE Heisenberg showed that the more precisely we fix the value of momentum the greater the random uncertainty in position of a particle. Similarly, if we can determine the time of an event more precisely then its energy has a greater random uncertainty. The energy–time uncertainty principle allows for the existence of virtual particles.

UNIFIED FIELD THEORY A single theory combining the strong, weak and electromagnetic forces. A Theory of Everything (TOE) would also incorporate gravitation.

UP A first generation quark flavour.

WAVE–PARTICLE DUALITY This is a term coined for matter and radiation since both are capable of wave-like behaviour (e.g. interference and diffraction) and particle-like behaviour (e.g. indivisible and transfer energy in quanta) even though the classical wave and particle models are mutually exclusive.

WEAK INTERACTION Force responsible for beta decays and able to change the flavour of quarks. It is mediated by the intermediate vector bosons.

Timeline

1803............Dalton's Atomic Theory.
1869............Mendeleev's first periodic table of the elements.
1895............Röntgen discovers X-rays. Wilson experiments with a cloud chamber.
1896............Becquerel discovers radioactivity.
1897............Thomson discovers the electron.
1900............Planck proposes that energy is quantised.
1902............Rutherford's transformation theory for radioactive changes.
1905............Einstein's photoelectric theory leading to the photon.
Einstein's Special Theory of Relativity and $E = mc^2$.
1909............The Rutherford scattering experiment.
1911............Rutherford's nuclear atom.
1912............Discovery of cosmic radiation.
1914............Discovery of continuous energy spectrum for beta particles.
1915............Einstein's General Theory of Relativity.
1919–21..... Evidence grows for a Strong Nuclear Force.
1923............de Broglie hypothesis: wave–particle duality of matter.
1925............Pauli Exclusion Principle.
1926............ Heisenberg, Schrödinger, Born, Bohr etc. construct a coherent quantum theory.
1927............Heisenberg's Uncertainty Principle.
1928............The Dirac Equation.
1930............Pauli proposes the neutrino to explain beta-ray spectra.
1931............First cyclotron. Dirac proposes and Anderson discovers the positron.
1932............Chadwick discovers the neutron.
1934............Yukawa predicts mesons in the nucleus to carry the strong force.
1935............Muon discovered by accident.
1939............Hahn and Meitner produce nuclear fission.
1946............First synchro-cyclotron.
'V-particles' K-mesons discovered. First strange particles.
1947............Discovery of charged pions.
1950............Discovery of the neutral pion.
1953............First bubble chamber photographs.
1954............CERN, the European Centre of Particle Physics Research.
1955............Discovery of the antiproton.
1956............Discovery of the antineutron.
First colliders used.
1962............Discovery of muon-neutrino.
1964............Discovery of the omega-minus. Quark hypothesis proposed.
1966............SLAC, the Stanford Linear Accelerator.
1967............Electroweak unification.
1972............Fermilab.
1973............Discovery of neutral currents.
1974............Discovery of the J/ψ.
1975............Discovery of the tau lepton.
1983............Discovery of $W^{\pm}$ and Z^0.
1989............LEP, the Large Electron Positron Collider at CERN
1990............Z^0 decays confirm only three generations of particles.
1995............Discovery of top quark.
1996............First atom of antimatter (anti-hydrogen) created in the laboratory.
1996............LEP II, upgrade of LEP to create W^+W^- pairs

Useful data and equations

Rest mass of electron = 0.000549 u = 9.110×10^{-31} kg = 0.511 MeV/c^2
Rest mass of proton = 1.007276 u = 1.673×10^{-27} kg = 0.938 GeV/c^2
Rest mass of neutron = 1.008665 u = 1.675×10^{-27} kg = 0.940 GeV/c^2

Speed of light in a vacuum	$c = 2.998 \times 10^{8}\,\mathrm{m\,s^{-1}}$.
Electronic charge	$e = 1.602 \times 10^{-19}\,\mathrm{C}$
Planck's constant	$h = 6.626 \times 10^{-34}\,\mathrm{J\,s}$
Unified atomic mass unit	$u = 1.66 \times 10^{-27}\,\mathrm{kg}$
Permittivity of free space	$\varepsilon_0 = 8.854 \times 10^{-12}\,\mathrm{F\,m^{-1}}$
Boltzmann constant	$k = 1.381 \times 10^{-23}\,\mathrm{J\,K^{-1}}$
Electron-volt	$\mathrm{eV} = 1.602 \times 10^{-19}\,\mathrm{J}$

Prefixes

atto-	a–	10^{-18}	kilo-	k–	10^{3}
femto-	f–	10^{-15}	mega-	M–	10^{6}
pico-	p–	10^{-12}	giga-	G–	10^{9}
nano-	n–	10^{-9}	tera-	T–	10^{12}
micro	µ	10^{-6}	peta	P	10^{15}
milli-	m–	10^{-3}	exa-	E–	10^{18}
centi	c	10^{-2}			

EQUATIONS

Accelerators

$W = eV$ work done accelerating a charge, equals its kinetic energy

$F = Bqv$ magnetic force on a moving charge (direction from FLHR)

$r = \dfrac{p}{Bq}$ radius of curvature of a particle in a perpendicular magnetic field

$T = \dfrac{2\pi m}{Bq}$ orbital period in magnetic field

$f = \dfrac{1}{T} = \dfrac{Bqr}{2\pi m}$ cyclotron resonance frequency

Newtonian kinetic energy and momentum

$$\mathrm{KE} = \tfrac{1}{2} mv^2 = \frac{p^2}{2m}$$

$$p = mv$$

In an accelerator $\mathrm{KE} = eV$ so $v = \sqrt{\dfrac{2eV}{m}}$

Relativity

$$\beta = \frac{v}{c} = 1 - \frac{1}{\gamma^2}$$

$$\gamma = \frac{1}{\sqrt{1-\beta^2}}$$

Total energy $E = hf = pc$ (photons)
Total energy $E^2 = E_o^2 + p^2c^2$ (particles of non-zero rest mass)
At high energy $E \gg E_o$ $E \approx pc$ for all particles.
$E = mc^2$ mass–energy equivalence
particle lifetime in the lab $t_{lab} = \gamma \, t_{particle}$

Quantum theory

$E = hf$ (photons)

$\lambda = \dfrac{h}{p}$ de Broglie relation

$\Delta E \Delta t \approx h$ energy–time uncertainty

$\Delta p \Delta x \approx h$ momentum–position uncertainty

Tables of data

Generation	Particle	Relative mass	Relative charge	Spin	L	L_e	L_μ	L_τ
1	electron	1	–1	$\frac{1}{2}$	1	1	0	0
1	electron-neutrino	0?	0	$\frac{1}{2}$	1	1	0	0
1	positron	1	+1	$\frac{1}{2}$	–1	–1	0	0
1	antielectron-neutrino	0?	0	$\frac{1}{2}$	–1	–1	0	0
2	muon	207	–1	$\frac{1}{2}$	1	0	1	0
2	muon-neutrino	0?	0	$\frac{1}{2}$	1	0	1	0
2	antimuon	207	+1	$\frac{1}{2}$	–1	0	–1	0
2	antimuon-neutrino	0?	0	$\frac{1}{2}$	–1	0	–1	0
3	tau	3490	–1	$\frac{1}{2}$	1	0	0	1
3	tau-neutrino	0?	0	$\frac{1}{2}$	1	0	0	1
3	antitau	3490	+1	$\frac{1}{2}$	–1	0	0	–1
3	antitau-neutrino	0?	0	$\frac{1}{2}$	–1	0	0	–1

Quark pair	Strangeness	Charge/*e*	Meson (spin 0)
d anti-u or $d\bar{u}$	0	–1	π^-
u anti-u or $u\bar{u}$	0	0	π^0 (u anti-u, d anti-d)
d anti-d or $d\bar{d}$	0	0	$\eta^0 \eta'^0$ (u anti-u, d anti-d, s anti-s)
s anti-s or $s\bar{s}$	0	0	
u anti-d or $u\bar{d}$	0	1	π^+
s anti-d or $s\bar{d}$	–1	0	$\bar{K}^0$
s anti-u or $s\bar{u}$	–1	–1	K^-
d anti-s or $d\bar{s}$	1	0	K^0
u anti-s or $u\bar{s}$	1	1	K^+

Quark triplet	Strangeness	Charge	Spin $\frac{1}{2}$	Spin $\frac{3}{2}$
ddd	0	–1		Δ^-
udd	0	0	n^0	Δ^0
uud	0	1	p^+	Δ^+
uuu	0	2		Δ^{++}
dds	–1	–1	Σ^-	Σ^{-*}
uds	–1	0	Σ^0, Λ^0	Σ^{0*}
uus	–1	1	Σ^+	Σ^{+*}
dss	–2	–1	Ξ^-	Ξ^{-*}
uss	–2	0	Ξ^0	Ξ^{-*}
sss	–3	–1		Ω^-

Quark flavour	Charge/*e*	Strangeness	Spin/$\hbar$
up (u)	$+\frac{2}{3}$	0	$\frac{1}{2}$
down (d)	$-\frac{1}{3}$	0	$\frac{1}{2}$
strange (s)	$-\frac{1}{3}$	–1	$\frac{1}{2}$
anti-up ($\overline{u}$)	$-\frac{2}{3}$	0	$\frac{1}{2}$
anti-down ($\overline{d}$)	$+\frac{1}{3}$	0	$\frac{1}{2}$
anti-strange (s)	$+\frac{1}{3}$	+1	$\frac{1}{2}$

Generation	Quark	Charge/*e*	E_0/GeV	Spin/$\hbar$	Lepton	Charge/*e*	E_0/GeV	Spin/$\hbar$
1	d	$-\frac{1}{3}$	0.008	$\frac{1}{2}$	e	–1	0.511	$\frac{1}{2}$
1	u	$+\frac{2}{3}$	0.004	$\frac{1}{2}$	ν_e	0	0?	$\frac{1}{2}$
2	s	$-\frac{1}{3}$	0.150	$\frac{1}{2}$	μ	–1	106	$\frac{1}{2}$
2	c	$+\frac{2}{3}$	1 200	$\frac{1}{2}$	ν_μ	0	0?	$\frac{1}{2}$
3	b	$-\frac{1}{3}$	4 700	$\frac{1}{2}$	τ	–1	1780	$\frac{1}{2}$
3	t	$+\frac{2}{3}$	~93 000	$\frac{1}{2}$	ν_τ	0	0?	$\frac{1}{2}$

Interaction	Gauge bosons	Acts on	Conservation laws	Typical lifetime	Typical range
gravity	graviton zero rest mass	everything	*Q, B, S, L*	no gravitational decays	infinite inverse square law
electromagnetism	photon zero rest mass	charged quarks and leptons	*Q, B, S, L*	10^{-18} s	infinite inverse square law
weak	W^+, W^-, Z^0 83 GeV/c^2, 93 GeV/c^2	quarks and leptons	*Q, B, L* but not *S*	10^{-10} s	10^{-18} m
strong	8 different gluons zero rest mass?	quarks	*Q, B, S* (leptons not involved so *L* = 0)	10^{-23}	10^{-15} m

Conservation laws

Charge Q – always conserved.
Baryon number B – always conserved.
Lepton number L – always conserved (electron- muon- tau- lepton numbers separately conserved).
Strangeness S – conserved in strong interactions, violated in some weak interactions.

Total energy, linear and angular momentum and charge are all also conserved.

Further reading

Relativity

Relativity for the Layman, James A. Coleman, Pelican 1969.
Relativity Revisualised, Lewis Caroll Epstein. Insight Press 1987.
Spacetime Physics, Edwin Taylor & John Wheeler, W.H.Freeman and Co. 1966.
Relativity – An Introduction to Space-Time Physics, Steve Adams, Taylor and Francis Ltd, 1997.

Quantum Theory

The Quantum Universe, Tony Hey and Patrick Walters, Cambridge University Press 1990.
In Search of Schrödinger's Cat, John Gribbin, Corgi. 1986
The Quantum World, John Polkinghorne, Longman 1984.
QED, Richard Feynman, Princeton University Press 1985.

Cosmology

A Brief History of Time, Steven Hawking, Bantam Press 1991.
Cosmology, Edward R. Harrison, Cambridge University Press 1989.

General

The Character of Physical Law, Richard Feynman, Massachusetts Institute of Technology 1977.
Hyperspace, Michio Kaku, Oxford University Press 1995.
About Time, Paul Davies, Simon and Schuster/Viking 1995.
The First Three Minutes, Steven Weinberg, Collins 1978.

Particle physics

The Particle Physics Pack (includes worksheets etc.), IOP Publishing/Open University.
The Particle Explosion, Frank Close, Michael Marten, Christine Sutton, Oxford University Press 1987.
The Cosmic Onion, Frank Close, Heinemann 1985.
The Forces of Nature, Paul Davies, Cambridge University Press 1979.
Particle Physics and the Cosmos and *Particles and Forces*, collections of Scientific American Articles edited by Richard A. Carrigan jnr and Peter Thrower, W.H. Freeman 1989, 1990.
Quarks, Leptons and Cosmology, J.A. Allday, IOP Publishing 1997.

Other resources

PPARC, Particle Physics and Astronomy Research Council.
World Wide Web sites: the CERN homepage is a good place to start, hyperlinks from here to useful resources throughout cyberspace. The Institute of Physics also publishes lists of interesting sites, but a simple word search will usually find what you need, whether it is the latest proposed experiments or a resume of past work.

Index